SEND DOWN A DOVE

SEND DOWN
A DOVE

by Charles MacHardy

Coward-McCann, Inc.   New York

To my family, Gordon and C.J.

SEND DOWN A DOVE

Chapter One

A cold wind blew down the loch, rippling the surface of the blue-green water and sending up little showering cascades of spray as waves broke against the hulls of the many ships gathered in the anchorage. The wild screeching of sea-birds and the plaintive bleating of sheep on the surrounding hills lent the scene a bleakness of atmosphere despite the brightness of the early morning sun. A crystalline blue sky, like an inverted china bowl, arched over the hills, its brilliance reflected in the waters of the loch.

On board the biggest of the ships which lay at anchor in the middle of the loch, and high above the surface of the water, sailors shivered on the upper deck as icy fingers of wind probed for gaps in their clothing. Most of them wore overalls buttoned up to the neck, but their bared hands and exposed faces were scrubbed to a bluish red.

Alongside the ship three submarines, sleek and menacing, were secured: two on the portside, nearest the landing jetty on the southern shore of the loch, and the third and smallest on the starboard side. Like long lean hunting dogs they tugged nervously at the ropes that bound them to their parent ship.

At the head of the starboard companionway, leading up to the well deck of the parent ship, a leading seaman stood rubbing his shoulders and stamping his feet. Leading seaman Titt was a man of nearly thirty years of age with heavy shoulders and powerful arms. He had squarish features and a small stub of a nose, slightly thickened at the bridge as a result of earlier years when he had boxed for the Navy. His frank, pale blue eyes matched the color of the sky, and his mouth was generous and well formed and indicated an unexpected sensitivity. The chin was cleft, and underneath the eyes where the tissue puffed slightly the tightened skin had permanently creased in two lateral wrinkles.

Feeling the early morning cold, he waited impatiently for the two seamen struggling up the companionway. Though the ammunition boxes they carried on their shoulders obscured their features, he recognized them without difficulty. Nearly thirty feet below the level of the well deck, the small submarine, berthed on the starboard side, rocked in the lively sea. Her gangplank lifted and fell in seesaw motion. At last the hands reached the deck. Breathing heavily, little puffs of mist forming around their lips, they staggered past Titt with a brief grunt, too weary and too cold to exchange pleasantries. He was about to descend the ladder when a peak-capped figure emerged from the forehatch of the submarine. It was the captain. Titt held back as the figure swiftly negotiated the ropes, wires and piled-up crates strewn over the casing and crossed the gangplank. A gust of wind blew down the loch, whisking the tops from the sea horses. Titt shivered, his hand automatically reaching to hold onto his cap.

For Christ's sake, hurry it up, he muttered to himself as he watched the captain ascend the ladder. *It's bloody well freezing up here.*

Almost as if he had heard him, the captain bounded up the ladder, taking the last steps two at a time. Titt stood back in the correct attitude of attention demanded by the code of naval discipline. Seemingly oblivious to his presence, Lieutenant Commander Cheney, D.S.O. and bar D.S.C., swept past, leaving the gangway clear once more.

Don't mind me, mate. I've got all bloody day, Titt breathed to himself as he hurried down to the submarine and threaded his way along the casing toward the opened hatch. Grasping the rim, which was cold enough to be painful to the touch, he lowered himself down the hatch, his feet finding the metal rungs of the nearly vertical ladder. Sheltered from the searing wind, he stood for a moment, blowing on his chilled hands.

The compartment he had entered was the torpedo stowage compartment, but it served a dual purpose. Known as the fore-ends, it was also the living quarters of the whole ship's complement, excepting the officers and petty officers. Re-formed in shape it might have made the size of a living room in a council flat. At sea it housed nearly two dozen men.

The scene in the fore-ends was chaotic. The tools, lifting tackle and torpedo parts scattered in profusion made it look like some sort of secret underground garage. Billy Wells, the torpedo gunner's mate, and his crew of three seamen were busy preparing to take on board six spare torpedoes and two reloads for the tubes. Slipping about the oily deck and sweating in the confined space, the T.G.M. and his hands cursed incessantly, a strange litany of foul language. From the fore-ends a strong smell escaped up through the hatchway—an odor compounded of shale and fuel oil, stale bread, grease, paraffin, sweat, un-washed bodies, damp canvas and old clothing. Lying over this compost, like a blanket of fog, was an air of dampness and musti-ness reminiscent of an empty tomb.

Titt, so long accustomed to the smell that he hardly noticed it, picked his way through the tangle of ropes and tackles that ran wildly about like creepers in a jungle. He ducked through a bulkhead door and entered a long narrow passageway. Like a tunnel it ran aft through to the heart of the submarine, where it suddenly expanded into a bewildering array of instruments, valves, pipes and gauges as it entered the control room. The passage itself was flanked by a maze of pipes and cables, but on the starboard side were the petty officers' mess, the captain's cabin, the wardroom and lastly the wardroom pantry.

Squeezing past the petty officers' mess, Titt was hailed by a voice from inside.

Chief petty officer William Blow, the submarine's coxswain and senior petty officer, stepped out of the mess, his freshly shaved pink cheeks glowing like newly sliced bacon. Setting his cap firmly on his head and squaring off the lapels of his neat uniform, he gave the tail of his jacket a couple of sharp tugs before addressing Titt.

"Stores, Tom? I meant to have a word with you earlier. Have you completed your list yet?" he asked briskly.

"Stores?" queried Titt. "Didn't Jock Bain give you the list?"

"Oh, Jock has it? That's all right then. Just as long as you gave it to him."

"Well, it was only this morning—"

The coxswain waved his hand. "Okay, Tom. As long as he has it. I just want to get everything buttoned up in good time—you never know what can happen in this lot."

Titt grinned. "What's this, then? Don't tell me you've heard a buzz about what we're doing? What's Jimmy been saying?"

C.P.O. Blow looked severe. "The first lieutenant's said nothing. And even if he had—well, you should know better than to ask silly questions."

Titt looked at the coxswain sideways: "Come on, 'swain. What's happening? Is it true that we're supposed to be going to Chatham for a refit?"

Blow pressed his lips together and threw his chest out. "I'd like to know who spreads all the buzzes on this boat. I'll give him *buzz* when I catch him. It's getting worse than an old wives' gathering. Who the hell starts it, anyway?"

Titt grinned again. "Wouldn't you like to know? Anyway, if you're not saying, I'll have to fall back on my own sources of information." He rubbed his chin thoughtfully: "Yeah, that's it. I'll just go and have a little word with the wardroom flunky. He's bound to know something about what's going on."

"Now, Tom—" warned the coxswain, but Titt was already on his way down the passage.

In the control room a couple of hands were busy polishing the brasswork. They looked up as Titt appeared. He stepped around the chief E.R.A., who was examining the afterperiscope while a stoker at the control lever slowly worked it up and down. The glistening massive steel column hissed as it moved out of the well. From just behind the control room a torrent of heavy noises beat out as engineers and stokers labored never-endingly at the diesels. The banging and clattering was deafening.

Titt slid around the periscope and cupped his hands to his mouth: "Mitch—Raggy? Stores this afternoon . . . two o'clock . . . and be there, we've a lot to do, okay?"

Both able seamen got the message and nodded. Titt was about to go when something about Mitchell made him take another look. The seaman looked pale and appeared to be sickening for something.

Titt cupped his hand to his mouth again: "Hey, Mitch—are you all right?"

Mitchell mustered a feeble grin, his voice sounding a little weak as he yelled back: "I'm all right, Tom. Feeling a bit off, that's all."

Titt crooked his finger, beckoning Mitchell to follow him through the bulkhead door. The A.B. put down his tin of Brasso. Wiping his hands on his overalls, he followed Titt out into the passageway where there was less noise and they wouldn't have to shout at each other.

"What's up with you, then?" Titt asked, eyeing him closely.

Mitchell put his hand to his brow, which glistened slightly with sweat. "I'm all right, Tom. Honest I am. It's just—"

"D'you go ashore last night?"

"Yeah. We were in Dunoon—"

"On the grog, were you?"

Mitchell gave a sickly grin. "Well, we had a couple of beers."

"More like a couple of barrels by the look of you. Anyway, if you're still feeling groggy later on, you'd better nip up to the sick bay—and I mean that. You look like death warmed up."

Mitchell looked alarmed. "Sick bay, Tom? I don't want to go to no sick bay. It was only the booze last night. I'd a bit too much, that's all."

Titt gave him a look. "Mitch, don't bugger about. If you're sick, then get up to the sick bay. That's all there's to it. What are you so worried about, anyway? If it was me I'd be up there quicker than that. Anything to get a break from this lot. You must be off your chump."

Mitchell looked concerned. "It's not that, Tom. I don't want to miss the boat and—"

"Oh, I get it," Titt butted in. "You don't want to miss the boat. I don't suppose you'd have heard anything about a refit, now. A little spell in dock for the old *Scorpion,* eh?"

Mitchell gazed at the deck. "Well, there *is* a bit of a buzz going around—"

"A buzz, eh?" Titt's eyes narrowed, but he sounded amused. "Well, you take my tip, son. Don't depend on buzzes. This little lot's not over yet. We might even be back on patrol yet. So you don't want to count your chickens, mate. Okay?"

Mitchell looked glum. "All right, Tom. Whatever you say."

Going back down the passageway, ducking his head to avoid the myriad of pipes and valves, Titt bumped into acting petty officer Jock Bain, the second coxswain.

"Hiya, Jock. Seen the 'swain?"

"I only just left him. Why? Did you want to see him?"

"Me? No. He was on about that list of stores I gave you. He's getting just about as bad as the skipper. You'd think he wanted to get back to sea. Anyway, you've given him the list?"

"Aye, but you know what he's like, Tom. Everything's got to be on time. There's no putting off with old Bill. Anyway, he's got the list, so that clears you. Where are you off to now?"

"Heading back inboard. Did you want anything? I'm going up to the bosun's store."

Bain shook his head. "Doesn't matter just now, but if you've time later on, have a look at that securing wire on the port fore-planes, will you? It could need renewing. I'd do it myself, but I'll have to do something about the afterperiscope wire. It's going to go for a Burton any time."

"Hmmph." Titt didn't envy Bain. Rigging periscope wires was a lousy job. "Well, the best of luck, mate. Better you than me. I'd sooner scrub the quarterdeck with a toothbrush."

Bain pulled a face. "Okay, okay. Don't rub it in. Don't think I'm going to enjoy crawling about upside down on my arse, sorting out that bloody monkey's puzzle, with the chief tiffy breathing down my neck, offering advice."

Titt stood for a moment, rubbing the back of his neck. "Here, Jock," he said, switching the subject, "have you heard anything about this supposed refit? I hear we might be going to Chatham now."

"Oh, it's Chatham, is it? Last time I heard it was Pompey. I don't mind personally where it is so long as we have the bloody thing."

"You think there might be something in it, then?" questioned Titt.

"I don't know about *think*—all I know is that we need the bloody thing or we'll be coming apart at the rivets one of these days. Christ, I wouldn't like to be on board if we ever have to do a deep dive. I reckon we'd fold up like a matchbox." Bain made a noise like a man ducking under a cold shower. "Anyway, I don't know what I'm doing here cackling the fat. I've enough on my plate to keep me going." He moved off, speaking over his shoulder, "Don't forget about that foreplane wire, Tom, will you?"

Titt nodded after the burly retreating figure. Continuing his way back along the passage and into the fore-ends, he climbed up through the hatch. On the casing, he decided to have a look at the wire. Bain was right. It needed renewing. He slipped out his knife and unclasped the spike, then unscrewed the small shackle pins which secured the stay. The frayed wire in his hand, he headed for the bosun's store. Old "Slasher" Tipton, the bosun's mate, would splice a new one up for him. He was too busy to do it himself.

As the day wore on, it brought little respite from the biting cold. The crew, up to the ears in work, crawled about the submarine like ants, too busy even to speak. After the midday meal Titt got hold of Renwick, Mitchell and the gunlayer, and they started bringing ammunition and stores down from the parent ship. They had only been at it an hour when all operations ceased. The T.G.M. was ready to take aboard the torpedoes. Sub-Lieutenant Joyner came to see Titt and told him to start rigging the loading rails. Normally this would have been Bain's job as second coxswain, but he was still busy with the periscope wire. Titt left Mitchell down below where it would be warmer and got hold of able seaman Corr, a big Scot. Together the four men went up top and, breaking open the casing, unshipped the rails and began erecting them. Their hands were numb with cold by the time they had finished. To add to their miseries Joyner kept getting in the way and offering meaningless advice. The rails they had rigged were supported on stanchions, about two feet above the deck, and ran halfway along the casing like a pair of tramlines before dipping down in a curve through the hatch and down into the fore-ends where they linked up.

Teeth chattering in the cold, Titt and the others waited for the first torpedo to swing over from the well deck of the parent ship. Joyner, his arms flapping about, signaled that all was ready, and with a warning hail from up top, the jib of the crane swung over the side. Slowly the first torpedo was lowered away. Titt and Big Jock Corr grabbed the nose and tail lines thrown down from the well deck. The two-ton, thirty-foot-long steel cylinder, swaying ponderously in the wind, sank slowly like a descending lift. A few feet above the casing Titt or Corr steadied it, making sure that the brass rollers on either side of the lifting band, encircling the torpedo, would engage the rails. The submarine, lifting and falling in the choppy sea, kept pulling away at the last moment. Or, coming up suddenly, it would punch the rails against the torpedo with an ominous clang. There were a few anxious moments before the torpedo was finally home and the rollers slotted into the rails. Once it was in position, Titt dropped the nose line down through the fore-hatch. Down below the crew caught it and ran it through a snatch block for'ard, on the bulkhead between the fore-ends and the tube space. They began to haul away. Slowly the torpedo was drawn toward the hatch as the cranesman up top eased away on his purchase. Titt heaved a sigh of relief as the tail vanished through the round hatchway.

There was a sudden, sickening lurch.

Angrily the wire from the crane began to vibrate. From somewhere below in the fore-ends a cry came. Titt sprang for the hatch, yelling wildly at the cranesman to belay everything. Dropping down on the deck he saw that the torpedo was lying at an odd angle. On hands and knees he crawled forward under its belly, glancing anxiously upward at its threatening bulk. About halfway along he spotted the source of the trouble. The gate in the starboard rail wasn't in position—it hung uselessly on its securing chain. The brass roller on the torpedo lifting band had plunged through the gap in the rail. With each fresh movement of the submarine the torpedo swayed dangerously. Only the roller on the port rail and the restraining forces effected by the purchase from the crane and the hands holding onto the nose line kept it from breaking loose. Mitchell, standing near the open gate, was paralyzed with fear.

Titt reached him. "Hold it, Mitch," he gasped, straightening up. "When I sing out, slip the gate back in, okay? Ready now?"

The A.B. shot him a terrified glance out of the corner of his eye. He licked his dry lips and nodded, unable to take his gaze away from the two tons of metal which threatened to tear the rails from their mountings and crush him against the bulkhead. Titt wasted no time. Seizing a tommy bar, he thrust it between the rails and the lifting band of the torpedo. He shouted to the T.G.M. to tell them to hoist away slowly up top. The rest of the hands hung on helplessly to the nose line as Titt put his weight on the bar.

With a terrifying, metallic groan the torpedo began to move in an upward direction as the crane began to hoist away.

Sweat poured from Titt as he struggled to lever the roller back through the gate in the rail. One slip now and the torpedo would jerk backward, plucking the rails from their moorings like twigs. With nothing to hold it in position the torpedo would drop free and smash the fore-ends and everything in it to matchwood.

Titt strained at the tommy bar, his heart pounding madly. To his horror the metal bar, nearly an inch thick, began to bend. Gritting his teeth, he put all his strength into one last effort. Jerking and shuddering, the torpedo rose. The roller cleared the gate.

"Right," he gasped. "Slip the gate in, Mitch. Quick now."

Mitchell collected himself sufficiently to whip the gate back into position. The crane lowered away again, and the torpedo nestled slowly down until it gained the security of the rails. Wells, now that it was safe, was free to move. He came across the compartment, slithering on hands and knees, coming upright to face Mitchell.

"Who the fucken hell left the gate out?" he shouted. "Was it you?"

The able seaman, still trembling, shook his head in denial.

"Well, some bastard left it out—or took it out. It didn't bloody well jump out by itself," Wells stormed, looking as if he were about to lash out with his fists.

Mulholland, one of the torpedo crew, squeezed forward. His long, yellow, grease-covered hair hung half over his eyes. He brushed it back with his hand. "It's old Joyner. He's doing his nut up top. He wants to know what's up," he said.

Wells, still seething with rage, didn't even look around.

"Tell him to go and get stuffed, that's what's up," he replied, biting the words off.

Mulholland grinned. Joyner, peering down through the hatch, heard the T.G.M.'s remark. His face went a fiery red. He hastily withdrew, biting his lip and pretending he hadn't heard. When they unhooked the crane to return inboard, he started flapping his arms about wildly again and shouting instructions in an effort to cover up his embarrassment. The hands exchanged grins with each other. They all knew Joyner.

There were no further incidents, but it took a long time for Wells to simmer down.

It was well after six o'clock before the last fish was safely on board. Titt and his helpers began dismantling the rails. The rest of the hands not on watch scurried off to get washed and cleaned up in time to get ashore. Titt stayed behind with the duty watch to help clear up. It was nearly eight o'clock before he got away. Feeling filthy and sweaty, he headed for the crew's mess on the parent ship. Hurrying along the casing he nearly fell over the gunlayer's bucket. Titt frowned as he saw the bucket contained parts of the dismantled gun. Stiff with fatigue he descended the companionway.

When he reached the mess he flopped down at the table. Most of the hands had already gone ashore, and only a few remained on board. Over by the mirror on the bulkhead, able seaman Oak stood combing his thick black hair. Dressed in his best suit, he was obviously intending to go ashore.

Titt found himself yawning. "Anybody seen the gunlayer?" he asked no one in particular.

"Trapper? I think he's gone ashore," a voice answered.

Oak spun around from studying himself in the mirror.

"Gone ashore? He'd better not. I'm waiting for the bastard. We're supposed to be getting the last liberty boat together," he said.

"Where's he gone, then?" Titt asked. "Anybody know?"

"Mebbe he's in the head," someone volunteered.

Titt rubbed his hand over his face. He felt absolutely dead beat; too tired to move. A minute later Trapper Lacey, the gunlayer, came into the mess. Like Oak he was dressed in his number ones, his gold service badges and the crossed guns standing out proudly on the dark blue background of his jumper. Titt looked up at him as he crossed over to the mirror.

"Hey, Guns," he called out. "What's the idea of leaving the bloody cannon in bits?"

Lacey swung around. "Eh?"

"The gun. It's lying all over the casing. You'd better nip down and do something about it. Get that bucket out of the way before rounds or Jock Bain'll be after your guts."

A look of dismay crossed the gunlayer's features. He swore softly to himself: "Oh, bollocks. I forgot all about the bloody thing." He turned to one of the hands seated at the table.

"Here, do's a favor, Kennedy? Nip down and stow that bucket away in the control room, will you, or we'll miss this bloody liberty boat." Turning to Titt he said: "Me and Gospel Oak have a date with a couple of civvy parties in Dunoon." He grinned and made a gesture of feeling his biceps. "It's my birthday tomorrow and we're celebrating in advance."

Titt looked at him coolly. "And how about the gun?"

"The gun? Aw, don't worry, Tom. I'll have it back together in the morning in no time," Lacey promised.

Titt hesitated. He wasn't too keen on the idea of the gun's being left unassembled, but he didn't want to spoil anyone's run ashore. He decided to let the matter go this time. "Okay, Guns. As long as the casing's clear for rounds, but remember you get that gun back in one piece tomorrow before you start celebrating your birthday, or the bloody thing'll still be in bits when we get in dry dock—if we ever do. Bugger off then, the pair of you."

Lacey smiled broadly. "Goodo, Tom. Come on, Gospel let's get going. We just got four minutes before the last boat shoves off."

Titt watched the pair leave the mess before he dragged himself to his feet. He walked around the mess and down by the back of the hammock netting. He stopped in the small alley formed by the men's lockers. Fumbling about in his overalls he found a key. He opened his locker and took out a towel and soap, together with his writing gear and ditty box. Before writing home to his wife he had a good washdown and changed into fresh underwear and a clean pair of washed-out, pale-blue overalls.

He spent most of the evening writing letters. After rounds, he went back down aboard the submarine to collect his laundry.

Jock Bain was duty petty officer. He was stretched out in the P.O.'s' mess, reading, when Titt's head appeared around the drawn curtain. Bain raised himself to a half-sitting position. He put down his book.

"Come in, Tom," he welcomed. "Fancy a mug of kye?"

Titt nodded and sat himself down at the green baize-covered table. Jock reached over to the enamel jug and poured out a cup of cocoa.

"What are you doing down here, anyway?" he asked, pushing the cup across the table.

"Oh, I just came down to get my dobeying. I want to crash

it out before I get my head down," Titt answered, sipping the cocoa.

"Good, you can do mine when you're at it." Bain bared his bone-white, irregularly spaced teeth. "You can save me the laundry money."

"You wouldn't like to drink my tot for the next month and all?" Titt replied sarcastically.

Bain laughed. For the next few minutes the men remained in conversation. Finally Titt stood up, his cup empty.

"Well, must get back aboard, Jock, and get this lot out of the way. You never can tell when we might shove off. By the way, you haven't heard anything yet, have you?"

Bain looked at him quizzically. "Heard anything about what?"

"Oh, come off it, mate. You're getting as secret as the coxswain. About the refit, of course. What do you think I'm talking about?"

"Oh, that. Well, seeing as I've been stuck in the control room all day with that bastarding periscope, I didn't have much of a chance to catch up with the local gossip." Bain paused, twisting his finger in his ear. "Tell you something I did hear though—"

"Go on," said Titt, taking the bait.

"We might be getting a new skipper." Bain leaned back on the bench to measure the effect of his words on Titt.

"A new skipper," Titt repeated unbelievingly. "You're joking."

Bain spread his hands. "That's the way I heard it. There's some word about the old man going back to Fort Blockhouse."

"Fort Blockhouse. Now I know you're joking. A shore job for Cheney? That'll be the day.'

Bain shrugged. "I don't know. Mebbe he'd even like to get back ashore, for all we know. He must have had about enough by this time."

"Enough what? Don't kid yourself. As far as old Cheney's concerned he wants to finish up like Nelson with all the gold braid and gongs you could pin on one jacket. He's not going to get that farting about in a shore job, is he? No, Jock, not on your Nelly. He's too much all for it to want to get back ashore," Titt said.

Bain twirled his empty mug in his hands. He looked at the tabletop. "You don't care much for the old man, do you? He's a good skipper, you know. I've sailed with a few of them and— well, say what you like about him, but he knows his stuff, mate."

Titt leaned forward. "I don't like any of them, Jock. Sure, he knows his stuff, but for my money they're all the same. Gong-collecting, the whole bloody lot. It's all right for them, you know. It's their job—their life. But what'll we get out of it when it's all over? Fat lot of good *your* ribbons will do in civvy street. Oh, it'll be great for a year or two. Picture in the local paper and folks looking at you when you go in the pub with the wife and all that crap. We'll all be bloody heroes for a day, but after that nobody'll want to know."

"It's not going to be the same as last time, Tom. A lot of things are going to change," Bain said with strange earnestness.

Titt curled his lip. "Hmmph. We'll see. But I tell you one thing that's not going to change, and that's the old rat race for promotion in the Navy. Extra stripes will be as scarce as horses with wooden legs. If you want promotion, now's the time to get it, or you'll be joining the queue, and every second bloke in it will be a lieutenant commander." Titt picked up his dobeying. "Anyway, I must get this lot done or I won't have any clean clobber. But I'll bet you, Jock, that if we go back on patrol again, it'll be old Cheney standing up there on the bridge giving the orders. This war's not going to last forever, and he'll be after all the medals he can get before there's nothing left over to dish them out for."

"Ach, you're a right old moaner, Tom. What are you so worried about? The skipper's only doing his job. You'd do exactly the same if you were in his shoes, wouldn't you? Anyway" —he got up with the air of a man who has the last word—"as I've said before, it all boils down to old Darwin: the survival of the fittest. And that applies to you and me and all the rest. That's what counts."

Titt snorted sarcastically. "I haven't read Darwin, so I wouldn't know, but if it's a question of survival then the best thing to do would be to get out of this lot. Mebbe we should have all been conshies."

Bain's black curls shook in despair. "The trouble with blokes like you is that you won't read—"

"I don't have to read a book to tell me what's good or bad for me, do I? The way we've been cutting corners this last couple of patrols we're just asking for it. One of these days our luck's going to run out and we're going to catch a right packet. And you can stuff your survival of the fittest."

"Ach, you're a Jeremiah, Tom. Why don't you leave it all to the skipper? He's seen us through before, and if it comes to it he'll see us through again. Stop worrying and go and get your head down," Bain advised.

Titt straightened up and drew the curtain aside. "All I hope is that we're not doing another patrol, Jock—Cheney or no Cheney. I've had enough. I just want to get back to the wife and kids and settle down to a nice peaceful life. That's all: a nice, simple, peaceful life."

A silence fell between the two men.

Titt finally said, "Well, I'm off, Jock. Get this lousy lot done. See you in the morning, mate."

"Aye, see you, Tom. Remember we're going over to the floating dock tomorrow. It's harbor stations at 0745. See you."

The fore-ends was quiet. Titt stopped, one hand on the ladder of the forward hatch. Only a single bulb lit the compartment. In the racks, the bulky cylindrical forms of the spare torpedoes they had sweated to load lay safely hidden in the shadows. Up forward near the tube space three hammocks swung gently. The duty watch, apart from the sentry up on the casing, were asleep. A strong smell of torpedo oil fuel permeated the atmosphere, thick and cloying. The table, which normally occupied the center of the space, was folded up and lay against the torpedo racks. For a brief span, in the everyday life of the boat, the fore-ends was clean and orderly. At sea it would be like a hellhole. The deckhead would be obscured by a pile of hammocks, the deck itself would be a slopping pool of dirty water, and the atmosphere would be foul with every bit of free space taken up by stores, equipment and the few personal belongings of the crew.

Titt felt sick to think of it. He had the awful feeling that they would be going back on patrol. A wave of despair came over him, and he couldn't get off the submarine quickly enough. He went back up to the parent ship. Changing into an old pair of football shorts, he headed for the washroom. For the best part of the next hour he scrubbed and pummeled the pile of dirty clothes in a frenzy of energy to rid himself of his depression. He hated the filth and gross disorder of life at sea, but even greater than his hatred was his fear. He'd always been frightened, as everyone else had, but he'd managed to keep it under control. Recently his fears had grown. Too many patrols, too many near things, had taken their toll, and even the mention of going to sea again created a sensation of butterflies crawling around in his stomach.

It was the small hours of the morning before he got to his hammock. The mess, on the parent ship, was quiet. Only the soft animal sound of the sleeping men's breathing and the never-ending purr of the ship's machinery could be heard. Stretched out on one of the forms was a drunk. Someone who had come back aboard too full of beer to bother to sling his hammock. Fully dressed, a stupified expression on his openmouthed face, the man lay in crumpled oblivion. For a moment Titt thought about waking him, but he changed his mind. The bloke wouldn't thank him for it. Best to leave him where he was. He climbed over the figure and hoisted himself into his hammock. It was a long time before he found unconsciousness in sleep.

All hands were up early the following morning. Harbor stations were piped at 0745. Bleary-eyed, and most of them suffering from hangovers, the crew shuffled about miserably. The wind continued to blow cold. On the casing the berthing party shivered and stamped their feet as they waited to cast off the breasts and springs.

Sub-Lieutenant Joyner fidgeted nervously. He kept looking up toward the bridge, waiting for the first lieutenant to appear. Cheney was remaining on board the parent ship, and the first lieutenant would take the submarine across the loch to the floating dock. Overhead the gulls screeched and wheeled in their incessant search for food.

Lieutenant Brangwyn came hurrying down the companion-way. He was late. He crossed the gangplank and with quick steps made for the bridge. Leading signalman Beer handed him the megaphone as he clambered over the conning tower and onto the bridge. The coxswain, standing stiffly at the wheel, glanced at his watch. He shook his head disapprovingly as he noted the time. They were three minutes late.

Brangwyn wasted no time. He ordered the motor room to obey telegraphs, and a moment later the casing party cast off. The submarine drew away from the parent ship on her motors, picking up speed. Waves broke against her saddle tanks as her bow began to dip in the choppy sea. The men on the casing were showered with stinging wet spray. There was no place they could shelter, and they cursed the weather, the war, the Navy and anything else that came to mind.

The docking earned the crew no rest from their work, and they carried on as usual. Those working up top shivered, and those down below sweated. Dockyard workers and naval engineers swarmed all over the submarine, covering everything in grease and oil and adding to the miseries of the crew, who had scrubbed the boat from stem to stern the previous day. The polished brasswork and washed-down paintwork were soon filthy.

By the middle of the afternoon they were clear of the dock. Cheney paid a visit during the operation but only stayed long enough to have a quick word with the engineer officer. Satisfied with the engineer's report, he sought out the first lieutenant to tell him he was returning as he had an appointment with Captain (S) on the parent ship. Lieutenant Brangwyn was in the wardroom. Like the petty officers' mess, it was screened off from the passageway by a curtain.

As Cheney drew back the curtain to enter the wardroom he was spotted by Cadbury, the wardroom steward. Eagerly, the steward scurried along the passageway, dropping the dish towel he perpetually carried as his badge of office. He picked it up again, nearly falling in his haste. Outside the wardroom he bent down beside the half paneling, straining his ears. The steward was a gossipmonger and spent his life picking up crumbs of information and peddling them around the boat. Within an hour, on the basis of what he'd heard, he had a rumor circulating among the crew: the skipper had been summoned to see Captain (S) immediately. That's why he wasn't remaining on board to take the submarine back alongside the parent ship. By itself this snippet would have aroused no interest among the hands. It, therefore, had to be suitably garnished. Cadbury allowed his imagination free rein, and the version that reached the ears of the crew had it that the *Scorpion* was being sent on a special patrol into the Baltic Sea, where they would pick up some high-ranking German officers. By late afternoon he had extended the story to include Admiral Doenitz among the officers to be picked up. Some of the newer members of the crew, unaware of the steward's notoriety, were crazy enough to ask him what it was all about. Cadbury replied, in whispering tones, that Montgomery and Doenitz were meeting at a secret place in Oxford where they were to produce a plan that would sweep the Russians all the way back to the Volga. The names sounded good to Cadbury, and he was half-roads to believing his own story.

Most of the veteran crew looked upon him as a sort of village idiot who from time to time gave them a good excuse for a laugh. But in a service that carried out a great deal of cloak-and-dagger operations, speculation was always rife. All rumors, no matter how improbable they sounded, were given a traditional airing and freely exchanged.

No sooner was the dock flooded than all hands went to harbor stations and the submarine was floated off. When they got back alongside the parent ship they had to clean up the mess in the boat all over again.

Titt and his two hands, Mitchell and Renwick, were in the control room. On hands and knees they scrubbed every inch of the deck before they started on the brasswork. Mitchell flung himself into the work as if determined to show Titt that he was fully recovered. They had finished by five thirty. Titt sent the hands inboard to tea and went to look for the coxswain. There was only Charlie Preece, the chief stoker, in the P.O.'s mess.

"Seen the 'swain?" asked Titt.

Preece shook his head, a scowl on his ugly features. "He'll be inboard. He's going ashore tonight, or so he said earlier."

Titt hesitated. "Oh, well, it doesn't matter. I'll mebbe catch him before he goes."

Preece grunted. "Who's duty P.O. tonight—you?"

"Uh-uh. Why, what's up?" Titt replied cautiously.

Preece picked at his yellow teeth with a match. "It's nothing. It won't affect you anyway. We're putting a topping-up charge on the battery after tea. Some bastards have always got bright ideas."

Titt groaned. "That's great. I never knew anything about that. When was this decided?"

Preece looked up. "What are *you* so worried about? You're not a stoker."

"No, but we just scrubbed out the control room. It's going to get in a fine mess again if we're putting a charge on."

Preece grinned sourly. "What do you want me to do? Tell everybody that they can't get through the control room because it's just been scrubbed out?"

Titt looked at the chief stoker. What a right bastard he was. Thank Christ he didn't have to work under him. Preece was the sort of bloke that was only happy when somebody else was in it. Never give them a break and put the boot in when they were down was his motto.

"When will the charge be finished?" Titt asked in a flat voice, holding back his anger.

Preece sucked at the match. "When the battery's up."

Titt's eyes glinted dangerously. "I know that, but what time will that be?"

"Mebbe eight o'clock—or nine. Depends," the chief stoker shrugged.

Titt could see he was getting nowhere. He gave Preece a hard stare. "Thanks for the information," he said and turned on his heel, leaving Preece grinning after him evilly.

Back up on board the parent ship he was late for tea. He was in no mood to go along and see the duty cook about a late meal. He didn't want to do any explaining and expose himself to the mercy of some wisecracking, smart-aleck P.O. cook. He grabbed towel and soap from his locker and headed for the washroom. Back in the mess he slipped on a pair of clean overalls. He went down again to the submarine to see that the gangway sentry was on watch.

Big Jock Corr was pacing the casing, the bulky, useless service .45 in its khaki webbing slung around his waist. Over his once white, rollneck, submarine jersey he wore a heavy watch coat. The sleeves seemed to come halfway up his arms. The noise of his boots rang out on the steel casing as he walked up and down. Even as Titt spoke to him, a tremor ran through the submarine, and from the conning tower a puff of oily blue smoke climbed upward as the diesels barked into life.

On board the parent ship Captain (S) looked up from his desk as he heard the knock on the door of his cabin. He threw a quick glance at the heavy brass clock on the bulkhead. That would be Cheney. Captain Osbourne bit his lip gently as he looked away from the door to face the opened port. It was beginning to get dark. He wished he'd been able to see Cheney earlier as he'd intended. The man wasn't going to be pleased with the news he had for him. Lost in thought for a moment, he gazed through the port. Deep shadows had begun to spread over the hills, robbing them of their vivid spring coloring.

Collecting his thoughts Osbourne returned his attention to the door. He cleared his throat and asked his caller to enter.

The heavy mahogany-paneled door swung open easily and silently on its hinges. Lieutenant Commander Cheney came in, removing his cap as he ducked under the doorway. With his face half hidden in the gloom of the cabin, he looked older than his thirty years. His prematurely graying hair helped to give this impression, but the appearance of age was accentuated by the two deeply carved lines that ran down either side of the nose. The eyes, in shadow, were completely hidden beneath the heavy bone of the brow. But the most noticeable feature of the face was his nose. It was large—too large. Thrusting forward from the brow it ran in a great vault toward the mouth. Though it robbed the face of any claim to good looks, at the same time it created an effect of an extraordinary, almost predatory, determination.

In the dimly lit cabin Cheney's uniform looked presentable. In fact it was grubby and stained with grease and paint. Even the tiny colored medal ribbons of the D.S.O. and the D.S.C. were soiled and faded, and the gold-braided rings on the sleeves were frayed and worn and beginning to part company with the jacket.

Osbourne half rose from his seat. "Ah, there you are, Cheney." He gestured toward the vacant leather-covered tub chair. "Sit down and make yourself comfortable."

Cheney sat down. A silence fell between the two men, broken only by the soft continual hum of the ship's auxiliary machinery, the cry of the circling gulls and now the soft *putt, putt,* of the liberty boat as it pulled away from the gangway and headed toward the pier at Sandbank.

Osbourne broke the silence. "Well, Cheney," he began guardedly, "I've no doubt you'll be anxious to know what's happening to you?" He shot the man opposite a keen glance at the same time as he leaned forward, his fingertips softly drumming the desktop. Cheney made no reply.

Osbourne drew a deep breath. "I'm afraid I haven't good news for you. I've tried to get you another command—one of the new T-boats—but it seems they're determined to have you down at the attack school at Blockhouse." He spread his hands helplessly. "I did what I could, but they're adamant. They need someone with your experience. . . . I'm sorry."

Only a slight stiffening of the shoulders betrayed Cheney's emotions. He made no move to speak.

Captain Osbourne withdrew his hands from the desk and shook his head. "I know how you must feel about it. I really am sorry," he repeated with genuine concern. He knew only too well that the chances that the lieutenant commander sitting opposite would get another command before the war finished were slim indeed. Inevitably it would mean a setback in his struggle for promotion. It might be years before he got his third ring up. Perhaps if he hadn't been so obdurate, had done a little more socializing, or even if he'd had another bar to his D.S.O. It was tragic. The man was a brilliant submarine commander and deserved promotion, but that was the Navy. It hadn't changed much from the days of Nelson.

Cheney had pushed back his chair and risen to his feet. "I'm sure you've done everything you can, sir." He picked up his cap from the desk. Cheney didn't believe in talking when there was no point to it.

"One moment, Cheney." Osbourne held up a hand. "There's something else—"

Cheney checked in his turn toward the door. The cap under his arm swung around slowly as he faced his superior officer, but he made no move to regain his seat. "Something else?"

"Yes. I'm going to have to ask you to do another patrol," said Osbourne.

The muscles on Cheney's face tightened imperceptibly.

"I know you badly need a refit, but I'm afraid it will have to wait." Osbourne suddenly rose from his chair and crossed over the length of the cabin to where a large map of Europe covered half the bulkhead. Standing in front of the map, he beckoned Cheney. He waited till the tall figure of the lieutenant commander joined him. Stabbing a finger in the direction of the chart, he said: "I don't have to tell you that as far as Jerry is concerned it's nearing the end. It could take six months, but on the other hand a few weeks could see it all over." He frowned heavily. "One thing worries us. As you know, Jerry has stepped up his program on the new type XXI and XXII U-boats. They're building them as fast as they can. We—or the Air Force, rather—have been making it hot for them. So much, in fact, that they've had to move their whole training school out of Danzig and up to Oslo Fiord." His finger stabbed at the chart again. "There they are, safe and sound and well out of our reach."

Cheney stared at the chart intently as he listened.

"Well, now," Osbourne went on, "as it stands they're no danger to us at the moment. But God help us if they ever manage to complete their trials and get to sea in large numbers. Make no mistake about it, Cheney, they could create absolute havoc—such a thing could alter the whole course of the war." He paused to emphasize his words.

"Now, we don't think this is likely to happen—we'll be in Berlin by then—but what we're afraid of is that the whole damned lot may scamper at the first sign of an armistice. I don't have to tell you that running at high speeds, and dived on their snorkels, they'd be able to slip out into the North Sea, and there's nothing we could do to stop them." Osbourne pursed his lips. "And of course there are the cruisers, *Prinz Eugen* and the *Nürnberg* at Copenhagen—though we wouldn't have much difficulty bagging them if they decided to make a run for it. Still we don't want any mad dogs running around once the show's over."

Osbourne went back to his desk.

The tall figure of Cheney, his shoulders hunched, stood staring at the chart. He spoke over his shoulder quietly: "And this patrol?"

"Well, now," Osbourne replied, seating himself, "the truth is that both the Air Force and our surface fleet have agreed upon a combined operation. We want to put on a show of strength to discourage any crazy ideas Jerry may have. Let them know we're there, and in force. And this is where you come in. With a submarine patroling outside the Skagerrak they'll know we mean business."

"You mean I'm to be a sort of glorified watchdog," Cheney said bluntly.

Osbourne frowned. "Well, there's a bit more to it than that. With a bit of luck you could bag one of them, you know." He tried to put conviction into his voice, but Cheney was right. He'd be little more than a watchdog, and with the new type U-boats running submerged on their snorkels he'd be lucky to catch even a glimpse of them. It was hardly likely to be a profitable patrol.

Cheney returned his attentions to the chart. British submarines hadn't patroled the Skagerrak since the German invasion of Norway. The whole area was thick with both British and German minefields. And more, the fresh water cascading down from the mountains created odd density layers, making a submarine difficult to control.

Submarine crews had learned to dread the very word Skagerrak.

Brows drawn, his great beak of a nose thrust aggressively forward, Cheney stared at the chart. He felt his anger rising. They wouldn't give him a new command, but they didn't mind asking him to carry out this futile patrol. And at the end of it, all he could look forward to was being dumped ashore at Fort Blockhouse. Was he to finish up in the Navy like his father before him —a mere three-ringer? He'd rather get out altogether than suffer that. Get out and join the humdrum, faceless, gray civilian ranks which he hated.

Thoughts churning over, he tried to concentrate his attention on the chart in front of him. The U-boats had gone up into Oslo Fiord. Well, that was out of the question. He might get in the fiord but he'd never get out again. He bit his knuckle. It was quite obvious that the decision to send a submarine to patrol the entrance to the Skagerrak was nothing more than a gesture on the part of someone at submarine G.H.Q. in London. The sort of thing that would look good on paper. Cutting through his anger an idea had begun to crystallize in his mind. He decided to say nothing to Captain Osbourne for the moment. The staff briefing on the parent ship would be the time to spring it. Staring at the bulkhead, he bit deeply into his knuckle, unaware that Osbourne was speaking to him.

". . . you'd better have a word with Commander (E) about your defect list," Captain Osbourne was saying. "Let me know what happens. There isn't much time, and we'd like to get the whole thing moving pretty soon."

Half preoccupied with his own thoughts, Cheney nodded briefly.

Captain Osbourne rose to his feet. "Good. Well, that's it, Cheney. You'll see Commander (E) right away and I'll let you know all about the staff briefing later."

Cheney wasted no time. Excusing himself hurriedly, he made his way out of the cabin and down to where the *Scorpion* lay berthed alongside.

He felt he was going to have a lot to do in the next twenty-four hours.

When Cheney had gone, Osbourne sat down heavily. Ill-temperedly he rummaged about in his desk drawer for his pipe. He found it and sucked on the empty bowl, his sense of irritation growing stronger as the minutes passed.

Jerking himself to his feet, he crossed the cabin toward the open port. The screeching of the gulls as they wheeled above the well deck by the gash chute suddenly sounded unbearably noisy. Normally it was a sound that comforted him, reminding him that though an appointment aboard a submarine parent ship was hardly seagoing at least it was better than being stuck ashore someplace.

He slammed the port shut, cutting off the noise. Gazing through the thick glass he could make out the outline of the hills. The moon had come up and the loch was the color of dull metal.

He couldn't help wondering how a man like Cheney would take to Blockhouse.

Chapter Two

The sea was the ugly gray color of lead. A hard wind, chilled by its passage over polar regions, drove at the rearing waves, shearing off their tops in a scattering of frozen spume. Though the month of May was near, the great refrigerating northern ice cap could still send signs of its presence across Europe. Dusk had begun to creep in. Already the moon and stars were hidden by a thick black overhang of cloud.

Eighty feet below the waves, His Majesty's Submarine *Scorpion* rolled. Even at that depth the turbulence above could be felt. At three knots she crept toward the distant coastline that marked the southernmost tip of Norway. Apart from her watch-keepers most of her crew were asleep.

Leading seaman Mulholland was on watch in the tube space. Standing on the raised platform behind the tubes, he thrust his bony hands into the pockets of his duffel coat and leaned against the bulkhead. Swaying with the roll of the deck, he kept his balance with the ease of a fairground attendant. Long greasy strands of hair hung limply over his eyes as he stared bleakly to his front. Behind him, through the opening of the bulkhead door, the crew were turned in. Only a couple of pilot lights glowed in the fore-ends. In the cold wet gloom of the compartment, underneath the ponderous, swaying hammocks, two of the hands lay face downward on the bench lockers flanking the mess table. Their arms wrapped around the lockers, they hung on grimly like monkeys.

Mulholland shivered in the damp cold. For the hundredth

time since coming on watch, he glanced at the heavy brass clock above the tubes. Jerking his gaze away, he pulled out from his pocket a copy of *Good Morning*, the paper issued free to submarine crews by the *Daily Mirror*. Listlessly he opened it out and began to read. From time to time, deliberately keeping his eyes from the clock, he would glance up at the complex array of dials and instruments packed thickly around the tubes. The scene was as familiar to him as the kitchen of his widowed mother's house in Mollison Street, Bootle. Automatically, he noted the pressure on the depth gauge, 42 pounds. Without having to think, his mind took the information in. At that sea pressure, they would be at an approximate depth of 80 feet. Even without the clock, he would have known by this fact that it was getting late. An hour or so before surfacing, it was customary to break off the periscope watch and go deeper. In bad light the periscope was almost useless, and a submarine wandering about blind at 30 feet could easily be rammed accidentally by a surface vessel.

Poor visibility, go deep—it was the iron rule of survival.

Mulholland folded the paper up and stuffed it back in his pocket. He didn't feel like reading. The print kept jumping in front of his eyes and the pictures dissolved into meaningless gray masses when he tried. Bored and cold, he shifted his position, leaning forward for an instant to look down over the platform at the pool of water slopping about in the bilges. He deliberately cleared his throat and spat into the oily blackness.

Some distance away, at the opposite end of the submarine, stoker first class McNally had the watch in the after-ballast pump station. McNally was thin and had pale waxlike skin. He suffered severely from the cold and was forever blowing on his hands and stamping his feet. To help keep his skinny frame warm, he wore several layers of clothing. Two thick, woollen vests and four jerseys—the topmost a sleeveless and no longer recognizable Fair Isle—covered the upper half of his body. A pair of long johns, two pairs of dirty football shorts and a pair of overall trousers, topped by service-issue bell-bottoms, protected his lower half. As if this were not enough, he had somehow managed to climb into filthy, grease-stiffened overalls. The grease, he said, helped to keep the cold out. During the whole of the patrol, McNally, like most of the others, never removed any of his clothing.

Bent almost double, he had managed to wedge himself into the tiny, boxlike pump space. His elbows propped up on the valve chest in front of him, he strained to read a grubby and torn paperback by the light of the single electric bulb. The book, a pirate copy of James Joyce's *Ulysses*, had been printed in Paris. Though Irish himself, McNally had never before heard of Joyce and was only reading the book because of the dirty bits it was alleged to contain. It puzzled him, the book. It even annoyed him, though just why, he couldn't say. But it also excited him. Seeing the vulgar, coarse words in print was so different from using them. It was almost like hearing a priest effing and blinding. Thinking about that, he had an uneasy feeling that he would have to admit to having read the book the next time he went to confession.

The book belonged to able seaman Rice, who seemed to collect unusual books. It had been going the rounds of the boat for some months. Rice had hesitated at first to lend it to McNally, but had given in finally with a warning to look after it as it was valuable and important. Most of the crew had thought the book was a great old laugh. They also thought that Rice was a bit bonkers to take it seriously. McNally's own view was that not only was Rice bonkers, but so was this fella Joyce. Imagine writing all that crap, he thought. Despite this, he kept on reading it.

Every now and then he would have to put the book down as the bell on the pump indicator rang and the light flashed on. Avoiding the sharp edges of the machinery that threatened to bite into his thin flesh, he'd get carefully to his feet. Why couldn't the officer of the watch keep a proper trim on the boat and stop buggering about with the pump? His fingers blue and chilled to the bone, he would start up the pump, cracking open the valves on the chest with a wheel spanner. Pumping water from one trimming tank to another, it might be as long as five minutes before the O.O.W. regained a trim. A period of inactivity followed before the process inevitably started up all over again. When this happened, McNally would pick up the wheel spanner, a murderous look in his eyes, and wave it wildly in the direction of the control room. From his thin colorless lips would pour a stream of indescribable filth.

The control room was at a spot approximately halfway between McNally and Mulholland. It was the center of the submarine's complex nervous system.

From the arch of the deckhead to either bulkhead, a circle cut in two by the deck, the control room was a bewildering maze of pipes, valves, instruments and machinery. It had the look of some wild scientific project that had got out of hand. In cross section it was perhaps the height and width of a London tube train compartment and about a third of its length. Every single cubic foot of space was utilized in some way.

In the very center were the periscopes, two thick gleaming columns appearing to support the arch of the deckhead. Enormously long, they plunged down into deep circular wells in the deck. On the port bulkhead, a pair of giant dials stared back into the compartment like the eyes of some subterranean monster. The dials were calibrated in units of feet from zero to five hundred. These were the depth gauges.

No one on board had ever seen the slender needles on the dials go beyond 350 feet. Nor did they want to.

Even at that depth, the pressure on each square inch of the submarine's hull was something like 175 pounds, or to put it another way, the weight of 144 heavy men standing on one square foot, if that were possible. In all, the total pressure on the hull amounted to many thousands of tons. Underneath the depth gauges were long curved spirit levels, the bubbles inside indicating the horizontal axial movement of the submarine.

Opposite, to starboard and surrounded by a Christmas tree of dials, a complex of long levers shone dully. This was the diving and blowing panel from which the main vents were operated. Right next to this and jammed between the panel and the switchboard, with its double banking of indicator lights, was a small gray box. It looked strangely like something out of an amusement arcade. This was the attack computer, but it was never referred to as anything but the fruit machine.

To the right of the telephone exchange and next to the long, tunneling passageway, was the helm. The brass-spoked wheel, which the crew spent many hours polishing when they were not at sea, was heavily stained and covered with verdigris. Immediately in front of the wheel was a gyrocompass repeater. Not circular in shape, like a normal compass, but long and boxlike, it enclosed a loop of printed film marked off in 360 degrees.

Just before the engine room bulkhead, a small space had been allocated to the asdic cabinet. The space was packed tightly with electrical equipment and gadgetry. In the corner of the cabinet a small console housed what appeared to be a compass dial with a large pointer in the middle. A knurled knob in the center of the dial allowed the operator to train the asdic unit through all the degrees of the compass. The bearing—relative to the ship's head—of any echo was read off from the pointer. The asdic unit itself, the Navy's most jealously guarded secret, was housed some distance away in the keel and carried a built-in detonation charge, should things go wrong and the submarine need to be abandoned in a hurry. From the compartment a crazy spaghetti of wiring ran to the bulkhead and, shooting upward, dispersed itself into cable channels fore and aft.

The wheel, planes, diving panel, switchboard and asdic cabinet were all manned by the duty watchkeepers. Only the fruit machine was left unattended for the moment. Scattered around the control room, the crew sat at their posts. One man stood, or half stood. Leaning against the forward periscope was the officer of the watch, Lt. Percival Robinson. As O.O.W. he was temporarily in command of the vessel.

Robinson, one of the four officers on board, was a regular. Prior to joining submarines, he had served on destroyers. This was his sixth war patrol, and the end of the month would mark his second year in the submarine service. He looked the typical naval officer. Tall and fair-haired, he wore an expression of haughtiness, as if he were permanently engaged in tracking down a bad smell. He was the keen type. A product of Dartmouth, he had a dictatorial manner of authority to match his arrogance. Robinson enjoyed the business of war. It gave him a sense of purpose that fitted in well with his Wagnerian idealism. His only regret was that it wasn't going to last long enough for him to get his own command. But he consoled himself in the belief that he would make first lieutenant yet. He was ambitious, but he had an alert mind, and there was no doubting his ability as a seaman.

Needless to say, neither his attitude nor his manner endeared him to the crew, who looked upon him as a first-class twit. But knowing he could be dangerous, they kept well out of his way. For his part Robinson viewed the crew as a bunch of rebellious malcontents who dodged and skived at the least opportunity.

He was watching one of them now. With an expression of sour displeasure on his face, he stared at the back of able seaman Renwick's head.

Renwick, on the foreplanes, was having God's own job to keep the boat at its proper depth. Varying density layers and the disturbed water made it extremely difficult. In such circumstances, Robinson should have known better than to expect accurate depth-keeping, but he had his own troubles in trying to keep a trim on and wasn't in the best of tempers. Further, he considered that the watch he was on with now—the blue watch —was, of the three watches, the most undisciplined. He was determined to shake them up.

Renwick, sweating it out, stole a despairing glance at his opposite number on the afterplanes. But leading seaman Titt's eyes were firmly glued to the depth gauge. He was watching the bubble like a weasel watching a rabbit. The moment it began to slither along the tube, Titt had the planes tilted over in a flash to check the movement. Anything could happen if a submarine took on too much of an angle of inclination. If the angle was by the stern, the submarine could plunge down out of control and nothing, short of blowing main ballast, would stop its descent—even that might not be enough.

At 100-odd fathoms they wouldn't stand a chance. The pressure hull would fold up like a matchbox.

Renwick looked over toward Titt again. Titt caught the glance this time. He rolled his eyes upward, echoing Renwick's mute protest as the foreplanesman jerked his head imperceptibly backward in the direction of the O.O.W. and made a little spitting motion of disgust with his lips.

The needle on the foreplanes gauge quivered and began to climb upward at speed.

"For heaven's sake, Renwick, what *are* you doing?" Robinson shrilled, straightening up hurriedly from the periscope as he saw the depth. "Get her down, man. Get her down." For God's sake, he'd have the captain in the control room in a minute to see what was going on.

Startled, Renwick put the planes hard to dive at Robinson's shout, but the submarine continued to rise. At 60 feet, he managed to hold her, but the stern was down at a sharp angle. Robinson's voice rose in fresh alarm as he saw the bubble slipping forward.

"Watch her, Titt. Hold it, man. Titt?"

But Titt had the planes full over, thrusting the stern up. The submarine regained even keel. Renwick, sitting tensed on the edge of his stool, licked his dry lips and began to coax her back down to 80 feet. Robinson had quit his stance at the periscope and moved right up close behind the planesman. The sound of his breathing was audible in the quiet of the control room. Both needles steadied on 80 feet. The bubble was held in the center of the level.

It was a full five minutes before Robinson was able to relax again.

Wiping the thin film of sweat from his forehead, he went back to lean against the for'ard periscope. Gradually his breathing returned to normal. With the submarine steady once more on her depth, he turned to survey the rest of the watch. He'd forgotten about them in the last few minutes. He eased his body forward and peered around the thick bulk of the periscope in the direction of the asdic cabinet.

Rice, the asdic operator on duty, was deep in concentration. A pair of enormous earphones clamped over his head, he slowly turned the control knob on the asdic bearing dial. Robinson nodded to himself in satisfaction and turned back to look at the helmsman. Immediately, his features clouded over with anger. Able seaman Oak, who had the wheel, had tilted his stool as far back as it would go. Legs and arms fully outstretched, he looked down over the length of his long nose at the gyro repeater. His vision wasn't helped by the fact that he wore a cap—an ordinary civilian cap—pulled forward over his head.

Robinson's mouth firmed in a straight line. This was the result of the first lieutenant's being far too lenient with the men. He should know you only had to give them an inch and they'd take a mile. Apparently Lieutenant Brangwyn didn't seem to care anymore how they behaved or how they dressed. All he'd insisted on was that they should wear at least one article of naval clothing in case they were ever made prisoners of war. The men had seen the logic of this—they didn't want to be captured in civilian dress and shot as spies—but at the same time they seemed to think the first lieutenant's edict entitled them to wear anything else they fancied. They'd be appearing in sports jackets and flannels next. In fact, he'd already seen one of them wearing a Polish officer's jacket. Let them get away with that sort of thing, and it was the beginning of the end. But he couldn't do much about it as long as the first lieutenant turned a blind eye. There was something he could and *would* do, however—and right now.

He crept up behind the unsuspecting Oak. "Helmsman," he barked loudly, hoping to startle him, "do you have to steer the boat in that slovenly manner?"

Oak gave no sign of having heard, but his voice floated easily over his shoulder. "No, sir."

Robinson nearly danced with rage. "Well, don't then," he yelled. "Do something about it. Sit up straight."

Oak, his feet resting on the signals locker in front of him, bent his legs so that the stool tilted forward. His knees came up near his chin, but his back was straight. He looked as if he were seated on a horse.

Robinson flushed hotly. His voice cracking with anger, he screamed at Oak. "Put your feet down. Yes, right down—on the deck—and for God's sake sit up properly."

Oak withdrew both feet from the locker and plunked them down, one after the other, on the deck, with great deliberation.

Robinson glared venomously at the back of the seaman's neck. For a moment, looking at the thick black hair straggling out from under the cap, he almost told Oak to get a haircut. He checked himself in time, realizing how ridiculous such an order would be at sea.

Seething inwardly, he returned to the center of the control room, his hands, thumbs showing out, thrust into his jacket pockets and his chin jutting forward. It was then that a movement, in the corner by the exchange, caught his eye. He looked around quickly to see the messenger draw himself up stiff as a poker, his back as straight as a guardsman's. The color rushed to Robinson's face and his eyes flinted hotly. Impertinent little swine. He stood for a moment, breathing through his nostrils, fingers clenching and unclenching in his pockets, but he held his tongue and returned his attention to the planesman. He knew only too well the messenger was inviting him to make some remark, but he wasn't going to make that mistake. He'd deal with them all in his own good time. He'd break their rebellious spirits yet.

Able seaman Stanley, the messenger, his face hidden from the O.O.W., winked cheekily at Oak. His little, brown, teddy-bear eyes danced merrily as he imagined Robinson's rage and frustration. Standing a bare five feet one inch and weighing not much more than a hundred pounds, Stanley looked frail as an invalid. In fact, he was a living terror. His fighting and epic bouts of drinking were legendary, and he spent his life in constant trouble. He'd done more punishment than the rest of the crew put together and had even survived a spell in the glass-house. Innumerable scars covered his face, and half his teeth had been knocked out, but despite this he still grinned cheerily and kept coming up for more. Toward officers he was notoriously cheeky, adopting a cringing and exaggerated manner of obeisance or bland innocence. Robinson knew he would get nothing but a barrage of earnest, straight-faced yes-sirs and no-sirs, if he challenged the bantam seaman. With effort he kept his mouth shut.

At a painstaking rate the hands on the control room clock crept round. Robinson, still seething, concentrated all his attention on keeping an exact trim. He stole a glance at the clock. It would be time to surface soon. He wondered how the cloud would be up top. By the behavior of the boat at 80 feet, he knew they were in for a rough time on the surface.

At 2100 hours precisely, Cheney came into the control room. He hadn't bothered to shave. The thick blue-black stubble on his chin, together with his habit of hunching up his shoulders, gave him a villainous appearance. His eyes, sunk back in his head beneath the heavy brow, were no more than twin flecks of white in the dim light. For a moment he stood in the center of the control room, sniffing, like a great hunting dog, for trouble. The eyes swung around, fixing on each of the watchkeepers for a brief second.

He nodded curtly to Robinson. "Bring her up to thirty feet," he said in a rasping voice.

Robinson repeated the order to the planesman, and carefully they edged the planes over to rise. The submarine began to come up slowly. Robinson looked at the gauge.

"Come on, Renwick. Put a little more rise on there," he admonished sharply.

Renwick exchanged a brief glance with Titt and, with a little shrug of his shoulders, tilted the control bar farther over. The submarine came up like a lift. Robinson's mouth dropped open, but he acted quickly. Using full power on both main motors, he was able to catch her before she broke surface. But it was a few anxious, sweating minutes before he had her under control again. Cheney made no comment but stood waiting, his hands clasped behind his back, his gaze steadily fixed on the for'ard periscope well. The submarine was still bucking about like a frolicsome pony when Cheney ordered the periscope up.

"Watch her, Robinson," he warned as the periscope came hissing out of the well.

Bending low, he grabbed the periscope handles as the massive lens mounting came clear of the deck. Snapping the handles open, he jiggled his head against the mask of the molded rubber eyepiece. A jerk of his wrist brought the lens into high power. With a circling, shuffling movement of his feet, he swung the periscope around to make a quick inspection of the horizon. In the failing light, visibility was down to a few hundred yards. The upper lens of the periscope was constantly awash in the broken sea.

"Bring her up to twenty-four feet," Cheney called out to Robinson, his voice sounding muffled because his head was close to the periscope. He made one further slow sweep of the horizon before snapping the handles together again and ordering the periscope down. Rubbing his eyes, he stood back, blinking for a moment.

"All right, Robinson, fifty feet. We'll go to diving stations in ten minutes," he said. Scowling moodily, he swept out of the control room.

The harsh metallic tones of the Tannoy bounced back off the steel walls of the boat, as diving stations was announced. Immediately there was a general stirring of bodies, followed by a chorus of groans and curses, as the crew wearily pulled themselves out of their hammocks. Stiff-limbed and red-eyed, they looked like a bunch of tramps being cleared off the embankment by a policeman. In an untidy heap, grabbing what spare clothes they could get their hands on, they formed up at the fore-ends bulkhead door and one by one emerged into the passageway to make their way aft.

Chief petty officer Blow was the first man to reach the control room. He was freshly shaved, and the white rollneck submarine jersey he wore under his uniform jacket was clean. He grinned as he pushed his solid bulk against Titt on the afterplanes.

"Come on, Tom. Move your fat arse over," he said, easing himself onto the stool as Titt slid over. Expertly Blow surveyed the bubble and looked at the depth gauge. "What is it? Fifty feet, Tom?" he queried.

Titt nodded.

"Okay, off you go then and let's get on with it," he said, his smooth-cheeked face beaming like a cleric's as he settled himself in.

Brangwyn, the first lieutenant, had taken over from Robinson, and a minute later, Cheney, dressed for the bridge, came into the control room. Brangwyn rubbed his face tiredly with his hands as he watched the planesmen and the behavior of the bubble, trying to get the feel of the boat before he took her up.

"Twenty-eight feet, number one," Cheney called out.

Slowly the boat began to rise as the planes were tilted. Preparatory to surfacing, all the bulbs in the control room had been changed over to red, so that the men going on the bridge would adjust to their night sight more readily. The compartment had a strange otherworldly appearance in the lighting. The pale chalklike faces of the crew were tinged with red, giving them a demoniac look. At 28 feet, Cheney ordered the periscope up and took a quick look around in the deep gloom. The bad light and the effect of heavy seas breaking over the lens made it impossible to see anything. The asdic cabinet had nothing to report.

Cheney clipped the handles of the periscope together.

"Stand by to surface," he called out, crossing over to the foot of the conning tower ladder.

There was an ominous quiet in the control room. Always before surfacing, a tension gripped the crew. They never knew what would be up top: a destroyer lying in wait with its engines stopped; an airplane poised directly overhead, ready to let its depth bombs go; a mine, broken free from its moorings, wallowing about blindly with deadly, probing horns. . . .

"Shut main vents." Brangwyn's voice rang out in the hushed silence.

Petty officer Preece, on the blowing panel, slammed the long levers home. There was a soft, heavy thud as the vents snapped shut, sealing off the upper openings of the buoyancy tanks but leaving open the lower inlets to allow the water to escape as air at high compression surged in. From various parts of the boat, reports filtered back into the control room that all main vents had been checked shut.

Brangwyn informed the captain he was ready to surface.

Cheney climbed a couple of rungs of the conning tower ladder and threw off the clips of the lower hatch. Signalman Beer, carrying the small Aldis lamp and the recognition flares, made to follow him. With a powerful heave, Cheney threw the heavy hatch cover back. A thin trickle of water, which had collected in the conning tower during the dive, dripped down on him.

Making an involuntary ducking motion, he twisted his head and yelled over his shoulder to Brangwyn: "Surface! Blow all main ballast!"

There was a roaring, hissing noise like a railway engine blowing off steam as Preece opened the valves on the blowing panel. Compressed air at 4,000 pounds per square inch rushed into the buoyancy tanks, forcing the water out.

The submarine began to rise like a cork.

Brangwyn, with a couple of quick steps, crossed over to stand at the foot of the conning tower, calling out the changing depths to Cheney.

"Twenty feet."

"Fifteen."

"Ten."

Cheney, at the top of the ladder, unclipped the upper hatch and flung it open. The water still trapped in the cockpit of the bridge cascaded down. Brangwyn, at the foot of the conning tower, was able to dodge out of the way, but Cheney and the signalman took the full, icy brunt of it together with the two lookouts who had moved up into the tower.

The first towering wave caught the submarine as she shook herself free from the depths. As she wallowed about like a half-drowned puppy, the seas poured over her bridge. Down below, the crew scattered as fresh cascades of water poured into the control room. A few seconds later, Cheney called down the voice pipe to start the main engines. The telegraphs clanged warningly, startling the diesels into life. A heavy tremor ran through the boat, and from the direction of the engine room bulkhead door the hammering sound of the engines shattered the silence. A puff of blue smoke, invisible in the gloom, came billowing out from the stern of the submarine.

For a moment she seemed to flounder about heavily, as if unable to get her bearings, before her bows swung slowly around to quarter the oncoming waves and she headed for the distant coastline of Norway.

Five minutes later the crew had fallen out of diving stations and the watch had taken over. Sub-lieutenant Joyner, the officer of the watch, was waiting to go up on the bridge. He braced himself to face the ordeal, but first the signalman had to come down. Cheney never allowed more than four men on the bridge at a time, in the event they should have to submerge in a hurry. Joyner didn't have long to wait. Puffing and blowing, Beer came clattering down the ladder, the Aldis lamp clutched tightly to his chest. His high cheekbones were scuffed by the wind, and his long thin nose was polished red like an apple. Joyner looked at the signalman distastefully, his spirit shrinking at the thought of two long hours on the bridge. Joyner's own face, normally pale, looked even paler now that the red bulbs had been changed back and a cold yellow-green glow permeated the control room. His eyes were red-rimmed and watered freely. He looked close to tears. Joyner was, in fact, beginning to feel seasick and would have liked nothing more than to crawl back into his bunk. Anything rather than face the grim reality of the weather-exposed bridge and two interminable hours of wet and icy misery.

Gritting his teeth, he grasped the bottom rung of the ladder and hauled himself up into the tower. The wind, sucked in by the pounding diesels, tore at him as he fought his way up to the bridge. He pulled himself up through the hatch and with an effort staggered out onto the swaying, windswept deck. For a moment he thought he was going to be sick. He lunged forward, and flinging his hands out, he clutched at the bridge capping. Shutting his eyes tightly, hoping that Cheney hadn't noticed, he hung on for a minute until the feeling had passed.

Cheney observed him coldly out of the corner of his eye. He distrusted Joyner. He felt the man was weak and unreliable. Unfortunately every submarine had to take its quota of rookies to enable them to get in sea time. The sub-lieutenant had been nearly eight weeks on board the *Scorpion* now and had one patrol to his credit. In a way he could be said to be unlucky. Normally the boat carried four officers and one extra for training purposes, but with the number of new submarines coming out of the yards and soaking up trained personnel it was difficult to get replacement officers. The *Scorpion* was shorthanded. Joyner, who was really only a trainee, did his best, but it fell far short of Cheney's standards. On the surface it wasn't so bad, as Joyner had two experienced lookouts to share the watch with him; but down below it was a different matter. A lot of things could go wrong with a submarine when she was dived. Dangerous situations could develop with terrifying rapidity. And the trim? Joyner was never able to master the delicate operation of keeping the submarine at the prescribed depth. With Joyner on watch the planesmen would work like mad and the stokers manning the pumps would spend their entire watch starting and stopping the motors as the boat seesawed about.

It was stoker M'Candless, in consequence of one such lengthy session with the pumps, who was responsible for giving Joyner his nickname. Coming off watch, tired and frayed at the edges, he announced in his rich Irish brogue and in full hearing of everyone—including the first lieutenant—that he "wouldn't put the basthard in charge of a boss." For some time after this Joyner was always referred to as the "bus conductor" by the crew. But then, and no one knew how or who was responsible, the tag underwent a mysterious change and he became known as the "ticket collector."

The "ticket collector" straightened up from where he was leaning against the bridge. Cheney looked at him suspiciously. Raising his voice to carry above the wind, he said: "Keep her on

045, Joyner. I'm going below. If you see anything at all call me; and call me in an hour anyway. All right?"

Joyner took a grip on himself, but before he had time to make a reply Cheney was halfway through the hatch and a second later had vanished from sight. Joyner glanced nervously around him. The lookouts, dark shadowy figures peering through binoculars into the black night, could have been miles away. He felt scared and terribly alone.

In the control room, though the crew had fallen out of diving stations, a round half dozen of them hung around smoking and talking in low tones. Jock Bain was petty officer of the watch, and Cheney was talking to Brangwyn over by the chart table. Too cold to hang about for any length of time, the men began to drift away, hoping to catch an hour's sleep before the main meal was served around midnight. A few minutes later Brangwyn left, leaving Cheney alone by the chart table. Brows drawn down, Cheney studied the markings on the chart before him. Still wearing his bridge clothes, his binoculars slung round his neck, he was lost in concentration as the coxswain approached. Blow had to cough again to indicate his presence.

"Ahem, ahem? Excuse me, sir—"

Cheney swung around, shooting an impatient glance at his senior petty officer. "Yes, coxswain? What is it?"

"Up spirits at 2330, sir? Dinner at 2400?" The request was a formality.

"Yes, yes." Cheney nodded brusquely and returned his attention to the chart. Blow remained where he was.

"Yes, what is it now, coxswain?" Cheney asked irritably, looking up.

Blow met his gaze impassively. "It's able seaman Mitchell, sir. He appears to be running a bit of a fever. I'm afraid I'll have to ask him to be excused duties for the time being, sir."

Cheney drew a deep breath. "What's the matter with him?"

Blow rubbed his smooth chin. "I'm not sure, sir. He says he's not feeling good. He's got a headache and—well, he's running this fever."

Cheney put his pencil down. "Is he in pain?"

"No pain, sir, only the headache and a bit fevered—"

"He hasn't any pain, just a headache and slight fever, and you want to excuse him duties. Is that it?"

"That's right, sir. I don't think he's well enough to keep a watch," Blow replied evenly.

Cheney stared unseeingly at the chart. He paused before jerking his head around decisively. "Very well, coxswain, but get him back on the watch list as quickly as possible. We can't afford to be shorthanded."

"Aye, aye, sir." Blow's feet came together and his shoulders squared. Turning on his heel, he strode off, instinctively adjusting his gait to the swaying deck.

When he'd gone, Cheney picked up his pencil again, a dour expression on his dark features. Glancing at the control room clock, he noted the time. He drew a mark on the chart. By midnight they should be just off Naze Point and approaching the entrance to the channel which would take them into the Skagerrak. The channel was known to be heavily mined. Cheney sullenly eyed the heavy red cross-hatching which marked off the area of the minefield. It would take them the best part of a whole day to get through it. But after that? A grim smile of satisfaction played for a brief instant at the corners of his mouth. After that he would be right on Jerry's doorstep. But the expression was short-lived, for he recalled the battle he'd had at the patrol briefing back on the parent ship. It had taken a lot of argument to get permission to extend his patrol billet beyond the entrance to the Skagerrak. In the end, with Captain Osbourne's support, he'd won, but it had been a struggle. It had left him with an even deeper feeling of contempt for staff officers. It was a damned good thing they didn't have to go to sea. Slide rules and statistics didn't sink ships or win wars—only action did.

Action! Action! Action!

His outspread hands beat out the rhythm of the words on the chart table. God, it had taken long enough for them to get it into their thick heads that the best way to discourage the U-boats from making a break for it was to sink one of the damned things. Go right into the Skagerrak and let them know it, instead of hanging about outside making barking sounds like an aging sheep dog. Hit them and hit them hard. That was the only thing they would understand. A kick in the guts would make them think twice about putting to sea.

Unconsciously he bit his knuckle as he turned his attention to the upper part of the chart, studying the many clusters of islands and numerous waterways that made up the complex of Oslo Fiord. It was there that the U-boat flotillas had gathered since being driven out of Danzig. He peered closer at the chart, trying to make out the fathom lines. His eyes felt gritty, and he found it difficult to get the tiny markings into focus. He stifled a yawn. During the passage from the Clyde and up through the Minches they had run into bad weather. Buffeted along the wild race of the Pentland Firth, they had finally broken out into the North Sea. A few winks on the Aldis lamp and their escort vessel had turned back, her hull quickly swallowed up by the gathering night. Alone and friendless—at sea a submarine had no friends—they made the crossing to Norway. The weather had steadily worsened and no one had been able to get much sleep or rest.

Cheney felt the yawn coming on again. He switched out the light above the chart table and drew the canvas cover over the chart. Placing a paperweight carefully on the stiff canvas, he made his way to his cabin. It wasn't until he was inside that he realized he was still wearing the damp towel, which he used as a scarf, around his neck. He peeled it off and hung it up beside the louver in the ventilating trunk. Fully clothed, he lay down on his bunk. He stretched out and tried to let himself go and relax. It seemed weeks since he'd slept. Reaching over to his locker, he found a pair of red goggles. He slipped them over his head and lay back again; they would help his night vision if he were suddenly called to the bridge. The goggles screened off the glare from the light fixture on the deckhead. He stared at the bulb. It looked like the sun viewed through a piece of smoked glass, reminding him of how he used to watch eclipses as a child. His eyelids felt as heavy as his tired limbs. Trying to

drain his mind of all thoughts, he shut his eyes. All his energies
and resources would be taxed in the days to come.

The steady throb, throb, of the diesels and the dull boom of
the heavy seas breaking over the casing above his head had a
hypnotic effect, but he knew he wouldn't sleep. He seldom did
when they were on the surface in enemy waters. With an inexperienced officer on the bridge he daren't even think about it.
Concentrating on the need for rest, he went through his nightly
relaxation routine. Starting at his toes he worked up through all
the muscle groups of his body, contracting and relaxing each
group in turn and then repeating the process. The drill had a
soothing effect and with its help he was able to keep at bay the
race of thoughts which clamored for attention.

While Cheney rested, Joyner paced about the bridge, restless
and ill at ease. He'd managed to work himself into a state of
near anxiety. The last patrol—his first—had scared him to
death. Safely back on the parent ship he was convinced he'd
never be able to go through with it again.

There was a chilling reality about setting out with the intention to kill and destroy. It was even more chilling when you
knew you mightn't come back. To talk about it all phlegmat-
ically in the comfortable, smoky, gin-and-whiskey-laden atmosphere of the wardroom was easy. It became something entirely
different when you were trapped inside the cold, oily, steel box
of a submarine's control room at a depth of 250 feet, with a
great, roaring destroyer up above shaking the living guts out of
you with depth charges.

Joyner had—along with his other ideas—believed that war
was a noble contest of arms. Visions of knights, cavalry officers and leather-helmeted, silk-scarfed fighter pilots had been
jumbled together in his mind. A sort of legion of heroes who
were ever ready to save the world from blacks, Jews and Reds.

He was beginning to regret he'd ever joined submarines.
He'd never imagined just how awful life could be aboard a
small vessel. Basically a weak type, he'd wanted to impress. Now
he was paying for it.

A fussy overemotional mother hadn't helped his development. Nor had his father. A vicar of a small parish near Tonbridge, the Reverend Mr. Joyner had succeeded in abstracting Christianity away from the vulgar needs of the everyday world. He avoided the poor like the plague and cringed before the wealthy. Even his saintlike meekness was a lie. The Reverend Mr. Joyner had no spine. His son was like him in many ways.

To this legacy from his parents Joyner had made his own contribution. He had a cruel streak and a hidden desire for violence. Before the war had begun he had admired Hitler. The man with the staring eyes and the music-hall moustache had appeared as a messianic figure who would cure society's ills. Words like "destiny" and "blood" had taken on near-sacred meanings to Joyner. Six years later his ideas had not basically changed, though his concern for his own skin now dominated his thought processes.

The submarine bucked into the rising sea, sending a cold shower of stinging spray over the bridge. Joyner, unprepared, caught the full force of it in his face. It took his breath away. For a moment his mouth jerked open in silent protest as the icy water ran down his neck. Twisting his head violently from side to side, he bent down to crouch behind the bridge structure. His binoculars were soaking wet. Glad of the excuse to shelter he began drying them with painstaking care. Busy wiping the last drop of moisture from the lens, he nearly dropped the glasses in fright as he heard the cry from the starboard lookout.

"Light bearing green 030!"

Joyner's heart gave a painful thump. A cold hand clutched at his insides. Fighting against the desire to call the captain immediately, he shot up hurriedly. Finding his glasses difficult to focus, he began to search the bearing.

A smudge of light seemed to jog about in the lens. Like a firefly it danced across the bloomed glass. God, there was something out there in the dark, all right. He stole a quick glance at the lookouts. Both men were calmly scanning their respective sectors. It was up to him to act—and quickly. He jerked the glasses to his eyes again, his heart thudding wildly. There it was again. But now to his astonishment he could see what appeared to be a diffused yellow glow behind the light. It seemed to spread upward from the horizon as if the ship—it had to be a ship—was encircled by a dim halo. His legs felt weak and they trembled, but he forced them to propel him across to the voice pipe. He seized it with both hands. His shout—or near shriek—almost knocked the helmsman off his stool, but it was effective.

Within seconds Cheney was scrambling out of the upper hatch.

"What's the bearing, Joyner? What is it?" he snapped, covering the bridge in a bound and leaping up by the night sight.

Joyner had difficulty in finding his voice. "It's a light, sir," he stammered. "Green 030 . . . it looks like—it's odd, sir, there's a sort of glow—"

But Cheney had already picked it up and was rapping out a stream of orders.

"Starboard twenty," he called down the voice pipe, "steer 210." His finger pressed the night alarm tit. The bows began to pay off. Presenting her beam to the sea, the submarine began to roll heavily as she backed off from the fast-approaching ship.

Long minutes passed. The glow surrounding the vessel could be picked up with the naked eye.

Down below, in the relatively peaceful atmosphere of warmth and light and the homely smell of cooking, disciplined havoc had broken loose with the sounding of the alarm. The crew, sleep still crusting their eyes, ran helter-skelter down the passageway. Unaware of pain or discomfort, they bumped into each other and the unyielding steel walls which enclosed them. Blind to everything else, they ran to their stations.

In the control room the attack team took over from the watch on duty. By the foot of the conning tower the gun's crew had closed up and stood around expectantly, talking in low, urgent whispers. The first lieutenant, hair tousled and looking like an overgrown schoolboy, took over command of the operations center. Standing between the periscopes he ticked off the "state of readiness" reports as they filtered in. Already the exchange was beginning to look like something from fairyland as lights flashed and flickered on the board.

C.P.O. Blow was seated at his diving station on the after-planes. His arm hooked over the back of his stool, he sucked his cheek as he eyed the gun's crew speculatively. He was a bit concerned with having had to replace Mitchell, who was sight setter on the gun, with the less experienced Kennedy. He hoped they wouldn't have to go to "gun action." It was easy to understand why the captain had appeared so annoyed earlier. Only the first night on their billet and a man had to be excused duties. It was a serious situation. In a submarine every member of the crew was valuable and had a specific duty to perform.

He would have to get Mitchell back on duty as soon as possible.

He shifted his glance to look over toward Titt. When they fell out again he'd have a word with him about the sick seaman. Titt was reliable; he'd keep a close eye on Mitchell.

The telegraphs clanged off like a fire bell. A shudder ran through the boat as the engines were opened out to full speed. Instinctively Blow wheeled around to face the depth gauge of the afterplanes. His grip on the control bar tightened. Full speed on both engines could mean that they were about to dive at any minute. But the minutes passed and nothing happened. Blow's grip on the planes lever relaxed a little. He turned to look at the gun's crew. They had stopped their whispered conversation and were looking up at the narrow entrance of the lower hatch. They had the tensed look of runners on the starting line, ready to get off their marks.

Blow eyed Kennedy carefully. The young seaman's face was drawn, and his eyes were bright with a nervous glaze. Blow shook his head and uttered a silent hope that there was nothing much the matter with Mitchell.

A submarine carried no medical personnel. In looking after the crew's health the coxswain had no more than a knowledge of first aid and his own common sense to guide him. Fortunately the most the men ever seemed to suffer from was constipation or an odd cut or bruise. A couple of number nines or a roll of inch bandage was all the therapy they usually required.

With the pressing of the night alarm tit "Bombardier" Billy Wells, the torpedo gunner's mate, had leaped out of his bunk. Jumping across the table in the P.O.'s' mess, he'd flung the curtain screen back. Out in the passageway he met the stream of bodies pouring out from the fore-ends. He jammed his greasy cap hard over his bulletlike head, bent forward and battered his way through the melee like a wing-three quarter coming out of a scrum.

By the time he'd reached the tube space the three hands who made up his crew were already closed up. Mulholland had cracked open the inlet valves and from the air pressure line had blown water into the tubes.

"Okay, Scouse?" queried Wells, still struggling to get his breath back.

Mulholland gave the thumbs-up sign. Wells nodded and squeezed past him. He wriggled his bulk into the space between the tubes, and his eyes flicked around, hurriedly checking the gauges. He reached the firing panel. With a quick heave from his muscular arms he hoisted himself up into the operator's seat. He settled himself in before unhooking the phone and calling up the exchange. Another quick glance at the gauges on the tubes and he flicked down the switches that would light up the master indicator in the control room.

The phone crackled and buzzed angrily. Wells adjusted the mouthpiece harness so that it sat easily around his neck. He ran his tongue over his lips. Speaking clearly and distinctly, he reported to the exchange that all tubes were brought to the ready. Above his head the tube space indicator board flashed on. One by one the little panels blinked into life until all six read "stand-by."

Wells drew out the locking pins from the manual firing triggers.

On the bridge Cheney had altered course again. Having first made a cautionary withdrawal, he had then gone in a large circle and was now creeping up on the ship that had been sighted. His glasses steady as a rock in his hands, he craned forward eagerly over the night-firing sight. Underneath the masthead light of the approaching ship he could just make out the heavy black shape of her hull framed in the yellow aura of light. She was obviously a vessel of considerable size—perhaps a 20,000-tonner from the look of her. From a point in the region of her bridge, little lights began to appear, like a village street being lit up at night.

The binoculars moved fractionally as his brows came down in a frown. One hand unconsciously gripped the bar of the night sight. The dark mass seemed to change in shape, and the lights telescoped into one single blob as the vessel, putting her helm over, made a large alteration of course.

Suddenly the explanation of the surrounding halo was revealed as the huge wall of her beam slid into sight, presenting an ideal target.

Joyner and the two lookouts heard the quick explosion of breath from Cheney and they tensed. Joyner, scanning the stern sector, dropped his glasses and wheeled around. To his astonishment Cheney had stepped down off the platform and was bending over the voice pipe. His words could be heard above the wind. "Call off the attack. . . . Port twenty. . . . Steer o6o. . . . Fall out diving stations . . . patrol routine."

Cheney's voice snapped off abruptly. He turned and stepped down off the platform. Joyner stood stiff and expectant.

"Keep your eye on her, Joyner. Keep clear of her if she alters course again. If she doesn't, come back on 045 in ten minutes. All right?" Cheney's voice sounded sour with disappointment.

Joyner nodded blankly. "Yes, sir," he replied, his eyes squinting to catch a glimpse of the ship, which was now ablaze with light. He was still unable to understand why the attack had been broken off.

Cheney made for the hatch. Then he stopped. Joyner, burning with curiosity to have a look at the ship, paused with his binoculars halfway to his eyes, not sure whether the captain wanted to speak to him or not. He took a couple of hesitant steps. Cheney waited on him, his face like stone. He bent forward at the waist as Joyner approached. In a voice that cut through the wind like a knife, he said: "She's a hospital ship, Joyner. All right? Just keep an eye on her." He gripped the hatch cover and in an energetic movement swung his legs over the coaming. A second later he had vanished from view down the tower.

Joyner's first reaction to the news was to feel an overwhelming sense of relief. Almost gaily he retraced his steps across the bridge. A hospital ship? The fear of threatened action removed, his tension began to drain away. Confidently he leaned over the bridge capping and lifted the binoculars to his eyes.

Lookout able seaman Moore had caught a brief snatch of Cheney's words. He had a quick glance over his shoulder to see what Joyner was up to. He saw the dim figure leaning out over the bridge. Though the brightly lit ship wasn't in his sector he decided to chance a quick look. He whipped his glasses around. Immediately he saw the great, towering slab of the vessel's hull and the large red cross painted on her side. The cross looked oddly distorted by the angle of perspective. For a moment an idiotic thought crossed his mind as he tried to imagine how long it would have taken to paint the cross. As he watched, the huge cross appeared to change shape and the row of lights, strung out like beads, began to merge into each other as the ship altered course again.

Moore would have liked to signal his opposite number, have a brief word with him. Anything to share the experience of having seen a hospital ship at sea. But he knew he daren't. Joyner would be down on him like a ton of bricks at the least whisper. A little feeling of guilt gnawing at him, he had one last look at the vessel before returning to cover his own sector. He realized that in the seconds he'd allowed his attention to wander, a fast-moving destroyer or an E-boat could have covered a few hundred yards—a distance that could make all the difference between getting down out of the way or being rammed. The thought made him shudder involuntarily.

An hour passed. The hospital ship had long since vanished. Resuming her earlier course the submarine closed the coast of

Norway; a tiny and insignificant vessel, alone in the wilderness of the black night.

Titt glanced at his watch and yawned. It had just gone ten thirty, or in naval language 2230 hours. At this time of night most of the crew would be up and about, but the passage across the North Sea had taken a lot out of them and they were catching up on lost sleep. Titt pulled himself up to a sitting position and looked at his watch again. He could feel the weight of bodies on either side pressing in as the hammocks swayed with each dip and roll of the boat. He wondered how Mitchell was. After they had fallen out of diving stations he had had a couple of the hands move the seaman's hammock from where it had been, near the center, to the outside of the bunch.

Throwing back the blankets, he reached under his pillow for his shoes. Leaning over the side of his hammock, as far as he could, he dropped the shoes carefully onto the table underneath. For a moment, reluctant to move, he sat rubbing his legs and shoulders before stretching up and grabbing an eyebolt on the deckhead. With a quick intake of breath he heaved himself out, his legs forcing a passageway through the dead weight of pressing bodies before his stockinged feet found the table. He put his shoes on, and keeping his head low, he worked his way underneath the bulge of hammocks to step over the man who was sleeping on the starboard locker bench. Brought up short by the spare torpedoes lying in their racks, he turned and placing his feet carefully on the locker so as not to disturb the sleeper, he wriggled his way up past the side of Mitchell's hammock. It was like trying to crawl under a dead elephant.

Mitchell's eyes were closed, and he was breathing through his half-opened mouth. There wasn't much color in his face, but this was not unusual; you didn't pick up a Riviera tan in a submarine. The skin shone greasily from his perspiration.

"You all right, Mitch?" Titt queried in a low whisper. There was no answer. Mitchell was sound asleep.

Titt, gripping the edge of his hammock, looked at the seaman for a while. He whispered again. No answer. He let go of the hammock and, ducking down, made his way back across the table, crawling carefully and quietly. Reaching his own hammock he slipped his shoes off and pushed them under his pillow. In a moment he was curled up underneath the blankets again. It was more than an hour before it would be time to get up and start preparing the mess for the evening meal. He would have another look at Mitchell then.

Titt pulled the blankets over his head and shut his eyes. In a few minutes he was fast asleep.

Chapter Three

As the night wore on, the smell of cooking grew steadily stronger. Pots and pans were bubbling and boiling on the small galley range. From time to time Steve Donahue, the cook, would open the oven door to see how the joints were coming along. The waft of heat, as it hit him, drew fresh beads of sweat from his perspiring features. Dinner would be ready in little more than half an hour. The time was 2330 hours.

Responding to some ancient instinct, the mass of bodies in the fore-ends had begun to stir. The restlessness grew as the crew yawned and rubbed their eyes. Gray figures, like animals awakening from a long period of hibernation, began to emerge from the hammocks. One or two lights came on, and the quiet was broken by the sound of bodies shuffling about and the soft murmur of voices. The two men lying on the bench lockers were rudely shaken, and some of the hands began to clear away the pile of spare gear that cluttered the table. More lights were switched on as the hammocks emptied. It seemed the first thing a man wanted to do whenever he got up was to switch on another light.

Titt, one of the first up, yawned heavily and scratched his chest. Two men still remained in their hammocks. Titt seized the sling ropes and shook the hammocks vigorously.

"Come on then, you two. Let's be having you. Come on, rise and shine, everything's fine—" He put his hand to his mouth as it yawned open again. Groans and protests answered him. One of the sleepers wanted to know the time.

Titt grabbed the slings again and shook them even more violently. "Never mind the time. It's time to get out of your pit, that's what time it is. Come on then, shake it up, you two."

Cursing Titt under their breath, the men got out and lowered themselves onto the mess table. The hammocks, now that they were emptied, were lashed back out of the way. Not much space was saved, but at least the men didn't have to duck down to sit at the table. Titt got hold of the biscuit tin that contained all the mess cutlery. He dumped it on the table with a jangling crash. The two late risers groaned again and screwed up their faces in pain, but they got off the table. Now that the table was clear, somebody got out the mess kettle containing the crockery and cups. Titt looked around the fore-ends. Able seaman Renwick was standing next to the table with a blank expression on his face, still half asleep.

Titt removed a tin from where it was hung up on the torpedo racks. "Here," he called out, flinging the tin across to Renwick, "if you're doing nothing go and get the rum, okay?"

Renwick blinked. He stuck his hands out and managed to catch the tin. He looked at Titt vacantly for a second, then the corners of his mouth twisted into a dopey smile as he caught on. "Well, chop-chop, mate."

Renwick needed no second telling. The man who collected the rum invariably got a few "sippers" from the rest of the crew. Titt, as leading hand of the mess, was supposed to collect the rum himself, but he switched the duty around so everyone would get his share of perks. Renwick shot off.

When he'd gone Titt went into his locker and got out the rum list. Everyone who was entitled to draw had his name marked down on the list. Titt put it down on the end of the table as one of the hands began laying out the cups. As yet conversation in the fore-ends was sporadic, but it began to pick up and become more lively at the prospect of "up spirits."

Renwick came back. He stepped gingerly through the bulkhead door, holding onto the tin with both hands. There was a ragged cheer from the fore-ends, and all the hands gathered as he picked his way through the mess and put the half-full tin down in front of Titt. Edging over, Titt made room for Renwick to sit down beside him. He pushed the rum list across the table. "Tick them off, Raggy," he said, taking charge of the rum. No one had a pencil. Everyone had to get up again as Titt went into his locker. Rummaging around, he found a chewed-up stub. He passed it over to Renwick and sat down once more. The men pressed in closer.

"Well, here we go, lads," said Titt, dipping a cup into the tin of rum. Carefully, holding the cup over the tin, he poured the rum into his "official" measure. In the light the dark-brown liquid sparkled and shone like Venetian glass. The eyes of the crew, dulled with fatigue, lit up, and they sniffed deeply as the thick, pungent aroma caught at the back of their throats.

Big Jock Corr was at the head of the list. He reached out his hand, and his thick fingers closed firmly around the mug Titt passed him. Eyes dancing merrily, he paused for a second as he savored the sight and smell of the heavy spirity liquid. His face creased into a broad smile and he gave a sort of dry, choking laugh. The mug came level with his eyes.

"Cheers, you lot," he said in a throaty voice. "Down the hatch." He tossed off the measure in one go. The fiery alcohol hit him, bringing tears to his eyes. He shut his eyes tightly, exploding his breath through slack lips.

"Brrrrhhh." He wiped his mouth with his fingers and put the mug down on the table. "Christ, that was great," he said, looking round the mess as if challenging the others to deny the truth of his statement. "Smashing. Ah could go the same again."

No one made any offers.

Only a thin film of liquid covered the bottom of the rum container. Everyone, including Titt, had had his ration, but naval regulations allowed a little extra in case of spillage. As leading hand of the mess and rum bosun, Titt was entitled to this by age-old tradition. He poured the rum into a cup. It was at least two thirds of a full tot. He passed the cup over to Renwick.

"Here you are, Raggy. Have a gulp."

Renwick rubbed his hands together. He chuckled as he

grabbed the cup. "Goodo, Tom." Taking a deep sip he handed the cup back.

Titt drained it. "Well, that's our lot for another day," he said.

The cups were pushed into the center of the table. Corr grabbed the rum tin, looking ruefully inside it as he shook it from side to side. "Ah reckon we should get two tots. One's no' enough," he complained.

"Two tots?" Stanley let out a derisive whoop. "Two tots, you bastard? You're half pissed on one already. Give you any more and you'd be wanting to jump ashore with a bloody great claymore in your hand. Yaaagh!" He let out a yell and waved his arm over his head, clutching an imaginary sword. "Watch out, you bloody German sassenaks, here comes Big Jock with his fiery cross and haggis bombs. Yaaagh!"

Some of the hands laughed.

"I'll do you yet, you wee Yorkshire bastard," Corr threatened.

"Lancashire," corrected Stanley.

"Lancashire or Yorkshire, you'll get done one of these days." But there was no real menace in Corr's tone. This sort of thing went on all the time with Stanley.

Stanley made a rasping noise with his lips. Suddenly he clapped his hand to his head. "Here, there's an idea. . . . Why didn't I think of it before? We should've sent Jock as a one-man boarding party on that hospital ship. That would've shaken them up. The Jerry pongoes would have been running around on their crutches shouting for help, thinking Uncle Joe had arrived with his kilt on."

"Yah." Corr made a face. "Why don't you go and get lost, you short-arsed English dwarf?"

The rum had eased the crew's tongues and raised their spirits. A new vitality flowed through their veins. Enthusiastically they joined in on the banter between Corr and Stanley. Titt couldn't help smiling to himself at the animated expression on the bantam seaman's battered little face. Stanley delighted in this sort of thing and was in fact encouraged by most of the hands, who looked upon him as a sort of court jester. One of the men wasn't smiling, though, as he looked sourly over the table at Stanley. As if he'd heard enough, he shoved his cup away from him forcefully. It hit the pile in the center of the table, making a little clinking sound.

The hands stopped and looked at him.

"Big joke, eh, Stanley?" able seaman Thornley said sneeringly. There was an uncomfortable silence. Thornley was nearly as big as Corr and had a reputation of being ready with his fists. He wasn't the most popular man in the mess, but his know-all, tough, sneering manner had earned him a number of followers. On top of that, as one of the few peacetime sailors on board and having served in the Mediterranean during the Spanish Civil War and the troubles in Palestine, he was accorded a certain respect. Most "hostilities only" ratings had a certain regard for the regulars, even if they never admitted to it. On the other hand, few of the regulars ever spoke any way but disparagingly of the "hostilities only" men. Thornley was a good example of this attitude. As far as he was concerned, the bulk of the men who made up the Navy in wartime were nothing more than dodgers who'd been winkled out from cushy jobs behind desks by the authorities. Whatever else Stanley was, he was an H.O., and in Thornley's book H. O.'s should only open their big mouths when asked.

"Yeah, big joke, Stanley," he repeated. "But I'll tell you something for nothing. If it'd been me, I'd have had a boarding party on that ship, quicker than that. Or better still, stuck a pair of kippers up its arse. Hospital ship?" he sneered again. "Bloody great troop carrier, that's what it was, I'll bet."

An awkward silence followed Thornley's remarks. It wasn't caused so much by what he'd said but rather his reasons for saying it at all. Stanley had only been joking as usual. Everyone knew that.

The silence drew out.

Thornley glared around the mess. The only sound, persistent and regular, like the dripping of a tap, was the slow *tack, tack, tack,* of Titt's pencil hitting the table. Thornley's expression changed. Slowly his eyebrows climbed up his forehead and his lips twisted in a sardonic smile.

"Here," he said with a short incredulous laugh, "none of you . . . none of you think that was a real hospital ship, do you?"

Some of the men coughed and cleared their throats, but there was no reply.

Thornley shook his head pityingly. "Well, what do you know? What a right bunch of goons. Imagine—"

"It's right enough." Mulholland's voice broke the silence.

Thornley whipped around, the muscles in his face tightening. "What's right enough?" he asked belligerently.

Mulholland ignored him, talking to the others. "It's right enough," he repeated. "I wouldn't piss about with them. They'd have had their little lot if it'd been me—bloody, great, square-headed bastards. I'd just like to see them letting one of our ships go. Like hell they would. They'd have sunk it, hospital ship or no hospital ship." Mulholland spoke quietly, staring trancelike at the table.

Corr frowned at this. A heavy, puzzled look settled on his eyes and mouth. His glance circled the men packed around the table. Ponderously, his big head shaking from side to side, he appeared to grapple with the ethics of the problem.

"Ah don't know . . . ," he began slowly, but Thornley was ready and waiting to cut down any opposition.

"*You* don't know?" he sneered sarcastically. "Well, *I* do. We should have sunk the bastards, that's what we should have done." He stabbed his thumb in the direction of Mulholland. "He's right, you know. They'd have done it to us."

A low murmur of assent came from some of the crew. Big Corr shook his head again. "Ah don't know. . . . You canna go around sinking hospital ships. It's no' right, even if they are Jerries."

The sudden upsurge of argument had split the mess right down the middle. The spark from Thornley had started a fire. Within minutes tempers had flared as the men took sides. Heated words were exchanged, and differences of opinion began to take on a personal note as the chance was seized to cross swords with old enemies. An open, violent slanging match was developing. It wouldn't have taken much more to set them at each other's throats.

In the babble of noise no one noticed that Titt's pencil had stopped tapping the table. Titt didn't shout or anything, but his voice had a quality in it that made it cut through, as he told all of them to shut up.

"Just stow it, will you? The lot of you."

Sullenly, some of them a little shamefaced, the men looked at Titt. They quieted down one by one, their angry voices dropping off. Finally only Thornley was left. Feeling more and more isolated in the growing silence, the big, blond seaman tried to bluster on, but when he got no response his voice began to die away in angry embarrassment.

"Are you done?" Titt asked quietly.

Thornley glared at him. "What's the matter with you, Tom? You're not another one of these bloody pacifists, are you?"

Titt met the infuriated glare coolly and easily. He rubbed his chin thoughtfully, but a tiny, dangerous smile crossed his features. "No, I'm not a pacifist, mate. But there's a lot worse things than that—like wanting to kill blokes that are in the hospital—"

"Hospital, my arse," swore Thornley. He flung out his arm, pointing vaguely. "Do you think they was injured, the blokes on that ship, then?" His arms threshed the air despairingly. "I don't know. I just don't know. How you can believe that old cock—"

"Listen, mate, I'm not going to argue with you. I've just one thing to say. Let's suppose they weren't troops and we'd stuck a fish in them, what then?" Titt asked.

Thornley made a sound of utter contempt. "Course they was troops. What else would they be?"

Rice's thin voice, tremulous and pedantic, wavered out. "But what about the Geneva Convention?"

"Fuck the Geneva Convention." Thornley turned on Rice, snarling. "Who asked for your opinion?"

Rice flushed deeply. He began to stammer a reply. Titt
stopped him with a wave of his hand.

"All right, Thornley. That's about enough. You started this
thing and now you can drop it. Just wrap it up, eh?"

Thornley's eyes went red with anger, but he held onto his
temper. He didn't want to tangle with Titt. His lips twisted in
an ugly grin. "Yeah, great. Just great. We let a shipful of Jerries
go and we're all supposed to cheer or something. How about
that?"

Titt's face was like stone. "How about nothing. I said to
wrap it up." The two men weighed each other. Thornley swallowed hard, looking at Titt narrowly. Titt leaned forward, daring him to have a go

Thornley shut up.

Titt now turned to face the rest of the crew. He folded his
arms on the table and took a deep breath. "I've listened to a lot
of you cackling your fat, but let me tell you one thing, seeing
there's a lot think we should have knocked off that ship. I was
on the *P*-98 in the Med when we sunk a trooper. It was an Eye-
tie trooper, only this one was carrying a lot of our blokes on
board. We picked up a few after—survivors, you know. We
could have picked up a few more, but they couldn't swim and
they all drowned." He paused to let his words sink in. "They
couldn't swim, see—the reason was that they were all injured
and on their way back to the hospital in Italy. So the next time
you talk about hospital ships you want to remember that. It
might make you think twice before going off at half cock."

There was a guilty silence. No one spoke. Titt got to his feet
slowly.

"All right then, you lot, if you've all done cackling let's get
the table cleared and think about getting dinner up." He
picked up the rum list and the pencil stub. He'd just got to his
locker and was bending over it when the boat gave a violent roll
to port. Titt was flung forward. His head cracked up against
the torpedo rack. All the cups on the table were sent flying.
One of them, behaving as if it were making a dash for freedom,

leaped across the fore-ends and smashed itself against the side of a torpedo.

Everyone had been caught off balance by the unexpected lurch, and more than a few heads and shins were cracked. There was a wild chorus of groans and curses. Titt jerked open the lid of his locker and fished out a thick scarf, wrapping it around his neck. He put the rum list and the pencil stub away and slammed the lid of his locker shut hurriedly.

Corr, who was standing right by him, blinked. "What's all the hurry for, mate? Where are you heading?"

Titt nodded in the direction of the control room. "That was no accident, Jock. Somebody up top's seen something and put the wheel hard over. You can stand by for the night alarm going off."

Titt was right, or nearly right. Up on the bridge the first lieutenant and the two lookouts were anxiously scanning the thick blanket of cloud overhead. Above the howl of the wind could be heard the faint, insectlike drone of a distant aircraft. It had come on them suddenly, appearing to circle once before it made off again. Brangwyn had taken no chances and put the helm hard over.

Lying in his bunk, eyes closed, Cheney had sensed a difference in the movement as the boat started to roll. In a flash he was up and out of the cabin. Cadbury, the steward, preparing to lay the wardroom table for dinner, a trayful of cutlery in his hands, had just time to step back smartly into the pantry as the captain tore past him.

Seconds later, his hair blowing about wildly and his unbuttoned bridge coat flapping about bat-winged, Cheney arrived on the bridge. Brangwyn wheeled as his ears picked up the scuffling sound of Cheney's boots.

Cheney bent forward, cupping his hands to his mouth. "What is it, number one?" His words were torn away like scraps of paper, but Brangwyn had heard.

"An aircraft," he shouted. "Stooged about for a minute. . . . Appears to have gone now."

Balancing himself against the heavy, swaying motion of the

bridge, Cheney cocked his head. He stood listening. The sound of the aircraft died away.

"All right, number one. . . . Let me know if she shows up again. . . . We don't want to dive if we can help it—must try and keep the charge on the batteries," he yelled at the dim swaying figure beside him.

Brangwyn nodded vigorously and raised a mittened hand to signal that he understood. Coat flapping wildly and noisily, Cheney reeled across the bridge toward the hatch.

Less than a minute after he'd gone, it began to rain heavily. Guided by the wind and chilled to near-freezing point, the rain drove in at a slant, lashing the exposed faces of the men on the bridge. Within minutes they were soaked to the skin. Miserable and cold, they peered into the night, their binoculars hanging uselessly around their necks. Without glasses to aid their sight in the heavy rain, visibility was down to less than a hundred yards. With the coming of the rain the wind seemed to pick up in strength, turning their lips blue and spreading the water that ran down their faces into dozens of tiny rivulets. Three small and insignificant figures entombed in a howling darkness, they hung onto the heaving bridge, trying to ignore the bitter cold and the insufferable discomfort.

All they could do was to look, listen—and hope.

Donahue had just opened his oven door to inspect the three joints of lamb he was roasting. A delicious smell escaped from the hot oven and stole along the passageway as far as the fore-ends. The crew stopped whatever they were doing and looked up, breathing deeply as their noses wrinkled and twitched.

With the opening of the door, everyone except Mitchell, who was too ill to eat, and Joyner, who felt seasick, was suddenly ravenous. Cadbury began setting the table, scurrying in and out of his pantry like a small animal and grinning all over his face for no apparent reason. Halfway through his preparations, he bowled along to see Donahue and find out when dinner would be ready.

Donahue was busy mixing up gravy powder with the fat from one of the roast tins. He shuddered when he saw the small bouncing figure of the steward.

"What do you want? Whatever it is I haven't got any," Dona-hue said sourly.

Cadbury grinned, showing spongy gums and bad teeth. "It's all right, Steve. Don't worry about me."

"I'm not worried about you," Donahue said flatly. "Now just tell me what you want and bugger off."

Cadbury seemed to find this a huge joke. "Hee, hee, hee," he giggled, his small round head bouncing up and down on his shoulders. "You're a right one, you are, Steve."

Donahue drew a deep breath and stared up at the deckhead. Speaking each word as if it were a separate sentence, he re-peated: "What . . . is . . . it . . . you . . . want?"

"Ah, that's just what I came to see you about, Steve," Cad-bury said.

Donahue groaned. "What . . . is. . . ."

The steward's expression became serious. He looked at the chef with some concern. "About the grub, Steve, you know? When's it going to be ready?"

Donahue's head tilted forward to stare at the hot plate. He ceased stirring the gravy mix and stood silently. Cadbury waited. Donahue slowly turned his head to face the steward. His voice free of all expression, he said: "Dinner will be ready in ten minutes. Now, will you please bugger off and let me get on with it?"

The steward's face split open again. "Ah, good, Steve. That's the stuff. I knew you'd say that. It's not me, you know"—he jerked his thumb over his shoulder—"it's that lot back there. They take a bit of handling, I can tell you." His manner had be-come serious again. "You should hear the way they go on at times. It's no joke."

Donahue had listened to the steward's ranting in silence. Now he put down the spoon and wiped his hands on his apron. His lower lip thrust out aggressively, he took a step forward. "Are you going to bugger off, Cadbury, or am I going to have to thump you?"

The steward's eyes widened and he took a little skip back-ward, holding up his hands in front of him with his arms out-stretched. "Ah, ah, ah. Now, now, Steve. You wouldn't do a thing like that, would you? You wouldn't hit an old shipmate."

Donahue cocked his fist. The muscles in his arm bulged. He spat out one single word.

"Get."

Cadbury let out his inane cackle and began backing off down the passageway. When he'd gone a few steps he turned and ran off in a strange skipping motion, shouting something unintelligible over his shoulder.

Donahue sighed despairingly. Shaking his head, he picked up the spoon again. He was still stirring the gravy a few minutes later when Titt came along the passageway. "Bugger off," he said without bothering to see who it was.

Titt looked at the broad back and the thick, perspiration-covered, red neck. *Oh, oh,* he thought, *someone's been needling him.* He cleared his throat once or twice and waited.

The cook turned around, nearly upsetting the gravy dish in his anger. "I told you to—" He stopped suddenly when he saw who it was. "Oh, it's you, Tom." He gave a lopsided, self-conscious grin. "I thought it was. . . ."

"That's all right, Steve," said Titt. "I know you're busy. I was just wondering how long it's going to be."

Donahue bent down and opened the oven door. A waft of hot air escaped, carrying with it the delicious smell of roast meat. Donahue closed the door and straightened up again.

"She's ready now, Tom. You can send one of your lads along in a few minutes."

"Mmmmm." Titt sniffed deeply. "Smells great, Steve. Even my old missus couldn't do any better." He swung a playful punch in the direction of the cook's heavy midriff.

Donahue flushed with pleasure and began fidding about with his pots and pans. Titt went back to the fore-ends. The mess had been fairly quiet since the boiling upsurge of the argument. Most of the crew had simmered down and their conversation was carried out in a low key. Only Thornley continued to look aggrieved. Heads turned questioningly with Titt's return.

"What's the score, Tom?" asked Corr. "Is it near ready yet?"

"It's ready now," Titt replied, turning toward Rice, who was sitting at the end of the table opposite Corr. Rice looked up.

"You can give Jock a hand to go and get it. Okay, Rice?" Titt said.

Rice nodded and got to his feet, followed by Corr. Both men grabbed cloths and made their way aft toward the galley. The rest of the hands began to lay the plates and cutlery out on the table, chattering excitedly among themselves at the prospect of a hot meal. The serving of rum, followed by the main meal, was the highlight of the day and was eagerly anticipated by the men. A few voices were raised in song, the sound lifting above the more regular tones of the crew's conversation.

There was a cry of "Grub's up" as Rice appeared in the doorway with a steaming hot tray of food held at arm's length. He had just stepped over the coaming of the bulkhead door when the klaxon situated above his head hawked madly, nearly tearing his eardrums out.

The steaming hot tray and its contents met the first mad rush of bodies. Rice was knocked off his feet as the tray soared upward, spilling out its contents. Corr, who was behind him, managed to keep upright, but his tray, like Rice's, was knocked out of his hands and the hot food scattered the length of the passageway. Fighting and kicking their way through the greasy mess that littered the deck, the crew struggled to get to the control room. Even though the hammering of the diesels had stopped, the noise in the passageway was like bedlam.

The deck had begun to tilt as Brangwyn and the two lookouts came tumbling down the ladder into the control room. Cheney was waiting at the foot of the ladder.

"What is it, number one?" he snapped.

"An aircraft, sir," Brangwyn gasped out. "I think she may have spotted us."

Cheney whipped around to the planesmen. "Eighty feet," he shouted. "Shut off for depth charging."

Robinson, the unhooked Tannoy speaker in his hand, repeated the last order. Everyone in the control room now looked at the depth gauges as if trying to force the indicator needles around by an effort of collective will. The needles seemed to hang for an eternity at 15 feet as if undecided whether to go up or down. Flickering uncertainly, they finally began to move. Everyone held his breath and cowered involuntarily.

Twenty-five feet.

Thirty-five feet.

Fifty feet . . . they would be safe soon.

Then came the terrifying crack of an explosion. The whole of the control room seemed to leap upward. Instruments and gauges together with everything else blurred as the compartment vibrated like a giant tuning fork. Lightbulbs popped off in a series of minor explosions as the lighting flickered and dimmed. From the deckhead the moisture-absorbent cork granules showered down like hail. The needles on the depth gauges began to spin crazily.

Above the noise and the confusion Bain's voice rang out warningly: "One hundred and fifty feet, sir . . . planes hard to rise."

The submarine had taken a deep angle by the stern. Blow fought to get the bubble back amidships, but it wouldn't budge.

"Two hundred feet, sir . . . still diving . . . planes hard to rise." Cheney leaned forward and gripped the back of Bain's stool, his eyes riveted to the gauge. The submarine continued to plunge downward. At 300 feet it seemed as if nothing would stop her descent to the bottom. Cheney was forced to take emergency action.

Quietly speaking over his shoulder, he said to Preece on the blowing panel: "Blow number one main ballast."

Preece sprang into action. Hooking his wheel spanner into the valve wheel, he cracked it open. There was a rushing, roaring noise as the torrent of compressed air poured into the ballast tank. Everyone started. There was something peculiar about the sound. It wasn't quite right.

Cheney whipped around at the same time as Brangwyn.

"The main vents, Preece, shut the main vents!" Cheney screamed across the control room in anger.

Preece flushed guiltily, nearly dropping his wheel spanner in his haste to shut off the blowing valve before slamming the main vent levers home.

"All right, Preece, now blow number one main ballast," Cheney snapped, eyeing the depth gauge anxiously as it approached 350 feet. Preece blew the tank again. The rate of descent slowed.

"Stop blowing," ordered Cheney as the stern began to come up and the deck leveled off. "Group up . . . half ahead both."

The telegraphs clanged. In the motor room M'Guinness and Thornley sprang to the switches, winding down the field regulators before throwing them open and then regrouping the motors from series to parallel before slamming home the main motor switches again and winding up the regulators to half ahead. The whole operation was done in split seconds.

The submarine now began to rise like an express lift. Cheney flooded number three ballast tank again, but they had ascended nearly 300 feet before he was able to get her under some sort of control. He turned to Brangwyn, who was still dressed in his bridge clothes, a pool of water forming at his feet.

"What's the damage report, number one?" he asked.

Brangwyn began unzipping his jacket. "Not too bad, sir. The chief's doing his inspection now, sir. Apart from the lighting the only thing seems to be a bit of a leak from the forehatch. He's in the afterends now, sir, so he shouldn't be long."

Cheney nodded coldly. "Very well, number one."

The exchange buzzed angrily. Both men turned to look at the messenger. Stanley flipped down the key and pressed his hands to his head over his earphones, listening intently. Then he said, "Report from engineer officer, sir. There's a leak from the port propeller gland. He says it's not a bad one, sir. And he's on his way back."

Dinsdale was back in the control room within minutes. He made his report to Cheney. Damage in the submarine had been confined to the lighting, the forehatch and the propeller gland. Cheney received the report in silence, stroking his chin thoughtfully. When Dinsdale had finished, he turned over the trim to the first lieutenant and crossed to the chart table. A few minutes later he called out to Brangwyn to fall out diving stations and go to watch diving.

"We'll surface in half an hour, number one," he concluded.

The bulkhead doors and the ventilation trunking, which had been shut off for depth charging, were opened up once more as the crew fell out of diving stations and began to file out of the control room. In the general movement and the low buzz of conversation, Cheney drew Brangwyn aside.

"How did it happen, number one? How did the plane get so close without being spotted?" he asked in a low, grating voice.

Brangwyn looked a trifle shamefaced. "I honestly don't know, sir. She just seemed to dive straight at us from nowhere. She came right out of the cloud as if she knew exactly where we were. I just can't understand." He shook his head in bewilderment.

"I see. I wonder. . . ." Cheney rubbed at the blue-black stubble on his chin. "Those were depth bombs she dropped, so she must have been on antisubmarine patrol . . . I wonder. . . ." He seemed to be speaking his thoughts aloud. His next question took Brangwyn by surprise.

"Why weren't the main vents shut after we dived?"

Brangwyn looked puzzled. "The main vents, sir?"

"Yes, why weren't they shut? You know my standing orders."

"But, sir," Brangwyn began protestingly, "I thought—"

"Thought, number one?" Cheney cut him off. "We don't think, we do."

Brangwyn flushed. Theoretically he was responsible for diving the boat, and normally he would have checked the vents shut, but he'd been on the bridge and the captain had taken over when he'd got down to the control room. "With all due respect, sir—"

"Never mind that now, number one," Cheney cut in again. "But it must never happen again, understand? Meantime I want you to warn all the lookouts to keep on their toes. All right, number one?"

Brangwyn drew in his breath. "Yes, sir. I understand, sir," he answered, tight-lipped.

"Good," said Cheney. "I'm going to my cabin. Call me five minutes before we surface."

For'ard in the crew's mess the hands were clearing up what was to have been their dinner. Bits of meat and vegetables were all over the place. The gravy, which had cooled instantly on making contact with the deck and the bulkheads, had thickened into a horrible, greasy sludge.

Mulholland was in a frenzy of rage. "The lousy bastards. Of all the shithouse tricks. Just when we were about to eat. The stinking, lousy bastards," he spluttered, flinging down the brush which he'd been using to try to clear up some of the mess.

"Easy there," warned Titt. "Let's get this lot cleaned up and we can all blow our tops later."

"And what about our dinner?" protested Mulholland. "What are we going to do about that?"

"Just get on with the cleaning up. I'll go and see the 'swain about what he can do," Titt said.

Mulholland, with a disgusted look, picked up his brush again and began wielding it vigorously, cursing under his breath. Rice was down on his hands and knees picking up the scraps of meat. He felt guilty about dropping the tray and set to with a will. No one really blamed him. It was just one of those things that happened. Most of them were accustomed by this time to the vicissitudes of life at sea in a submarine.

Most of them, that was, but Thornley. He didn't quite see it this way. Only a goon like Rice could have been responsible for dropping the dinner. If the others had nothing to say, he had.

"I suppose that's our lot then," he said, glaring in the direction of Rice, who was down on his knees with his back to him. "Bloody great. It'll be bully beef and pickles now—if we're lucky."

Everyone was too busy to pay much attention to his remarks. Annoyed by the lack of response, he tried again.

"Yeah, great. Our dinner gone for a Burton just because somebody flaps when the hooter goes off."

Rice stopped what he was doing but didn't look around.

"Fat lot of good that'll do now, mate," Thornley sneered.

"What are you going to do—take it all back to the galley and get the chef to heat it up again?"

Rice turned this time. He was feeling miserable and looked as if he were about to make some kind of apology, but Big Jock Corr stepped in.

"You'd be a lot better gi'n' us a han' to get this lot cleared up instead of standing there cackling your fat, chum," he said dryly.

Thornley, still looking at the kneeling figure of Rice, said: "I didn't drop the scran. The bloke that did it should be made to clear it up on his own."

Rice straightened up. Two pinpoints of color came to his cheeks. "I don't mind cleaning it up," he said in a hurt tone. "It was an accident, you know. I didn't mean to do it."

"Oh, that's great, mate. You don't mind cleaning it up, heh? And how about our dinner? What about that? Saying you're sorry now isn't going to fill our bellies, is it?" Thornley said sneeringly. "Accident, heh? Some bloody accident. That's how boats get lost—through some goon making a balls-up."

Rice flushed angrily. "That's got nothing to do with it and you know it. I said I was sorry and"— For once Rice seemed lost for words as his anger got the better of him. "Well, I *am* sorry and—" He looked around appealingly at the others.

Thornley felt he had him now and plunged the needle in. "We'll get fat on that, won't we—'I'm sorry I chucked your scran away, boys,' " he mimicked in a whining tone. "We've all got to go hungry and all you can say is you're sorry."

"Aw, can it, will you?" Big Corr broke in disgustedly. "It wisna anybody's fault, so stop picking on Ricey. If you want to blame anybody blame the Jerries."

Thornley swung to face Corr. "What's up with you then, haggis? Is Ricey a big mate of yours all of a sudden? You should tell him to be more bloody careful if he is."

Corr's eyes glinted dangerously. "Just watch it, mate," he replied. "Don't push your luck."

"Who're you telling to watch it?" Thornley snapped back. "Have you got a hook on your arm all of a sudden that you're chucking your weight around?" No hostilities only rating was going to tell Thornley what to do, even if he was an old hand in submarines.

Corr wiped his hands on his overalls. His head sank down into his shoulders in the manner of a fighter. "I don't need any hook on my arm," he said menacingly, "so just belt up, will you?"

The sudden dive and the near-thing bombing together with the loss of their dinner had set all the crew on edge. Tempers were back at flashpoint. It didn't help that Corr and Thornley disliked each other. Some months before, they had nearly come to blows. Since then they had kept out of each other's way in a sort of mutual truce. Corr looked upon the two-badge regular seaman as a loudmouth. Thornley didn't really know why he didn't like Corr. Corr was an H.O., and Thornley felt that H.O.'s should keep their place. But the real reason was that he envied Corr's popularity and resented that he was the biggest man on the boat. And again the big seaman had something of a reputation as a hard case. Thornley wasn't afraid of him. Years in the Navy had taught him to look after himself, but there was some hidden wildness in the big Scot that prompted caution. He certainly didn't want to tangle with him over Rice. What he really wanted was to hang one on Rice and teach him to keep his trap shut.

The situation was a dangerous one, as neither of the two men was prepared to back down. Fortunately, at that moment Titt came back in the mess after his visit to the coxswain. The first thing he saw was the two seamen glaring at each other, their fists clenched and breathing heavily.

"What's this, then? What's going on?"

Thornley and Corr both turned. They were silent for a moment. Corr shrugged and turned away. Thornley began speaking, but Titt cut him off short.

"I don't want to hear any stories or take sides. Just take a reef in, the pair of you, will you? Let's get on with what we're supposed to be doing. We'll be surfacing soon, so how about getting our fingers out."

Thornley choked back on what he was about to say, but he shot a venomous glance at Rice and then Corr. Gritting his teeth, he bent down and seized the handle of one of the bench lockers, jerking it savagely aside so someone could get around the back of it with a broom. The hands worked like beavers to clear up the mess before surfacing.

Rice wiped the sweat from his bony forehead and went over to Titt.

"What is it?" Titt asked. "What do you want?" He knew that Rice had been somehow connected with the incident between Corr and Thornley. But God help him if he thought he could come sneaking over with his story of it.

Rice saw the hostile look and flushed. "I was just thinking, Tom," he said uncertainly, unable to understand Titt's seeming hostility, "I could mebbe brew up some tea before we go to diving stations." He glanced around awkwardly. "I don't mind cleaning up or anything but—well, I thought a cup of tea would be a good idea."

Titt looked straight into his eyes. Rice shifted his feet, uncomfortable under the steady gaze. Titt gave him a pat on the shoulder. "Okay, mate. But you'd better hurry it up—we'll be surfacing soon."

A relieved smile came to Rice's features. "Okay, Tom. I'll do it right away," he said eagerly. He was gone at the double.

Five minutes later the tea was ready. The hands all gathered as Renwick put out the cups. Titt got his and moved over to the far end of the mess away from the crowd. He sat down on a packing case and slowly sipped the sweet, hot liquid. From time to time his glance strayed toward Thornley and then Corr. They'd both have to be watched or they'd come to blows one of these days. To have the crew fighting among themselves at sea was the last thing he wanted to happen. He wondered what had caused the latest fracas. In all probability Thornley had been needling Rice about the dinner and Corr had only been too glad to jump in. He'd have to watch Thornley, who was far too ready to bear down on Rice. Still he could handle the blond seaman all right. It was Big Corr that might be the problem.

There was something about him that he didn't quite get. He was cheery enough and a good worker; the lads all got on well with him. And he could take a joke. Look at the way little Stanley was always ribbing him. On the surface he appeared to be nothing more than a big amiable bloke. But underneath? There was some dangerous quality, a near-fanatical thing. Titt felt that if the big Scot ever really got wound up he could be murderous.

Titt had an odd respect for the Scots, but they had this fanatical thing about them. It came out in the way they drank and their crazy, almost religious attitude to football. They were an odd lot. You could never be quite sure when they were going to take the needle or what they were going to do next. Look at Corr. Some of the hands could call him haggis and he would just grin; with others his face would go as cold as granite if they used the name. He remembered one night in Dunoon. They'd been standing in a bar knocking back pints when some bloke from another ship had come over and slapped Jock on the back with a "Hiya, haggis." Jock had gone stone cold and raised his glass as if he were going to smash it into the chap's face. Whether he would have or not no one would ever know because the bloke had shot off like a frightened rabbit. And no wonder. Of one thing Titt was sure, and nothing would convince him otherwise, the Scots—they were a mad lot of bastards.

The pipe to "diving stations" disrupted his train of thought. Joining the queue filing out through the bulkhead door, he made his way aft to the control room. Rice had just made tea again, and now it would grow cold and wouldn't be fit to drink by the time they had surfaced the boat. Grumbling and bemoaning the loss of their dinner, the crew closed up at their stations.

Though it was still very dark the cloud had been torn in long shreds by the wind. From time to time the men on the bridge were bathed in a soft illumination as the moon peeped through. There was no sight or sound of the aircraft which had attacked them.

Normally when the submarine was surfaced, the main ballast tanks were completely emptied by running the low-pres-
sure blowers; only then was the submarine able to gain full
buoyancy. To be able to dive as quickly as possible, Cheney
hadn't emptied the tanks. In a heavy seaway it was a practice
not without danger. The submarine, trimmed down low on
the water, her movements tired and sluggish, was at the mercy
of a heavy wave breaking over the bridge and flooding the control room. As a precaution, Cheney leaned against the rear periscope standard, his foot on the hatch ready to slam it shut at
the slightest sign of danger. This too was not without hazard.
It had happened once before, more or less by accident. Joyner,
in diving the boat hurriedly, had slammed the upper lid shut
before he'd sounded the diving klaxon. Unaware that they were
diving, the engine room chief hadn't stopped the diesels.
Within seconds the engines had gulped up all the air in the
boat and had created a vacuum that threatened to tear everyone's eardrums out. Gasping for breath, the chief had just managed to shut the engines off in the nick of time. The experience
had · shaken everyone up considerably and hadn't helped
endear Joyner to the crew.

It was a full half hour before Cheney decided to run the L.P.
blowers and clear the tanks. Inch by inch the submarine came
out of the water, her movements becoming more sprightly as
she gained buoyancy. Cheney moved up to the forepart of the
bridge, chewing his knuckle thoughtfully. The idea had begun to form in his mind that the aircraft must have been using
some form of radar. He knew the Germans had been experi-
menting with it for some time. It looked as if their efforts had
met with success—how else could the aircraft have attacked
them with such certainty in the surrounding darkness? If this
were so they were in for a rough time of it. It almost certainly
meant they would have to dive repeatedly. In such conditions
it would be difficult to keep the battery up, and without the
battery to propel them underneath the water a submarine was
little more than a useless hulk.

His features took on an angry worried look. He paced the

bridge for ten minutes before he decided to go below and get some rest. It looked as though he was going to need it.

He turned to Brangwyn and shouted above the roar of the wind, "Keep her on 045. We'll try and get a full charge on. When the battery's up we'll make a quick run in before we dive. Call me in an hour. Keep a good look out for aircraft— might be using some kind of radar."

There were a few false alarms during the rest of the night, but though now and again they thought they detected the sound of aircraft, there were no further attacks. An hour before dawn Cheney was up on the bridge again. The clouds were beginning to clear, stripped from the sky by the violence of the wind. It was still bitterly cold in the freak resurgence of wintry weather that had gripped the whole of the northern latitudes.

Anxiously Cheney awaited a report from the motor room that the battery was up to peak. It came at last. Immediately the charge was broken and at full speed ahead on both engines they began their run in toward the coast and the Skagerrak.

Down below the crew slept fitfully. Within a few hours they knew they would be deep within the minefield that guarded the entrance to the channel.

Chapter
Four

It was early morning. As the first dim diffusion of light edged the rim of the eastern horizon the submarine crept toward the entrance to the Skagerrak. To port lay Naze Point, a faint smudge in the surrounding gloom. The wind had died to a light breeze. A long swell, cold, gray and menacing, rolled out from the Baltic and into the North Sea, lifting the bows of the submarine with a gentle, drawn-out swish.

The only other sounds that disturbed the quiet of early dawn were the deep throbbing note of the diesels and the wild rising cry of the gulls, as they circled near land. It was as if they were sounding an alarm at the presence of the intruder.

Lieutenant Robinson, who had the watch on deck, shivered in the coldness of the dawn as he reached with stiff fingers to draw the collar of his duffel coat more tightly around his neck. His nose and cheekbones felt like bits of ice stuck to his face, but with no wind to penetrate his clothing, his body was reasonably warm. Stamping his feet, as the cold bit into his toes, he glanced at the two lookouts. The shapeless figures might have been carved from stone. Robinson carefully wiped the lens of his night glasses and returned to scan his own sector of the horizon.

Since he had come on watch, a mood of excitement had steadily grown within him, shooting little nervous tremors down his spine. The feeling, though aroused by fear, was not unpleasant. In fact Robinson's fears were acting as a stimulant as he tasted the sour-sweet essence of approaching danger. In just a few hours they would be in the Skagerrak and could expect to meet enemy forces. It was a prospect that thrilled the lieutenant and tingled his nerve endings with an electric charge that gave pleasure at the same time as it hurt.

He scanned the dark waters ahead. Only a few hours now. But first they had to get through the minefield that barred their path like a giant booby trap. The thought of the deadly, invisible canisters of explosives sent fresh galvanic surges of energy through his nerves; but this time the feeling was entirely unpleasant and offered no thrills. Robinson tried to shut the thought off, but it kept returning, like a twinge of toothache, to disturb his mood of swashbuckling gallantry.

He glanced at his watch, screwing his eyes up as he tried to make out the position of the hands on the faintly glowing luminous dial. 0540 hours. Time to call the captain. He bent down and cupped a hand over the voice pipe.

A few minutes later Cheney arrived on the bridge. He wore no coat, but he'd wrapped a heavy towel around his neck, tucking the ends into his jacket.

He grunted sourly to Robinson and, moving over to the far side of the bridge, craned his head upward to look at the overhanging cloud. For a long minute he inspected the sky, sniffing about like a dog trying to pick up a scent, as he read the weather signs. He turned to Robinson.

"We'll go to diving stations in ten minutes," he said in a growling voice. Without waiting for a reply, he crossed over to the hatch and clambered back down the conning tower ladder. In the control room he went immediately across to the chart table and with a quick, decisive movement whipped back the canvas cover. Five minutes later Brangwyn, having been called by the control room messenger, arrived, rubbing his eyes and working his mouth open and shut as if he'd swallowed something unpleasant. He hung around for a few minutes, pacing about and rubbing his shoulders, before he picked up the Tannoy and announced diving stations. Within seconds of his replacing the speaker, the crew began to filter into the control room, grumbling among themselves in low tones as they shivered in the early morning cold.

Cheney, in the corner, seemed oblivious to everything as he studied the chart with deep concentration. His whole attention was absorbed by the warning red cross-hatched marks that indicated the position of the minefield. He stroked his chin thoughtfully. There would be slack water in about an hour. After that they would have the advantage of the flooding tide. By his calculations they would enter the minefield at 0900 hours. Three hours to go. He drew back the cover on the chart.

"All right, number one. We'll dive now. Stand by," he said, crossing the control room and pausing for an instant with his foot on the bottom rung of the ladder before he made his way up top again. A few seconds later Robinson and the two lookouts came clattering down the conning tower as the klaxon squawked out its warning cry. Echoing down from the top of the tower came the dull sound of the upper hatch slamming shut.

Before the first light of dawn the submarine had slipped quietly beneath the waves and buried herself in the depths.

Leveling off at 100 feet, Brangwyn caught a trim. The hands fell out of diving stations and crept quietly back to their sleeping quarters, tiptoeing their way forward in the sudden silence that had fallen with the stopping of the diesels when they'd dived. It was as if they were fearful of making the slightest noise now that they were approaching the minefield. They turned in, but few of them slept. Though the day had only begun, they longed deeply for the night to fall, when they would surface free of the terrors of the mined channel ahead.

Breakfast would be ready in a couple of hours, but no one had any appetite for food.

Cheney stood by the chart table sipping the cup of hot coffee Cadbury had brought him. Since the first light Cheney had been keeping a periscope watch in between frequent visits to the chart. The time was 0845. Cheney drained his coffee in one

gulp, had one last look at the chart and crossed over to the big
for'ard periscope. A dozen pairs of eyes followed him.

"Up periscope."

Silence gripped the men in the control room as the periscope
hissed out of the well.

Cheney snapped the handles open from a squatting position,
unflexing his legs as it rose. He nestled his forehead firmly into
the contours of the molded rubber eyepiece.

"Hold it."

The long column slid to a halt. Cheney began a circling
movement with his feet as he swung the periscope through
an arc, scanning the horizon. He took a deep breath and straightened up, knuckling his eyes for a second before he bent forward again and repeated the procedure.

The sidestepping motion of his feet slowed and finally
stopped. For a long time he remained motionless, breathing
audibly.

Clack, clack. The handles snapped back into the periscope
housing. Cheney straightened up as the periscope slid away
down into the well.

"All right, number one. We'll go to diving stations now. Shut
all bulkhead doors and ventilation trunking. Shut off for depth
charging."

They had arrived at the minefield.

"Diving stations . . . diving stations . . . diving stations."
Brangwyn's voice, distorted by the Tannoy, rang out through
the submarine. The first members of the crew came lurching
bleary-eyed into the control room.

Cheney waited till Brangwyn had reported all hands closed
up. He walked over to the Tannoy and unhooked it from its
bracket. Holding the speaker up to his mouth, he cleared his
throat once or twice before pressing the contact button.

"Hello, hello. This is the captain speaking. We are now
about to go through the minefield. During passage we will remain at diving stations and the boat will be shut off for depth
charge routine. Only under exceptional circumstances will the
bulkhead doors be opened. They will be opened of course to

allow meals to be served. The coxswain has arranged that leading cook Donahue will supply tea and sandwiches. These will
be served by the petty officers' messman and the wardroom
steward at intervals during the day. This will be the only occasion I will permit the opening of bulkhead doors—except in
emergency. You all understand? Good. I needn't remind you
we are quite close to the coast of occupied territory and you
will go about your duties as quietly as you can. It is known that
Jerry has a number of listening posts in the area. . . ." The
Tannoy crackled and the voice broke up into meaningless
sounds. It was some seconds before he was heard again. ". . .
you will be very careful not to drop anything. Go about your
duties as quietly as you can. We don't want Jerry nosing around
on top of us." The voice paused for a few seconds and then
resumed, as everyone waited expectantly. "It will probably be
early evening before we're clear of the minefield. When we
surface I want everyone to be on their toes. We can expect to
get some attention from enemy antisubmarine aircraft patrols.
That is all." The voice broke off abruptly.

Slowly and methodically, following the captain's address,
the crew began shutting off the boat for depth charge routine,
cutting off the ventilation trunking and swinging the heavy
bulkhead doors shut, finally knocking on the dog clips. Within
a few minutes they had sealed the submarine off into separate
compartments. The only link now was by means of the telephone exchange. Their job done, with nothing now to do but
wait and hope, the men sat down and began nursing their
private claustrophobic fears.

In the fore-ends chief petty officer Wells had just finished
checking the dog clips on the rear watertight door. He was going forward to check the door dividing the compartment from
the tube space when from somewhere above his head he heard
a faint voice hailing him. He looked up toward the deckhead.
Mitchell, the sick seaman, was leaning out over the edge of his
hammock. He didn't look well and his skin had a strange color.

"What's up then, Mitch?" Wells asked. "Feeling a bit
groggy?"

"What's going on, chief?" The voice lacked strength. "What are you shutting the bulkhead doors for? Have they spotted something up top?"

Wells reached up an arm and patted Mitchell on the shoulder. "Take it easy, Mitch. Nothing's happening. Nothing to get worried about. Just routine, that's all." Mitchell must have been sleeping when the captain was on the Tannoy, Wells realized.

"We haven't been spotted or anything?"

"I told you. Stop worrying. Nobody's seen anything."

"But the doors?"

Wells inspected the thin pallid face peering over the edge of the canvas. There was no point in trying to deceive the bloke. After all it wasn't his first patrol in submarines. "Well, the skipper thinks there might be some mines about."

"Mines?" Mitchell made the word sound like a dread disease. His mouth worked for a moment, and then he leaned back in his hammock. Wells could no longer see him but he could hear him.

"I wish somebody would tell me what's going on. What are we supposed to be doing? Are we at Norway yet?"

Even though Mitchell's face was hidden, Wells forced his own features into a grin. "Listen, mate, I'm only the T.G.M.— remember? If you want to find out the answers to those questions you'd better nip along to the control room and ask the skipper. If you catch him in a good mood he might even tell you. Now get your head down and get some sleep and forget about it."

Wells slipped under the hammocks, beckoning to Mulholland as he went forward. The tall lanky figure got up from the locker. Wells took his arm.

"Just keep your eye on Mitch, Scouse," he said in a whisper. I think he's feeling a bit dicky and—well, just keep an eye on him."

Mulholland sneaked a glance at Mitchell's hammock. "Right, chief. I'll do that. What was he on about just now, anyway?"

"He wasn't on about anything. Just keep your eye on him, that's all I want you to do."

Mulholland shrugged and looked round at the sealed-off compartment. "Well, he's not likely to go anyplace."

"Neither are you, or me for that matter, but I'm making it your responsibility, you long bugger. Okay?"

Mulholland spread his hands. "All right, chief. Anything for peace and quiet." He turned lazily on his heel and made his way back to the locker. Leaning forward on the table, he pillowed his head on his folded arms and closed his eyes.

Wells said nothing. He knew Mulholland wasn't asleep and the slightest alien sound would have him up on his feet as alert as a cat. It was just a habit that Mulholland had, this trick of closing his eyes at odd moments. He never suspected that it might get him into serious trouble one day.

Barbour, another member of Wells' three-man torpedo crew, was stretched out on the other locker, gazing vacantly up at the deckhead.

"What was all that about, Scouse?" he muttered from the corner of his mouth.

"The chief was asking me to tally up the hours you spend lying on your back. He thinks it might be a record," Mulholland answered without bothering to open his eyes.

"Yaaagh." Barbour made a sound of deep disgust. "Go and get knotted."

"You shouldn't speak disrespectfully to senior ratings or you might find yourself painting out the bilges when we get back," Mulholland mumbled in a tired voice.

"Yeah, when we get back. I'll worry about it then."

Kennedy, the third member of the T.G.M.'s team of torpedomen and the youngest member of the ship's company, heard the brief exchange between Mulholland and Barbour, but he was too engrossed to pay much attention to it. He was too busy playing the role of faithful dog to the T.G.M. to bother about anything else. For Kennedy had a sort of hero-worship feeling for Wells, and he trotted at his heels hanging on every word and faithfully carrying out each instruction. Perhaps his attitude wasn't all that surprising. Kennedy's father had died long before he had the chance to get to know him. Childhood had been an unfortunate and unhappy affair. He had lost not only his father but also both his brothers. One had died from pneumonia in infancy and the other from diphtheria at the age of nine. This combination of losses was far too great a mystery for a five-year-old to even begin to comprehend, and he was glad to accept his mother's explanation that they had all departed from earth to a place where they would be safe and happy.

The Kennedys had been farmworkers and had lived in a small house some miles away from the nearest village. At school young Kennedy was able to laugh and play with the other children, but he would fall into unnaturally silent brooding moods on his return to a home from which all warmth and vitality seemed to have fled.

Fortunately, being born of peasant stock, he'd inherited an ability to survive, along with a kind of stoical, Calvinistic independence of mind. Although this helped, the absence of a central, dominating guide in his life was something he was to feel throughout his childhood and early teens. It was no surprise, therefore, that when he found himself plunged into a new environment, the rugged, masculine figure of the T.G.M., with his almost godlike authority, became the focal point of Kennedy's thwarted emotions. For the first time in his life he had a hero he could worship.

Wells had finished inspecting the dog clips on the bulkhead door. He stepped back, adjusting the angle of his cap and frowning slightly.

Kennedy had put the clips on the door. "Is it okay, chief?" he asked anxiously.

Wells started. He'd been thinking what a fat lot of good the door would be if they hit a mine. He gave a short dry laugh and struck the vaultlike door with the edge of his fist. "It'd better be, laddie. There's an awful lot of water out there."

The youthful skin on Kennedy's forehead furrowed. "What's it like, chief? The . . . the. . . ." He hesitated as if frightened to put his thoughts into words.

"What's it like? Bloody cold, son. And wet."

"No, not that. I don't mean the water." He grinned sheepishly. "I mean the . . . the minefield. W-what's it like?"

The T.G.M. folded his arms and shook his head. "Of all the daft bloody questions. You've seen a mine, haven't you?"

Kennedy nodded dumbly.

"Well, that's what it's like then, only a lot more of them and all hanging like coconuts waiting for some daft bastard to have a go."

Kennedy looked a bit hurt at this. He'd hoped to get a serious answer to his question. Wells misinterpreted the look.

"Don't let it get you down, son." He slapped Kennedy on the back. "We've been through a lot worse than this. Don't you worry. Just leave it to the skipper. We'll get through all right."

Kennedy opened his mouth to put the question again, but Wells held a warning finger up to his lips, at the same time jerking his thumb in the direction of Mitchell's hammock. "Keep it down."

A tinge of color crept to Kennedy's cheeks. "Sorry, chief," he whispered.

Wells held up his hand. "Okay, forget it. Now follow me."

Mulholland looked up from the table at the T.G.M.'s approach.

"We're going to be a long time closed up, Scouse. A couple of you might as well get your heads down and grab some sleep. Kennedy here and Barbour can have the first go. All right?"

"Great idea, chief. Will you make us a cup of tea an' all?" Mulholland cracked.

"Listen, you long Liverpool bastard, I'll have you polishing the brasswork."

Barbour, already halfway into his hammock, stopped and grinned. "That's right, chief. It'll do him good."

Mulholland's answer was to yawn and straighten up from the table. "One of these days I'm going to go on strike." He screwed up his eyes painfully. "I suppose those two goons had better have the first go. They'd be just as well with their heads down for all the good they are. Well, what are you waiting for, kidder? You heard what the chief said, or do you want to stay up and polish the brasswork? He wasn't kidding, you know."

Kennedy stepped forward eagerly. "I don't mind staying up, Scouse, if you want to turn in first."

Mulholland looked at the T.G.M.

"Suit yourselves," said Wells.

"Okay, kidder." Mulholland pulled himself to his feet. "There's one thing about it—my old mum said I'd never die in bed, so you're all right for a bit." He climbed slowly up onto the table and hoisted himself into his hammock.

Wells turned to Kennedy. "Don't mind that dismal bastard. He's always dripping about something or other."

"A Jeremiah." Kennedy smiled.

"Eh?" Wells frowned suspiciously.

"That's what Jock Bain says: a Jeremiah. You know, from the Bible."

"Oh? Well, right then, me lad, Jeremiah or no Jeremiah, the bastard was right about one thing," Wells said, surveying the compartment. "You *are* going to polish the brasswork. Just look at the state of the place. It's like a broken-down pawnbroker's shop. Take a look at this lot—it's just covered in shit." He pointed to the copper urn. "It's a wonder you don't all have gyppo gut drinking out of that lot."

Kennedy followed him cautiously, not very sure whether he was being kidded or not. He'd never heard of anyone's polishing brasswork on patrol before.

"Just look at that mess." Wells' finger stabbed the air.

Kennedy looked. The urn had long since lost its metallic sheen and was covered in dark brown stains and thick patches of dull green. The brass tap dripped steadily, overflowing the drip tray and adding to the water slopping about the deck.

Wells pushed his cap back on his head. "Get a kettle," he said. "Go on. Chop-chop. Get a kettle, I said." The T.G.M. was determined that he would keep the young seaman busy so he wouldn't have a chance to brood or think about the barrier of mines that surrounded them.

Kennedy came back with the kettle. "Okay. Now when you've emptied the copper I want you to clean it so's I'll be able to see my face in it. I'll strip that tap out and fix it once and for all. The bloody thing drips every patrol. Let's get cracking then."

A few minutes later the copper was emptied. Kennedy laid it down on its side on a tea chest and literally covered it in Brasso. He rubbed away furiously as the T.G.M. fitted a new washer to the tap. If it took him the rest of the day he was going to get the urn shining like a mirror. Absorbed in his task, Kennedy forgot all about where they were, and where they were heading, for the moment.

The control room was as quiet as a grave. The air hung heavy. It was like the still, hushed period before the outbreak of a thunderstorm. Except for the helmsman and the two planesmen, who had jobs to do, the rest of the crew stood around, changing position only when their limbs began to ache and cramp up. Solemn-faced and silent, they resembled a group of pallbearers waiting for the coffin to arrive.

Titt leaned against the for'ard watertight door and licked his dry lips. Since they had gone to diving stations and the heavy door had clanged shut behind him, he had been staring fixedly at the foreplanes depth gauge—not really seeing anything but just gazing abstractedly at the soft green light that spilled over the giant dial. In other circumstances the light might have had a soothing effect, but now it had an ominous quality, like some fearful phosphorescent glow in a damp subterranean cavern. It reminded him of a film he'd seen as a boy. The film had been about a group of miners trapped in a pitfall, and the whole sequence had been shot in monochrome red to create a heightened effect. The result had been awesome and terrifying.

Titt shifted his gaze to where the captain was standing in the center of the control room.

Cheney was standing by the for'ard periscope, his shoulders hunched and his body inclined forward slightly in an attitude of deep concentration. Now and then the whites of his eyes would glint briefly in the dim light as he raised his head to look over the helmsman's shoulder at the gyrocompass. Apart from this slight movement Cheney remained as still as the others.

Titt became conscious of the gradual tightening of his chest muscles. Though his mind was well under control, his body had reacted independently to the tension induced by their arrival at the minefield. He tried to relax, slow down his breathing rate which had imperceptibly quickened. He'd learned from long experience that it was difficult to keep calm if your breathing wasn't under control. At the same time, the moment you consciously thought about breathing the rate had a tendency to increase and you would begin to suffer from feelings of slow suffocation. The air would seem to get thinner, causing your lungs to pump wildly and your heart to race. As the symptoms of hyperventilation developed, a trembling feeling would take possession of your limbs and a sensation of giddiness would follow. The odd bodily sensations would be reflected in your brain, inducing a feeling of panic.

Titt took a long, deep breath and let his shoulders drop. With the back of his hand he wiped away the sweat on his brow as he watched Cheney retrace his steps from the chart table to the center of the control room.

"Port ten . . . steer 060." Cheney's voice rang out like a pistol shot.

All eyes swiveled toward him.

Cheney stepped forward a pace, closing the gap between himself and the helmsman. The film strip in the gyro repeater started to edge its way across the visor as the vessel answered to her helm. Cheney stood back. He turned to face the asdic cabinet, his features drawn up into a snarling expression.

"Winch," he snapped, "start the M.D.U. Sweep five degrees either side of the ship's head."

"Steady on 060, sir," the helmsman reported quietly. "M.D.U. started, sir. Sweeping five degrees either side of ship's head."

Cheney gripped the hoist wire of the periscope. "Very well, Winch," he nodded. "Carry on your sweep."

The ticking of the control room clock could be heard as the minutes passed. Instinctively Titt straightened up and craned his head to look over the crowded control room toward the asdic cabinet. Winch had the headphones glued to his ears. Alone, of all the men on board, he was in contact with the world outside. It was a heavy responsibility, but Winch bore it with calm concentration.

Titt could just see the top half of the two-hundred-pound figure jammed into the asdic operator's seat. Winch's face was clearly etched in profile as the light fell on it from the console. With a little feeling of surprise Titt noticed for the first time how Jewish he actually looked. He'd never really thought of Winch as a Jew before. It was the sort of thing that hadn't meant anything; neither to Winch nor to the crew. As far as the fore-ends was concerned, he was just another bloke who happened to be the H.S.D. on the boat and that was all. Some of the crew liked him, some of them didn't, but it had nothing to do with his being Jewish. Stanley was about the only one who ever referred to it, offering him a fag and asking him if he didn't mind its not being kosher and that sort of thing. But Winch had never taken offense and seemed to find the idea just about as amusing as the bantam seaman did. But then Stanley baited everybody. There was a colored chap back on the parent ship he even called Sambo, going through a mime routine of strumming a banjo, and the bloke would just flash his white teeth in a broad grin.

An odd thought crept into Titt's head. Here they were, all on a submarine, and perhaps somewhere ahead there was another submarine, only it was called a U-boat. There would be men on board doing the same kind of jobs they were and suffering the same kind of hardships. They would even have an H.S.D. on board (or whatever they called it in the kriegsmarine), he might even be as good at his job as Winch was, but there was one thing certain—he wouldn't be a Jew.

Titt looked at the senior asdic rating with renewed interest, trying to discover what it was about him that made a Jew so different from anybody else, as some people claimed. Was it something to do with the nose? The dark wiry hair? But then look at the skipper. (He looked at him, studying the face carefully.) The nose might be a bit thinner and the hair straighter than Winch's, but that was all. There was no doubt that they both looked like members of the same race or religion—it was only when you came to things like speech and manner that they were as different as chalk and cheese. What was a Jew anyway? Was it a race, or was it a religion? Christ, Titt thought to himself, here's me wearing a Palestine medal on my number ones, spent eighteen months in and out of the place, been to Tel Aviv and Jerusalem, and I don't really know whether the Jews are a kind of clan or a religious sect. . . .

Winch's head twisted fractionally.

"Mine dead ahead, sir." There was no sign of panic or urgency in the flat Yorkshire tones.

Cheney gripped the periscope hoist wire more tightly. "Starboard ten," he said.

The seconds ticked away.

"Another one, sir: dead ahead."

Cheney bit into his knuckle. "All right, Winch. Let me know when it's on the port bow."

The tiny clicking sound of the gyro repeater could be heard as the ship's head paid off.

"On the port bow now, sir."

Cheney turned to the helmsman. "Wheel amidships."

Titt had a quick mental vision of the bulbous horned metal spheres that were strung out in front of them. He felt a quick pang of fear as a cold hand seemed to clutch his intestines. His muscles twitched as nerve endings sparked off, and sweat began to ooze through the opened pores of his skin. And all the time an alarm system clanged off in his head, telling him to run, to get the hell out of it.

"Contact lost, sir."

"Very well, Winch. Carry on your sweep."

Titt felt the tension ease out of his muscles. He took a deep breath, preparing himself for the next contact report, thinking he'd rather be in action anytime. And this was only the beginning; there was the whole day to get through. Hours and hours of it yet. Christ, it was worse than the rack.

Jock Bain, on the foreplanes, happened to look around and catch sight of Titt leaning nonchalantly against the watertight door. He wondered what the hell he was grinning at.

In the next hour Winch picked up no fewer than fifteen positive contacts. Almost monotonously he reported each one and went on calmly with his sweep. The tension in the control room began to build up as the submarine turned and twisted in her efforts to avoid the mines. Mingled with the heavy smell of diesel oil, a new odor arose as fear prized open skin pores and activated the sweat glands of the half-crouching men. With the rise in tension concurrently came a rise in temperature. Air leakage from the high-pressure line and the inhalation and exhalation of the same volume of air by the jammed bodies had begun to push the thermometer up. But the change went unnoticed. Like animals feigning death, the men had frozen into rigid positions—listening.

The use of the mine-detecting unit for all its advantages only made the crew more uncomfortably aware of the nearness of the deadly explosive bulbs. Most of them would have preferred to run the gauntlet blindly. They had their reasons. The moment you altered course to dodge a mine in front, the stern, swinging around, could collide with one you had previously avoided, in the way that a man walking along a thoroughfare with a long plank on his shoulder could catch someone behind him a blow as he swung around to dodge someone in front. Another serious disadvantage arising from the use of the unit was that the high-frequency signals it transmitted could be picked up and plotted by detection devices ashore. Though the M.D.U. was able to give a physical picture of what was happening, it had a severe psychological effect on the members of the crew in the control room. For the rest of the crew, scattered throughout the boat, it didn't matter—they were cut off anyway and had no way of telling whether they were within a yard or a cable's length of a mine.

Head lowered slightly, Cheney stood by the big periscope clutching the hoist wires as a support. Occasionally he would move from this position to consult the chart. The rest of the time he spent evaluating reports from the asdic cabinet and keeping a hawklike eye on the compass.

Eleven long minutes had passed since Winch had last reported a mine. Strangely enough, with each sweep of the second-hand of the control room clock, the men's anxieties, far from being diminished, were increased. There seemed something ominous about such a long gap without anything being reported. It was almost as if a trick were being played on them. A cunning device to soothe their senses and lull them into a false sense of security, then—

"Mine dead ahead, sir."

Practically the whole of the control room jumped.

"All right, Winch. . . . Port ten, helmsman."

The bows began to swing around in an evasive action.

"Mine, red 05, sir . . . 04, sir . . . 03—"

"Port fifteen. . . . What is it bearing now, Winch?"

"Now bearing . . . green 01."

"Midships, helmsman. Steady as you go."

No sooner had the helm been put on than Winch reported again.

"Mine head, sir." And before Cheney could make a further alteration of course Winch gave another warning: "Another one bearing red 05, sir."

The crew tensed and looked at Cheney at the same time as they made their own split-second deductions from the asdic report. It looked as if they were approaching a whole string of mines at the worst possible angle. In this the minefield could be compared to a fence with a number of gaps in it. Approaching it head-on allowed maximum opportunity for success, but the moment the angle of convergence was changed the gaps would correspondingly narrow and the chances of slipping through proportionately lessen.

Cheney released his grip on the hoist wire. His head came up. "Starboard fifteen."

The helmsman spun the wheel over madly.

From somewhere for'ard, possibly the tube compartment or the fore-ends, a sound was heard. Everyone immediately recognized it as alien. They held their breaths, not daring to move as they listened. A big, unspoken question revolved in their minds—*What was that?*

Cheney acted instantly.

"Wheel amidships." There was a low note of urgency in his voice. "Now steady as you go."

Eeeeekk. Eeeeeeeekkk. The ominous sound grew and filled the control room. It was as if an enormous door was slowly being dragged upon its rust-stiffened hinges.

No one could doubt it anymore.

They had picked up a mine wire. And somewhere at the end of the wire was a mine, its glasslike horns ready to break off at the slightest touch and allow seawater to get in and set up a chemical reaction that would spark off its firing circuit. Within a second of that happening they would all be blown clean out of the water.

Mulholland shot up out of his hammock when he heard the noise. He landed with a heavy thud on the mess deck. Kennedy spun around as if a grenade had gone off. The Brasso ran out onto the deck from the tin he held in his hand, but he wasn't aware of it. The strange noise and the sight of Mulholland leaping from the hammock had frightened him. His mind filled with fear. He could only dimly associate the two incidents as being connected; but they were in some unfathomable way.

The sound grew louder, jarring the nerves like a dentist's drill. Perturbed and shaken, Kennedy looked for the T.G.M. Wells had also stopped what he had been doing. He put the tap down quietly and looked at Mulholland. The eyes of the two men were linked in common understanding. They both knew what the sound implied.

"What is it, chief?" Kennedy asked in hushed tones.

Wells took a deep breath. "It's a mine wire, son. It looks as though we've picked up a mine."

Kennedy shrank back as if he'd been touched by a leper.

Then the fear, which he'd been struggling hard to control, gave way to a wave of terror. An enormous sense of claustrophobia gripped him. He wanted to scream, to flee from this water-surrounded steel dungeon in which he suddenly found himself imprisoned like a trapped animal.

The sound came again, threatening to tear his nerves to shreds as it seeped through his eardrums and reached down as far as his bowels. His body felt as if it were coming apart. He no longer seemed to be in control of it. It was like those awful dreams he'd suffered from following the death of his father and brothers. Momentarily he became disorientated, feeling his presence in the submarine was all a mistake; it was a joke that had somehow turned ugly and dangerous. In the whirl of his thoughts he found he had an almost irrepressible urge to cry out to the one person who had been closest to him all his life, his mother. But she couldn't help him now. He was on his own. With the shock of a knife being plunged into his stomach it came to him that he might never see her again.

Suddenly he wanted to vomit.

Wells took him by the arm. "Okay, son," he said, steering him firmly toward the mess table where Mulholland sat. He knew what the youngster was going through. At all costs he had to prevent Kennedy's feeling isolated and alone. For a moment he thought of waking Barbour so that the whole torpedo team would be mustered, but he dismissed the idea. Barbour was asleep and blissfully unconscious of what was happening. It was better he was left alone; there was nothing he could do anyway. Nothing any of them could do.

He pushed Kennedy down onto the locker bench and sat down himself on the edge of the table. Mulholland sat silently with his arms folded tightly across his chest.

The awful grating sound had stopped.

Wells shot a glance at the sea-pressure gauge on the bulkhead. The needle was creeping around slowly. He noticed that the angle of the deck had begun to tilt forward. They were gradually gaining depth, but the movement seemed to lack control. It was as if they were just sinking. There was still no sound. Had they got free of the mine wire or had it snagged up somewhere, anchoring itself to the hull?

Wells cocked his ears. He couldn't hear the soft purr of the motors. Had the captain stopped them and was he trying to hold a static trim? Or was he allowing the boat to sink slowly downward? If the mine wire had been caught up on the hull they would be like a rabbit trapped in an explosive snare, not daring to struggle. To move forward could bring the mine down on them like a descending lift. Maybe that was Cheney's plan then—to move downward, not forward, and use the mine's own buoyancy to effect their escape. If they dragged the mine down with them, it would have all the more tendency to shoot upward and perhaps free the wire, in the same way an empty bottle would if held under water. But whatever the captain did now, there was no telling what could happen. It was a gamble. Wells loosened the top button of his overall suit. It was becoming unbearably hot.

"Looks as if we're hooked up," Mulholland said flatly.

Wells ignored the comment and turned to face Kennedy, who was sitting upright with grotesque stiffness, his face the color of chalk.

"Go through the drill of blowing up the tubes," he said brusquely.

Kennedy's eyes widened and his lips twitched as if he'd lost the power of speech. He couldn't believe he'd heard the T.G.M. right. "Eh?"

"I said go through the drill of blowing up the tubes. What's the matter with you? Have you got cloth ears?"

"The t-t-tubes?" Kennedy stammered, looking toward Mulholland as if seeking confirmation that the T.G.M. had suddenly gone mad.

"Never mind him. He can do it in the dark with his eyes shut. It's you I want to hear the drill from. Now let's have it," Wells prodded mercilessly.

Kennedy's head wagged bewilderedly. "But—"

"Do I have to tell you again? Go through the drill, I said.

You might have to do it on your own one day. Now get cracking. Right from the start." His voice crackled with authority.

Kennedy licked his lips, stole a glance at the impassive Mulholland and hesitatingly began: "The first thing you do is to
crack open the valve—"

Wells interrupted. "At the order 'Blow up tubes' . . ."

"Oh. At the order 'Blow up the tubes' you first crack open
the valve from the—"

"No, you bloody well don't."

Kennedy took a deep breath and sighed despairingly.

Wells said, "Now start again. What do you check first? The
very first thing."

The young torpedoman bit his lip and concentrated. "You
'mmmm. . . . Yes, that's right, y-you check that the bow cap
doors are closed. Then you—"

"What was that you said?" The T.G.M.'s lips were a tight
compressed line. "Just say that again."

Kennedy flushed nervously. "I said that you checked the bow
cap doors were—"

"Were what?" Wells asked in an iron voice.

Kennedy realized his mistake. "Were *shut*," he replied
in a guilty whisper.

"That's better. Shut! That's the word; don't forget it. I won't
tell you again. Never, repeat, never, use the word 'close' on
board a submarine. That's a dirty word to a submariner, and if
I ever hear you use it again I'll have the skin off your back."

Kennedy stared miserably at the space between his feet.

"Now there's a good reason for that," Wells went on. "Like
everything else in the Navy it has a purpose and its purpose is to
prevent misunderstanding. When you have misunderstandings
you have accidents, and a submarine's no place to have accidents. You might get away with an accident on a surface ship but
not on a submarine—not very often anyway. So remember, the
word is 'shut.' In our language 'close' does not exist, okay? Now
start again."

Kennedy looked crestfallen. He kneaded the skin of his forehead with probing fingers. "Sorry, chief."

"Okay, son. Just remember never to use that word again. . . . Now carry on."

Racking his brains to get the complicated procedure right, Kennedy began a recital of the drill all over again.

Wells had guessed right. They were in a tight spot. They had picked up a mine wire. Dragging along the hull, it had snagged up somewhere midships near the control room.

The crew heard it scraping along the side of the hull like the approach of a blind man fumbling with a stick—and then it had halted. Cheney immediately stopped both motors. To make further way with the mine wire fouling the hull would have been to court disaster. Without way on, the submarine began to sink like an inert whale. Cheney had anticipated this, knowing how impossible it was to achieve a state of absolute negative buoyancy in which a submarine could remain suspended at the same depth.

He shot a look at the depth gauge. The bubble had begun to slide aft, indicating they were slightly heavy by the bow, and the big needles on the gauges were quivering nervously.

"Get the angle off," he snapped to Brangwyn.

Brangwyn, in charge of the trim, reacted quickly. "After pump, pump from for'ard," he called out.

The switchboard operator shot his hand out and flicked over the pump indicator switch while at the same time he rang up the pump station in the afterends. The light on the pump indicator panel flashed on and was followed a second or two later by a red light that indicated the pump was operating. From somewhere under the deck a low gurgling sound was heard, like a bath emptying, and then there was silence again as the pump stopped.

Cheney stepped over to Brangwyn and muttered a few words in his ear. Brangwyn nodded and unhooked the Tannoy.

"First lieutenant here. I want you to listen carefully." The echoing sounds generally associated with the system were strangely absent, screened off as they were by the heavy water-tight doors. "It appears that we may have picked up a mine wire. The captain is trying to keep a static trim. No one is to move from his present position until further orders. Is that clear? Everyone must remain absolutely still." He flicked off and hung up the instrument.

In the far corner by the exchange Stanley grinned widely. "I'm glad I wasn't in the middle of a slash," he remarked. There was a slight titter of nervous laughter from the corner. It stopped abruptly as Cheney wheeled warningly.

Now all eyes watched the bubble again. Trying to hold a static trim was a difficult and delicate operation. Like balancing a knitting needle on the edge of a razor blade. A little too much one way or the other and the needle would tilt and slip off its point of fulcrum. They wouldn't have much chance if they plunged down in 90 fathoms of water.

It was an awesome dilemma they found themselves in. Above was a mine. Beneath was a cruel tonnage of water that could crush the life out of them as effortlessly as a man crushes an ant with his boot. And for all they knew, the shore listening station might have picked up the high-frequency signals from the mine detection unit. Perhaps the whole place was about to seethe with antisubmarine forces.

The possibility of detection had occurred to Cheney. He had a talent for seeing all possible exigencies and dealing with them. It was this talent that had kept him, and his crew, alive in the past. It was also the reason he was a highly successful submarine commander.

"Start an asdic sweep, Winch. Stop the M.D.U."

"Aye, aye, sir." Winch switched off the unit and readjusted his headphones.

Brangwyn inched closer to the planesman, watching the bubble as if it were some strange kind of deadly insect. It had crept back amidships. He prayed that it wouldn't begin to slide forward now as so often happened when you desperately needed a trim. Had he pumped too much water aft? Were they now stern-heavy? The bubble seemed to be holding, but for how long? How long could he expect to keep this up without using the planes or the motors? And another thing—they were making depth. Not much but slowly and surely like a waterlogged hulk.

He half turned to speak over his shoulder to Cheney, never taking his eyes off the bubble for an instant. "One hundred and five feet, sir."

"Yes, I know," Cheney said, the tone in his voice clearly implying he didn't need to be reminded.

Brangwyn stiffened slightly at the rebuke.

He heard Cheney's voice again asking for an asdic report, and automatically he swung to face the cabinet. But Winch had completed his sweep and anticipated the question.

"Full sweep carried out, sir. Nothing to report."

The control room itself seemed to breathe a relieved sigh.

The needles on the gauges trembled and moved forward again in a clockwise direction. They were still sinking slowly. Suddenly it dawned on Brangwyn what Cheney was trying to do. He was deliberately pulling the mine down with them. Instead of tugging at its sinker on the seabed, it would be tugging at the wire attached to the hull. Somewhere above, it would be struggling like a kite on the end of a line in a high wind.

"Do you think it might work, sir," he whispered over his shoulder. The question was genuine, but it also let Cheney know that the first lieutenant was alive to his purpose.

Cheney grunted an unintelligible reply.

"Watch her," he suddenly said. "She's losing the trim."

Brangwyn's eyes flicked over the spirit levels. The bubbles appeared to be nailed to the center.

"Pump from aft, man. She's stern-heavy," Cheney urged in warning tones.

Even as Brangwyn gave the order to pump there was a barely perceptible movement from the bubble. The red indicator by the switchboard flashed on as the pump started up and sucked greedily at the water in the trimming tank.

"Stop pumping," he cried.

The bubble came to a halt just abaft the center line and

began to ease back. He had just caught her in time, but it had been thanks to Cheney.

They were now at a depth of 115 feet. The mine must be tugging madly at the wire that was holding it back in its efforts to shoot upward. Would it break free? Brangwyn, like everyone else, strained his ears to note the slightest sound that would indicate the wire's parting company with the hull. Everyone was keyed up, listening. When the sound came it caught them unawares. Winch's voice hit them like a bombshell.

"H.E. bearing red 80."

Cheney twisted around. "What is it, Winch? What does it sound like?"

Winch shook his head negatively. "Difficult to say, sir. It's a bit mushy, but . . . it sounds like diesel."

"Revs?"

"Can't really tell, sir. Mebbe around two hundred or something like that, but it's hard to say."

"Very well, Winch. Keep an eye on her."

Oh, God, Brangwyn thought. *Just what we need. A bloody A/S trawler coming out for a snoop around.* Brangwyn was worried that she might drop a few patterns of depth charges if she thought there was a submarine about. She wouldn't come into the minefield, of course, but the effect of compression waves on the trim would be disastrous.

One hundred and twenty-two feet.

Winch's voice came from the cabinet. "Range appears to be closing, sir. H.E. still a bit mushy. Now bearing red . . . 82, sir."

Cheney withdrew the knuckle of his forefinger from his mouth. "Very well, Winch. Keep reporting her. Let me know if you can get a range."

The minutes dragged past.

For Brangwyn it was becoming more and more difficult to keep a trim. The bubble looked unstable and threatened to slip away. Still no sign that the mine wire had broken free.

Cheney came to a decision. He had to act before they lost the trim altogether and went into an uncontrollable dive. It might free them, but to check the dive he'd have to blow main ballast. Anyone listening on hydrophones would be bound to hear it. But worst of all, he'd have to cope with the boat's behaving like a wild stallion bang in the middle of a thickly sown minefield.

"All right, number one. We'll start the motors. Use the starboard. Right, let's get moving."

Brangwyn sucked in his breath and braced himself. He turned to the stoker manning the telegraphs. In a voice he tried to keep firm, he said: "Slow ahead starboard."

Within seconds a sound was heard like that of a distant powerhouse generator. A faint pulse rippled through the deck as power was sucked up from the battery cells and transmitted to the screw. Once more the submarine felt alive.

"Starboard ten," Cheney ordered.

Making way through the water, the submarine crept forward gingerly in a circling movement as helm and screw forced her around.

A loud creaking sound filtered through the hull. Like an enormous foot treading on a loose floorboard in an empty house.

Eeeeeekkk. It sounded again—an ominous scraping noise that pierced the eardrums.

Before the crew had recovered their wits the sound came to an abrupt halt. Then a series of hammerlike blows fell, terrible sounds that made the blood run cold. *Bang. Bang. Bang.* Another tortured squeal of metal rubbed against metal—then silence.

They were free.

Chapter Five

The crew drooped in the control room like wilting flowers. Their eyes bulged and their mouths sagged open. It had just gone 2000 hours. For fourteen hours they had been closed up at diving stations.

Fouling the mine wire in the morning had shaken them up. They jumped at the slightest sound. Winch's voice, all the more terrifying because of its calm persistency, grated wildly on their nerves. Staring, white-faced, in the direction of the asdic cabinet, they wished he'd shut up. It was almost as if they held the bulky H.S.N. responsible for the presence of so many mines. Trapped in their steel surroundings, unable to find relief in action, the crew sweated it out. Despite the extremely low temperature, their bodies perspired freely in the oily chilled atmosphere.

It was late in the evening before reports from the mine-detecting unit began tapering off. The flat tones of Winch's heavy Yorkshire accent were heard less and less frequently.

It looked as if the minefield was thinning out.

Though they exchanged meaningful glances, no one dared mention this. They even tried not to think about it. In their superstitious way the crew believed that the moment you displayed or entertained premature signs of optimism you were asking for trouble. It was more comfortable and safe to believe in the worst. That way you covered all your bets. If it didn't happen, you felt grateful and relieved; if it did, well, that's what you had expected anyway. So they held themselves close and nursed their private thoughts, but like the accused who anxiously awaits the return of the jury with the verdict, each man suffered from feelings of loneliness and apprehension.

With the passing of the hours the air in the control room had become heavy and poisonous. Inhaled and exhaled repeatedly by the dozen or so men, its vital properties were nearing exhaustion. Almost as if it were visible it hung between the periscopes like a blanket of gas over a foul swamp. In a few more hours it would barely be capable of sustaining life.

Even now the men were showing the first slight symptoms of carbon dioxide poisoning. As the oxygen was irrecoverably removed from the air and the level of carbon dioxide gradually rose, the crew were more and more disturbed by unrelated feelings of apprehension and shortness of breath. Before they surfaced, most of them would have headaches ranging from mild to severe, depending on each man's metabolism.

Cheney had a slight headache now. Stirring himself to action, he pushed himself forcibly away from where he leaned against the periscope and crossed over to inspect the barometer on the bulkhead. The crew watched him weary-eyed and disinterestedly as he tapped the glass with his finger. It was a dull routine matter and of no great significance. Cheney inspected the delicate instrument, automatically converting the reading to pounds. 17.5. Nearly three pounds above normal atmospheric pressure. The buildup, caused by leakage of compressed air from hundreds of valves and joints in the main line system, was no more than normal. He returned to lean against the periscope, breathing a little heavily, his expression heavy and brooding.

A burst of explosive coughing shook the quiet of the control room. Cheney turned angrily. Able seaman Oak, eyes watering and shoulders shaking, put his hand to his mouth to stifle the sound and cover his embarrassment. Everyone looked in his direction. For some reason the sound of someone's coughing when they were dived disturbed them. It was ten minutes before Oak was able to get control over his wheezing chest and bring his spluttering to an end. Meantime it appeared to have escaped everyone's notice that the asdic cabinet had gone strangely quiet. Winch no longer reported any contacts. But the significance of this didn't escape Cheney.

"Switch off the M.D.U., Winch. Start an all-round asdic sweep."

All at once the control room crew realized that they could be clear of the minefield.

Winch had nothing to report on asdic.

Cheney stood for a moment, gazing into the depths of the periscope well at his feet. Decisively he swung to face Brangwyn.

"All right, number one. Bring her up to periscope depth. . . . Winch? Start the M.D.U. again."

Immediately everyone in the control room became alive again as Cheney rapped out the orders. It was as if they had been cooped up in a slow-moving bus in a traffic jam and now suddenly found themselves clear with an open road in front of them. The telegraphs rang out with an almost festive sound after the long silence. With both motors surging at half ahead and the planes hard to rise, the submarine came up from the depth like a pearl diver seeking air.

Cheney, as usual, had positioned himself ready to grab the periscope handles when the long tube came out of the well. He glanced over his shoulder at the depth gauge. Forty feet. The boat had begun to roll slightly, indicating a bit of a seaway up top.

"Give me a quick sweep on asdics, Winch," he called out. "Twenty-eight feet, number one," he added as the first lieutenant opened his mouth to ask the depth required.

With an oily hiss the big for'ard periscope snaked out of the well. Cheney snapped the handles down and screwed his eyes to the lens. He swung the 'scope around the compass. The surface was completely clear of shipping. He had another look around, much slower this time. He took a couple of quick bearings from coastal promontories and put the periscope down.

"A hundred feet, number one. . . . Start the M.D.U. again, Winch." He rubbed his eyes with his fingertips and in one continuing movement ran his hands through his hair. "We'll surface at 2200 hours."

"Very good, sir," Brangwyn replied, unable to keep a relieved note from creeping into his voice.

Cheney gave him a cold stare.

The next hour passed as slowly as a mile-long funeral cortege. The crew held their aching heads and tried to slow their breathing rate.

Cheney picked up the Tannoy.

"Captain here. We are now clear of the minefield and will be surfacing quite soon. From now on we can expect to receive some attention from Jerry. The success or failure of our patrol will depend upon every man discharging his duties to the very best of his ability. The waters we are now in are heavily patrolled. They are also extensively used by U-boats making passage. I needn't add that we can also expect the U-boats to be heavily escorted by destroyers and aircraft. The advantage will lie with us, but we must never lose it. It is up to every man then to see that we don't; this applies especially to lookouts. An early sighting will make all the difference and can favorably affect any course of action we might have to take. You understand? Very good. Carry on with your duties. Open up watertight doors and ventilation trunking."

A few seconds of silence followed. His remarks with their ominous implications had revealed to the crew a little of what might be in store for them. Despite the fact that this unexpected piece of information—a diplomatic way of telling them they were in for a rough time of it—had jolted them, they also experienced an immense surge of relief that they were clear of the minefield. Eagerly they sprang to the heavy bulkhead doors and knocked off the dog clips. The ventilation trunking was next opened up, and the blowers began to circulate the air through the submarine. It was the same old sour-sweat permeated air, but the emergence of drafts and currents from the louvers in the trunking gave it the illusion of freshness. The opening up of the doors also helped bring relief to the feelings of deep claustrophobia that came about as a result of their being shut off from each other in isolated groups.

At precisely 2205 hours the submarine blew her tanks and, with water cascading from her casing in torrents, pushed herself triumphantly to the surface. Darkness had fallen. The coast of Norway was little more than a turbid streak of tone against the black waters of the Skagerrak.

Overhead the cloud had begun to break up and the wind that had blown so fiercely the previous night had eased to a light breeze. It was still bitterly cold for the time of the year.

Lieutenant Brangwyn had the first watch on deck. His head ached sickeningly; an iron band of pain was behind his eyes. All day long he'd had to bear the strain of keeping the submarine trimmed. Robinson had relieved him during breaks for tea and sandwiches, but as first lieutenant, as long as he remained in the control room the prime responsibility for depth keeping was his. Now stretching before him was a two-hour watch on the ice-cold bridge. He prayed they wouldn't sight anything—he was so worn out with lack of rest that he felt he would never be able to cope.

Moore's voice came as an unpleasant shock.

Brangwyn stifled a groan. He cupped his hand to his ear to pick up the sound of the aircraft the lookout had reported. Like the far distant purr of a motorized lawn mower it could just be heard above the dull rumble of wind and water. Brangwyn debated whether to send for the captain. He was reluctant. Cheney would need all the rest he could get, now that they were in enemy waters. Should he disturb him for something that might turn out to be a false alarm? Even as he debated the question the sound died away. Within ten minutes it was back, and all during the rest of the watch the plane, or planes, stooged around, never seeming to get any nearer. Finally Brangwyn was forced to inform Cheney there were aircraft about. Knuckling his eyes and scowling heavily, Cheney came up on the bridge, but after a short time he went below again, apparently satisfied that the darkness of the night gave them sufficient cover against surprise attack.

By the time the watch had changed over at 2300 hours, the skies had begun to clear. The covering of cloud was stripped away and a huge moon hung above, sitting on top of the periscope standards like a ball cut from solid ice. The wind had almost died. In front of them the Skagerrak stretched away for miles like a piece of crinkled tinfoil. Cheney swore when he came up on the bridge and saw the sudden change in the weather conditions. No longer were they protected by the cover of darkness. Leaning out over the bridge, he looked aft at the long fluorescent wake they trailed. He bit his lip and returned to the forepart of the bridge. He spoke to the O.O.W.

"We'll trim down, Robinson. We're far too big a target in this light. Open three and four main vents."

Cheney leaned over the bridge again, eyeing the level of water as it surged the length of the hull.

Swhooooszh. With an explosive sound a gout of water leaped skyward from the ballast tanks as the main vents were opened. Robinson shot an anxious glance toward the black straggle of cliffs that marked the distant shoreline.

"All right. Shut main vents!" Cheney cried, as the water level rose, covering the ballast tanks and swirling up as far as the casing. Cheney watched the rise of water carefully. Trimmed down now, the submarine was sluggish and difficult to maneuver, but it presented a much smaller target; it also had the advantage of being able to dive quicker. But as the battery was nearly flat after the long passage through the minefield, the last thing he wanted was to have to dive.

In the crew's mess the evening meal ritual was in full swing. All the hammocks, with the exception of Mitchell's, had been lashed back and the lockers cleared. Everyone froze at the sound of the vents thudding open.

"That was the vents," Renwick exclaimed, his jaw slackening and his mouth dropping open. "Did you hear that, Tom?"

"Of course I heard it. Do you think I'm deaf or something? Don't worry, kid. We're only trimming down with all these planes pissing about."

Renwick still looked a bit worried as he began putting the cups out on the table.

Monkhouse stuck his head through the fore-ends doorway. "Up spirits!" he cried.

Stanley jumped to his feet. "Stand fast the Holy Ghost," he yelled, bringing himself to attention and cutting off a salute.

Titt swung a playful punch at him. "Okay, shorty. You seem to be the only one around here that has nothing to do, so you go and get it."

Stanley's eyes danced. He saluted again. "Very good, chief." He turned about smartly. "The book says you've always got to obey orders from a senior hand," he said over his shoulder, bending down and grabbing a liquor can. He shot off through the bulkhead door like a scurrying rabbit.

Some of the hands laid cups out on the table. Titt went to his locker to get his rum list. He stopped at Mitchell's hammock on the way. Squeezing past the torpedo rack he gave the canvas sack a light shake.

"You all right there, kid? How's it going?"

There was a mumbled protesting groan from beneath the blankets. Mitchell's head emerged slowly like a tortoise sniffing the air. "What's that? What did you say?" He rubbed his eyes. He saw Titt. "Oh, it's you, Tom."

"Well, how's it going? Do you think you'll be able to knock back your tot? Rum's up."

Mitchell screwed up his face. He shook his head. "I couldn't look at it. You have it, Tom."

Titt tried to get a closer look at the A.B.'s features, but the mass of lashed-back hammocks were screening off the light from the deckhead. "Okay, Mitch. Is there anything I can get you, though? Would you like something to eat? I'll see the 'swain—mebbe he'll get the chef to cook up something special for you. How about that?"

Mitchell waved his hand weakly. "No, I don't want anything to eat. I—I don't feel like it." He twisted his features and licked his dry cracked lips. "I'll tell you what—could you get me a drink of water?"

"Water? Sure. Is that all you want? Just hang on—I'll go and get it."

There was no cold water in the fore-ends. Titt had to go as far aft as the galley. When he came back Stanley had arrived with the rum. The hands had gathered at the end of the table.

"Hold on a second. I'll be there in a jiff when I've given Mitch a drink."

Mitchell took the glass of water gratefully. He sipped at it. "Thanks, Tom," he murmured.

Titt made a chopping motion with his hand. "Forget it. Look, are you sure you wouldn't like me to see the 'swain—"

Mitchell handed the cup back and shook his head. "No, it's okay. I'll be all right in a day or two."

Titt shrugged helplessly as Mitchell crawled under the blankets again. He hesitated, wondering if there was anything he could do for him, but by this time some of the hands were singing out demanding their rum. They were right enough; there was little else for them to look forward to. He ducked under the hammock and made his way to the table.

"All right. Just take it easy," he muttered as he approached. "You're worse than a bunch of O.D.'s queueing up at a brothel."

He sat down at the table and handed the rum list to Stanley. Abstractedly he began pouring the rum as Stanley sang out the names. He couldn't help feeling a bit worried about Mitchell. Maybe he'd made a mistake by not insisting that the seaman go to sick bay when they were alongside the parent ship. He should have ignored his protests and sent him packing. But then it had been so late in the afternoon when he'd noticed that it was probably more than a hangover the A.B. was suffering from. Only a couple of hours away from sailing, he'd hesitated to report it to the coxswain, knowing only too well the trouble it would cause to get Mitchell drafted inboard and a relief in his place. So late in the day nobody aboard the parent ship would want to know about it. They'd be too bloody busy getting ready to nip ashore in a mad dash to the pubs or some married bird's pad, ashore as Dunoon. Anyway, what the hell. He hadn't had a minute to himself that day. Loading stores right up to the last minute and then Lacey going and getting himself boozed up to the eyeballs so that he had to be helped aboard and half the gun lying in bits. Christ, what a panic that had been. Good thing that Corr and Renwick between them had managed to get it all back together in one piece before someone had started asking questions. Some blokes should have their heads examined or their behinds kicked—both maybe. Great, everybody got a bit grogged on his birthday, but to get a skinful a few hours away from harbor stations was pushing it. He should have put Lacey in the rattle and let him take what was coming to him. The only thing that had stopped him was that he knew they would fling the book at the gunlayer. He'd have got chokey for sure and probably lost his good conduct badge along with it, and all because he was so solid between the ears that he didn't even have the sense to come in out of the wet. Christ, what did you do with a bloke like that? He'd even warned him about it the previous day. Titt bit his lip in annoyance thinking about it. Maybe if it hadn't been for the gunlayer and his stupidity messing everything up that day, he would have gone to see the coxswain about Mitchell. And now the poor bugger was lying in his hammock and the patrol hadn't even started yet. But why in the name of Jesus hadn't he gone to the sick bay if he felt that groggy? All because there was chance of leave which they might never get anyway? It was crazy. Still a fat lot of good that was now, and a fat lot of good he was to anyone lying in his hammock. It would be just great if they had to go to gun action with a new sight setter in the gun's crew. That would help a lot. Titt poured his own rum and angrily swallowed it back.

Now that the crew had had their issue of rum the mess buzzed with conversation like a public bar on a Friday night. This was their great moment, the highlight of the day. Fortified and already feeling heady from the effects of the burningly strong alcohol, they could sit back and let themselves go. For one brief span, as fleeting as the life of a butterfly, the mess glowed with warmth and conviviality.

Moore, sitting to the left of Titt, felt the liberating effects of the alcohol. His thoughts were stimulated but not in a cheerful way like most of the others. He was thinking deeply about his girlfriend, Alice. Her last letter, received just before they'd sailed, had shaken him. He'd read it over and over and was still unable to get the real sense of it. Somewhere at the back of his mind he knew it contained a hidden message, a warning, if only he could put his finger on it. What was it? The question nagged at him and wouldn't let go. That feeling of warmth and response was absent from the written words, scattering seeds of doubt in his brain. Something was going on and he had to know the truth (or was he just imagining the whole thing?). If only he could see her and talk to her. Tell her how much she meant to him; how much he needed her. Christ, didn't she understand? The thoughts swarmed about in Moore's head like angry flies. He leaned over toward Titt.

"Hey, Tom?"

Titt looked up from the table at which he'd been staring moodily. "Hunh?"

Moore squeezed along the bench. "Hey, Tom? Have you heard anything yet? You know? About where we're going? How long's the patrol going to last? What about this buzz that we're on a cloak-and-dagger job?"

Titt, still concerned with his own thoughts, answered irritably: "Do you think I've started slinging my hammock in the wardroom or something? What do you want to ask me for?"

"Well, it was funny, wasn't it? One minute we're all lined up to go in for a refit and the next thing we've shoved off on patrol. You must admit there's something funny about it, eh?"

Titt made a clicking sound with his tongue. "Something funny, mate. Christ, you've been in long enough to know that everything's bloody funny in this lot. You should know a lot better than to listen to buzzes."

Moore's dark features flushed at the rebuff. "Okay, okay. I just thought you might have heard. Anyway—"

Renwick cut in from across the table. "Here, Pony," he said jokingly, "why don't you ask your townie, Cadbury? He's a mate of yours and full of buzzes. He'll give you the gen, Pony."

Moore flung a wintry look at the laughing Renwick. "Why don't you just drop dead, Renwick? And don't go around saying Cadbury's a mate of mine. I don't like it."

Renwick's smile died and he shut up.

But the subject of Cadbury, now that his name had been brought into the conversation, was always good for a laugh.

"Hey, you know what the daft bastard was telling me?" someone said. "He said that we're on our way to Germany to pick up some Jerry bigwigs. Hitler and all that lot. Straight up, that's what he says—and he believes it."

There was a burst of laughter. Rice looked thoughtful. As the laughter died he chipped in: "Perhaps that's not so farfetched as you seem to think." He didn't actually mean his words to be taken seriously in connection with the wardroom steward's alleged buzz. What he wanted to get over was that a lot of things went on behind their backs that they were not aware of. Secret deals and meetings in so-called neutral countries. Politicians carving things up at the same time they egged the troops on. But the way it came out it sounded as if he'd come to the defense of Cadbury. There was a renewed burst of laughing and catcalls.

"Come off it, Ricey. Don't give us that old cod's wallop."

Rice flushed. "All right. Then what about the *Seraph* in the Med? They picked up General Giraud from France, didn't they? *And* they landed General Clark in North Africa for a secret meeting with the French. What about that?"

"Yeah, but they was Froggies, not bloody Jerries, mate."

Rice shook his head despairingly. "I'm not saying that we're supposed to be picking up Hitler, or anything silly like that. All I'm saying is that it's quite obvious the Nazis"—he pronounced it properly with the *tz* sound—"are near the end of the road. It's quite possible some of them might want a deal before the Russians get into Berlin—"

"That's the stuff. Give it to them, Karl. Up the Reds," shouted Stanley.

Rice ignored him and went on. "As I was saying, the Red

Army could be in Berlin any day, and a lot of people won't like that—people on both sides. It wouldn't surprise me then if there's a lot of secret talks going on." There was a barrage of derisory shouts. "All right, all right." Rice raised his voice aggrievedly. "Why don't you read your history? Read about the last war and see what happened then. You might all get your eyes opened."

"Balls." said Thornley, just itching to get at Rice. "Absolute bloody balls. I suppose you're going to give us that old crap about the Reds being a lot of heroes and a lot of bloody saints."

Rice shut his eyes, realizing the utter futility of arguing against such crazy logic. Anyway, he didn't want to get involved in an argument with the big blond seaman. It would only give Thornley the excuse he was looking for. At the same time a little stubborn streak within told him that if he shut up it would look like he was climbing down. From the far end of the table Corr came to his rescue. Thrusting his head forward, his green cat's eyes glinting and the pockmarks in his face coming up in sharp relief as he was caught in the harsh glare of the overhead lighting, Corr said: "There's mebbe something in what Ricey says. Ah mind mah old man telling me that the Jerries—some of the heid yins—was never done coming ower here afore the war. Visiting some big lord's house in the country and a' that." His mouth twisted in a lopsided grimace. "Ah widna trust ony of them. Not one of the bastards. . . . And there's another thing. What about that bloke—what do you call him—him that came ower in the airplane and landed in a field to see some of his mates?"

"You mean Hess," said Rice helpfully.

"Aye, that's the bastard—Hess. That's his name. How about him, then? He was one of the big Nazis, wasn't he?"

The big Scot's intervention had annoyed Thornley, but he hid his feelings for the moment; it was Rice he was after. "You want to grow up, mate," he sneered. "Here's us knocking seven bells of shit out of the Jerries and you're as good as telling us that underneath it we're all pals. You must be off your rocker."

Rice took a deep breath. Thornley's undisguised hostility

scared him, but now that he had started he felt he had to go on. Butterflies fluttered in his stomach. He avoided Thornley's malignant gaze.

"I'm not saying it's as simple as all that. What I'm trying to say—and Jock agrees with me—is that the ruling classes of both Germany and this country were friendly before the war, and once this is all over they could be friends again—given time. And a lot of people in both countries would like to see the Russians knocked out somehow. After all it wasn't long after the armistice had been signed in the last war before German troops and ours were fighting side by side in Russia to try and put down the revolution."

Thornley exploded.

"That's a lot of old cock, that is. Who told you that?"

"It's true," said Rice firmly. "Read your history. It's all there. Read it. You'll find out a lot of things you didn't know before."

Thornley went red with anger. "I'll read what I bloody well want to read and not all that muck you're always on about. It's just a lot of propaganda. Half of it's published in Moscow, I'll bet, for a start."

Rice shook his head.

"No? Well, if it isn't, it's written by Reds in this country and that's the same thing—they'll get paid for it by Moscow. Anyway, seeing you're always on about Russia, you're so keen on it, why don't you go and live there? You have a bash at it, mate, and you'll only be too keen to get back to old blighty, I can tell you."

Rice gave up. There was no use arguing with Thornley.

"That's got nothing to do with it." Able seaman Purgavie looked across the table at Thornley.

"Eh?" Thornley said belligerently. "What's that?"

"What you've just said. It's got nothing to do with what Rice was saying."

Thornley put his hands to his head and snorted. "Oh, Christ, don't tell me we've got another one of Uncle Joe's boys in the mess. Going to give us a bit of *Das Kapital,* are you?"

"Stick to the point. And anyway, what's so wrong about Uncle Joe? He's knocking the Jerries for six, isn't he?"

Thornley leaned forward, his eyes narrowing. He jabbed his finger at Purgavie. "You don't know what you're on about, mate. You've never seen them, have you?"

"No," said Purgavie coolly. "Have you?"

Thornley's mouth came down in a tight line. "For your information, mate, I have. I've seen the bastards all right. I seen them in Spain when we was out there and half you bastards were still at school or pushing a pen in some office. You don't have to tell me about the Red Army, mate. I know. You should have been out there and mebbe you'd know what you were cackling about. Bloody lot—looting all over the place, shooting priests and raping nuns—"

"What was up with you, then? Jealous?" cracked Stanley. "I've always fancied a bit of nun meself."

Thornley's eyes blazed. "Very funny. Very bloody funny, mate. But you wouldn't have thought it was funny if you'd been out in Spain and seen what we did. You're all great at cackling the fat, aren't you? You civvies are all the same. Been in the Navy about two minutes and you know it all."

"I was in the Med then," Titt broke in quietly. "Where were you, then, when you say you saw all this?"

Thornley forgot all about Stanley. He'd always counted on using his weight and length of service in arguments, but he couldn't do that with Titt. Everybody waited for him to speak, but the big seaman had been put right on the spot by the seemingly innocent but penetrating question. He decided to bluff it out. "Oh, so you were, Tom. What was it you were on again?" Thornley was stalling.

"I was on destroyers then—the *Bulldog*. What were you on?"

"The *Bulldog*. Yeah, I remember her. Wasn't she up at Santander when that Spanish cruiser was blocking the port?"

"The *Almirante Cervera*."

"Yeah. That's the one. I remember it now," Thornley said. "There was two or three of our merchant ships in the harbor couldn't get out for her. And there's another one steaming about outside and the *Cervanta*—"

"*Cervera*," corrected Titt.

"That's what I mean—the *Cervera*. The cheeky bastard sends a signal to the *Resolution* saying that this merchant ship's her prize. The old man near did his nut and tells her to go and get knotted."

"You were on the *Resolution,* then?"

"That's right. I was in battlewagons then. But I remember the *Bulldog* being there all right. But—can you remember the name of that cargo buster the Spaniards were after?"

Titt thought for a moment, his eyes never leaving Thornley's. "The *Gordonia*," he said.

"The *Gordonia*—was that it? I think you're right. It was a kind of Scotch name."

"How'd you manage to get ashore?" asked Titt.

Thornley looked puzzled. "Ashore? What do you mean?"

"Well, you were telling us all about the Reds and seeing them rape nuns and all the rest of it."

Thornley leaned back and spread his hands in indignant appeal. "Aw, come off it, mate. You were there. You know what went on the same as I do."

"Yes, I was there and I heard about a lot of things that went on, but I only heard about them—you said you saw them."

The rest of the crew craned forward eagerly. More than a few of them were glad to see Titt putting the screws on the loud-mouthed Thornley.

"Well, you know what I mean," Thornley blustered as he felt himself getting caught in the pincers of Titt's relentless questions. Was Titt getting at him because of the argument about the hospital ship? What was the bastard up to? He felt his temper rising, but he tried to match Titt's easy tones.

"Christ, everybody knew about it. It was all over the mess-deck. I mean—well, everybody just knew. . . ."

Titt got to his feet nonchalantly. He pulled at the lobe of his ear. "I see. It was all over the messdeck. Everybody knew about it, but nobody saw anything. Just another messdeck buzz. . . . Ah, well," he yawned, "I never pay much attention to buzzes myself. Still, you never can tell—if you push your story hard enough there's always somebody who'll be willing enough or daft enough to believe it." He stretched and slapped his belly. "Anyway, it's about time we saw about the grub. Two volunteers are better than ten pressed men, so how about it, some of you?"

Rice, who was sitting at the end of the table, got to his feet. So did Renwick. Renwick could hardly conceal his delight at seeing Thornley brought down a peg. He got Rice by the shoulders and pushed him toward the bulkhead door in playful exuberance.

Thornley was crushed. He could find nothing to say. Inside he burned with a furious rage, its rays focused on Titt as if from a magnifying glass held in front of the sun. He'd never forgive Titt for showing him up in front of the crew. Struggling to control his anger, he made a great play of having forgotten to do something in the motor room. He shot out of the mess behind Rice and Renwick.

The two seaman had reached the galley and were speaking to chef Donahue as Thornley came along the passage. Because of some remark of Renwick's, Rice started laughing in his high-pitched, almost girlish, way. The sound affected Thornley as if a broken bottle had been thrust in his face. Shaking with fury, he pushed his way through the galley, shouldering Rice fiercely out of his way. Rice stumbled against the oven.

Donahue turned to stare after Thornley. "What's the matter with him, then?" he said angrily. "He'll shove his weight around once too often."

"He's got a right old widgy on. Old Titt's just taken a reef in his sails. Made him look a proper monkey. You should have seen it."

Donahue mopped his streaming face. "It's about time, too. He thinks he's a bit of a hard case, that one, but he doesn't want to bugger about with Tom or he'll find himself cut down to size in no time at all."

Renwick laughed dryly. "He got the chop tonight. That's what he's so wild about and wants to take it out on Rice here."

Muttering something about Thornley's sailing close to the

wind, Donahue bent down and opened the oven door. A gust of hot, steamy air hit the passageway.

"Yummmm! Smells great. What is it, Steve?" Renwick asked.

"Toad in the hole, and don't screw your face up or I'll give you something to screw it up for. There's custard and duff to follow for afters, and if anybody's got any complaints, well, they know where to find me. Anyway, it's not ready yet—it'll be another five minutes."

Renwick, with Rice at his heels, trooped back to report to Titt. Most of the hands had risen from the table and were setting out the plates and cutlery. Corr stood beside Titt.

"You shook him there, Tom. He'll keep his big trap shut for a while."

"Mmmm. Mebbe, but you just take it easy, Jock. I don't want any punchups in the mess. If you've got anything to sort out, sort it out ashore and not on board."

Rice came over. "Be ready in five minutes, Tom."

Titt nodded and made to put his things back in his locker.
Tom?" he asked.

Rice caught him. "How long were you out in the Med, Titt looked at him quizzically. "When? I've been there on three commissions."

"I mean that time you were speaking about—before the war."

"Oh, a couple of years, I suppose. But why do you ask? Don't ask me anything about it. I couldn't tell you. You don't see much what's going on ashore when you're at sea."

"Yes, but you must have heard about it. You know stories and things. Was it true . . . I mean . . . well, what Thornley was saying? Did you hear those stories about rape and the rest of it? Did the men believe them?"

Titt laughed. "Well, I don't know if they did or not. I suppose you'll always get some blokes to believe anything they're told."

Rice's eyes sparked with enthusiasm. "You're right there, Tom. It's all part of conditioning the troops so as they'll do what they're told and not ask any questions."

Corr, head canted to one side, was listening intently. "Aye, that's right enough," he agreed. "They'll tell you anything to keep you happy. Ah wouldn't trust the bastards. You know something? Ah mind mah old man telling me about the last war in the trenches. Know what the bastards did? Well, it was Christmas, see, and the troops were lashed up to a bit of grog and were giving it laldie, singing away and all that. Anyway, afore long the Jerries started singing too, and the next thing they were all at it together. It was like a big chorus. The next thing that happens the Jerries start lobbing grub over from their side into the trenches, and then our blokes start doing the same." Corr paused for a breath. "Well, the officers got to hear about it and they got together and had a bit of a chinwag. A few hours later the sergeant comes up with a load of bully beef tins he says are from stores. 'Here you are, lads,' he says. 'Whit's this?' says the old man. 'It's for the Jerries. Help yourselves, lads.' So they grabbed the tins and started lobbing them over to the Jerries just like they do with the bottles at Hampden Park, and shouting Happy Christmas and a' that lark. Well, the Jerries got the tins of bully beef and they blew up in their faces when they opened them. Just like hand grenades. You can imagine what happened then. In no time they were back at it hammer and tongs knocking mortal fuck out of each other."

Rice's eyes opened in horror. "Of all the filthy tricks. My God! What beasts!"

Titt said nothing. His face was expressionless. He made to go.

"Eh, but just a minute, Tom." Corr stopped him. "That's no' the end of it. You know what? Well, the funny thing was that later, when it was all over and they got back to blighty, some of the blokes were going around saying it was the other way about and it was the Jerries had done it to them. Would you believe that, eh?"

Rice shook his head. "Man's inhumanity to man," he muttered.

Corr looked surprised. "Good for you. I see you've read

Burns. Aye, Rabbie knew a thing or two. He knew what he was on about." He slapped Rice's shoulder. "I see there's hope for you Sassenachs yet."

Rice smiled. He began reciting softly:

> A fig for those by law protected!
> Liberty's a glorious feast!
> Courts for cowards were erected,
> Churches built to please the priest.

Corr's eyes widened in respect as Rice finished. "How about that, then? Did you hear that, Tom?" He slapped Rice heftily on the back this time. "Good for you, mate."

"Great," said Titt, "but poetry's not going to fill our bellies, and the grub should be ready by about now, so how about it?"

"Aw, Tom." Corr's big head wagged despairingly. "Have you no soul, man? You've just got to hand it to Burns—"

"I'll hand it to anyone, Jock—when we've eaten. So let's get cracking, eh?" Though he didn't show it in his face, Titt had been impressed with Rice's knowledge of Burns. With big Jock? Well, you expected that. The Scots probably got Burns along with the salt in their porridge. Maybe there was more to Rice than just a lot of old waffle. Underneath the didactic manner perhaps there was a bit of real learning tucked away. Funny that Rice should quote the only bit of Burns Titt really knew. Jock Bain had read it to him one night, almost a year ago, when they were alongside the parent ship. "Liberty's a glorious feast." The words had a bite and a snap to them, none of that flowery effeminacy he had always associated with poetry. Like whiskey they had a dangerous potency. They made you think and that was a risky thing to do for a man serving his time out in the service. . . .

They were all gathered around the table finishing off their meal. Thornley had made a brief and silent appearance, bolted back his food and left again for the motor room. Corr was brewing the tea. A heavy sulphurous smell permeated the compartment as matches were struck and the crew lit up. Corr came back with the giant teapot and began sloshing it into the cups. He filled his own last and sat down beside Titt.

"Christ, Ah wish it was rum," he said, pouring an enormous quantity of sweetened milk into the dark-brown liquid. "One tot's no' enough for a big fella like me." Out of the corner of his eye he caught Stanley grinning. "And you keep your wee face shut or I'll flatten it. And properly this time. I won't leave it half done like the M.P.'s did." Having dealt with Stanley he turned to Titt.

"Well, we've had our grub—who's for ashore?" he said laughing and rubbing his hands together.

"What are you on about?" said Titt.

"Well, you said you'd rather have your grub than liberty. We've had the grub so how about it—how about organizing a run ashore?"

Titt gave him a pained look.

"Is that supposed to be some kind of a joke?"

Corr laughed. "Come on. Liberty men fall in. We'll piss off ashore and find a good boozer and I'll give you all a song." Without warning he threw back his head and in a tuneless voice began singing "The Star o' Rabbie Burns." The sound was dreadful. The crew shouted at him but he went on, ignoring their pleas to shut up.

He finished a verse and turned to Titt. "How's that, Tom? A good tune, eh? Did you like that?"

Titt groaned. "Christ, I hope Jock Bain didn't hear it or he'll be through with his bagpipes to join in. Don't tell me that was a tribute to your national poet—I wouldn't believe it."

"Aye, Rabbie Burns. The greatest poet that ever lived," said Corr, thrusting his chin out melodramatically. "The greatest poet in the world. And he was only a plowman, not one of your long-haired, half-deid, English university twits. That's all he was—a plowman. But it didn't make any difference to him. Aye, 'a man's a man for a' that.' And he should have known, he said it."

Even the normally serious Rice seemed to be amused at Corr's fervor. "You want to be careful, Jock," his voice twanged thinly, "you'll be up in front of Jimmy the One for preaching socialism on board one of His Majesty's ships."

Titt got up from the table. "Oh, come on. Let's get the table cleared and the dishes done or we'll be cackling all night. Pony, you can get the water."

As the crew began clearing up in the fore-ends, Monkhouse was collecting the dishes from the P.O.'s' mess. Monkhouse wished they'd all shut up and let him get on with it. Percy Bissel, the electrical artificer, had been trying to pump the coxswain about the patrol, so far with little success.

"Come on, Bill, you old sod, let's have it," he tried again. "Where are we supposed to be heading?" There was no reply, so he went on: "Look, don't try and kid me there's nothing in the wind. When was it a boat last operated in the Skagerrak? Must be years ago. Don't tell me we came all the way through that bloody minefield just as an exercise. No, there's a reason for it, and my guess is you know it. What about it, Bill?"

Blow smiled good-naturedly, his clean-shaven cheeks glowing healthily in the soft lighting. "Now, now, Perce. You know as well as I do, that I don't get a copy of sailing orders. Only the old man does, and up to now he hasn't had time to read them out to me."

"Ha-bloody-ha. You can save the sarcasm," said Bissel. "But if you ask me, you know something and you're not telling."

Bain leaned forward. "What are you worrying about, Perce? There's no need to bother the coxswain. Why don't you ask me?" He winked at the other petty officers. "I've got all the gen."

Bissel made a derisory noise.

"You don't believe me, eh? Well, let me tell you I've had the latest from Cadbury, and he's the boy on this ship that knows what's going on."

"Has that bugger been spreading buzzes again?" Blow interjected. "I'll give him buzz, right in the ear, if *I* catch him. And you, Jock, you should know better than to encourage him."

Bain laughed. "Och, there's no harm in him—he's just a bit daft and likes to natter."

"Daft?" sneered Preece. "The bastard's clean off his rocker and should be locked up out of harm's way. I'm telling you, Bill, you want to keep an eye on him—he's right round the bend."

As the petty officers debated the question of the steward's sanity, the object of their investigation was sneaking along the passageway, soft-footed as a cat. A quick look toward the galley confirmed that Donahue was busy cleaning his stove. There was no one else about. Eyes bright with excitement, Cadbury squeezed himself against the mahogany paneling outside the captain's cabin. Normally only a curtain screened off the interior from the passageway, but for some reason the door had been shut. From behind the paneling came a muffled sound of voices. Eagerly Cadbury pressed forward, his ear to the door. Robinson had the watch and Joyner was in the wardroom. It could only be the first lieutenant with the captain. He pressed up closer. Was Brangwyn getting a bollocking from the old man? It sounded like it. He listened intently, his round features screwed up like a rubber ball. Cheney's voice was raised. Cadbury imagined he heard both the coxswain's and Mitchell's names mentioned. There was a confused jumble of sound. Both Brangwyn and Cheney seemed to be speaking at the same time. What was that? He thought he caught the word U-boat and then something about Oslo before he leaped back in alarm as the voices ceased and he heard the scuffle of feet. Springing erect, he scuttled back to the safety of the pantry. Once there, he kept hopping about from foot to foot and continually poking his head around the corner to see if any important member of the crew was heading toward the control room. He was dying for the opportunity to launch his latest, and greatest, buzz.

His fantasy was cut short as the buzzer in the pantry rang, summoning him to the wardroom. That would be that little shit Joyner, demanding more coffee. Well, he'd take care of him all right. He smiled archly to himself. Only the other day Joyner in his usual bullying snot-faced manner had insisted on another helping of stew. He'd got it—and a great big dollop of grease scraped from the bottom of the hot plate to go with it. Hee, hee, hee. That would teach the bastard. It wasn't the first time that he'd slipped him a Mickey Finn, no, nor Mr. Fancy-Face Robinson either.

Joyner, tousle-headed and stifling a yawn, saw the curtains part in answer to his ring. The bland, smiling face of the steward appeared.

"You rang, sir?"

"Yes, Cadbury. I would like some more coffee."

"Coffee, sir? Certainly, sir. And how would you like your coffee, sir? Black, white, or would you prefer brown?" Cadbury asked with bland sincerity, his head cocked to one side like a small fat bird..

Joyner's eyes narrowed and his lips came together. "Just as usual, Cadbury," he said sharply. "You should know by now. The first lieutenant will be back shortly—he may want some too, so you'd better hurry it up," he added threateningly.

Cadbury gave just the hint of a bow before he slipped back through the curtain. Joyner could hear him whistling as he made his way back to the pantry. God! how the man infuriated him. Damned insolent oaf. He wouldn't have dared behave like that if either the captain or the first lieutenant had been in the wardroom. One of these days he'd make him sit up. . . .

Brangwyn was still closeted with the captain. Cadbury's guess hadn't been far out—he *was* giving the first lieutenant a dressing down. He was referring to the incident with the plane.

"I'm not particularly concerned about them spotting us— in one sense. Part of the idea behind the operation is that Jerry should know we have submarines patrolling the area. It might help to discourage them making a break for it if it ever comes to that. No, it's not that. But that attack was too damned close. We should never ever be taken completely by surprise like that. It should *not* happen," Cheney finished angrily.

"But, sir," Brangwyn protested, "no one could have possibly seen the plane beforehand. And they certainly could not have heard it in those conditions." He paused. "You did say yourself, sir, that they might be using some form of radar."

"Yes, yes, yes," Cheney replied impatiently, "but it's the whole thing I'm concerned about, not just one incident."

"The whole thing?" Brangwyn looked puzzled. "I'm sorry, sir, I'm afraid I don't quite—"

Cheney waved his hands. "Brangwyn, a slackness has crept into the ship's company's performance. I see evidence of it in many ways. This is a very important patrol. A good deal can depend on the outcome of it. I want this slackness to be tightened up. Be as severe as you think necessary, but I want every man on his toes. And I mean *every* man. You understand, Brangwyn?"

Brangwyn stiffened. "Yes, sir. Is that all, sir?"

"Yes, that's all—for now," Cheney said curtly, reaching up for his bridge coat. "I'm going on the bridge. Tell the steward to make some coffee. I'll have it when I come down." He slipped on his coat.

"Oh, and another thing, Brangwyn," he said, as the first lieutenant made to leave. "You might teach Joyner to keep a proper trim. He takes far too much out of the battery when he's on watch. I want the battery saved as much as possible. Do a watch or two with him till he gets the hang of it, all right?"

Brangwyn opened the door. "And, number one"—Brangwyn stopped as Cheney's voice resumed—"I want Mitchell back on watch as soon as possible."

"Of course, sir." Brangwyn frowned. "I *have* had a word with the coxswain and he's keeping an eye on him."

"Did he say what was the matter with him?"

"Well, no, sir. He apparently has a temperature and feels sick—he didn't say it was anything specific."

Cheney nodded. "Hmm. Perhaps you'd better go along and have a look at him yourself."

Brangwyn looked hesitant. "But, sir, the coxswain—"

"Yes, you've already told me. The coxswain's seen him. Now I want you to see him."

"Very well, sir. As you say." Brangwyn went out of the cabin. He shut the door behind rather forcibly.

Chapter
Six

Cadbury had made a fresh pot of coffee and placed it on the wardroom table. Brangwyn sat staring at the pot. A curl of blue smoke rose from the cigarette he held in his hand. He very rarely smoked, but the interview with Cheney had upset him. Joyner watched him furtively from behind a book he pretended to be reading. He could see the first lieutenant was angry.

Brangwyn ground his half-finished cigarette into the base of a three-inch shell which served as an ashtray. He rang the bell for the steward. In a moment Cadbury appeared.

"You rang, sir? More coffee, sir?" he queried obsequiously.

Brangwyn shook his head. "Tell the coxswain I would like to see him in the control room right away."

"The control room, sir?"

"Yes, Cadbury. Do I have to repeat myself?"

Joyner peered over the top of his book.

"Very good, sir." Cadbury shot off. O-ho. What was all this about? Wants to see the coxswain. In the control room. That means whatever it is he doesn't want Joyner to know. Cadbury rubbed his hands together; things were happening.

Finishing his coffee, Brangwyn rose and put on his jacket. He drew back the curtain and headed for the control room. Blow was already there. He stood at the far end, by the chart table, out of earshot of the P.O. of the watch and the helmsman.

"Ah, there you are, coxswain. I just wanted to have a word with you."

Blow straightened up attentively.

"It's about Mitchell, coxswain," said Brangwyn, coming right to the point. "How is he?"

"Well, he still feels sick and he has a bit of a temperature. I don't think he's all that bad, sir—though he hasn't eaten—but he's not well either, if you know what I mean."

"Of course, coxswain. And you've seen him this evening?"

"About a couple of hours ago, sir. But I'll be going along again. I've asked Titt to sort of keep an eye on him."

"I see," said Brangwyn, gazing at a spot on the deck. "Well, coxswain, let me know when you intend to pay your next call. I think I'll come along with you. I'd just like to see how he is. Is that all right, coxswain?"

"Of course, sir."

"Very well. You'll let me know then?"

Blow made to go, but Brangwyn stopped him. "Oh, and one other thing, coxswain. . . ." He hesitated, not sure how to begin. "Well, I've had a word with the captain. He—well, he has stressed once more to me the importance of keeping everyone on their toes. I can tell you in confidence, coxswain, that our present operations have a strategical importance." Blow remained impassive. "And so there must be no question of relaxing or taking things easy. I know that there's a good deal of feeling about that Jerry is nearly finished and that it's only a question of time. Such an attitude among the men must be discouraged as dangerous and irresponsible. I think you understand, coxswain."

Blow remained silent.

Brangwyn frowned at this seeming lack of cooperation from his senior petty officer. "It is the duty of all petty officers to nip these sort of rumors in the bud and prevent their circulation. As far as this ship is concerned the war is far from over and we must never relax our vigilance, all right?"

Blow coughed, clearing his throat. It sounded like a protest, but his voice was even as he answered: "Very well, sir. Is that all, sir?"

Brangwyn felt uncomfortable. The coxswain must be wondering why he had been summoned to the control room. After all, he hadn't told him anything about the patrol, and saying that the men must keep on their toes seemed rather like stating the obvious. If anyone doubted that they were back in the business of war, the passage through the minefield would have dispelled that illusion, to say nothing of a near miss from a hundred-pound depth bomb. Originally he had intended to pass on the captain's criticism, but faced with the coxswain he felt it would have been an act of hypocrisy. As far as he saw, the crew's behavior was no worse, or better, than it had always been. He knew there was a lot of talk going about, of course, but that was only to be expected. It was common belief back home that the war was in its closing stages. It would have been much better if Cheney had told the men the objectives of the patrol. That, more than anything, would kill the wild rumors and speculations that were spread. He regretted his action in sending for the coxswain. Annoyed with himself, he spoke sharply.

"That will be all, coxswain. You'll let me know when you are going to see Mitchell?"

"Aye, aye, sir." Blow turned, carrying his shoulders rather stiffly, and in his slow, rolling gait walked out of the control room.

In the mess he faced a barrage of questions. What had Jimmy been on about? Was it true they were expecting a recall? Were the Germans really about to sling their hands in? Blow skillfully evaded the questions by saying exactly nothing. Seeing they were getting nowhere the little group at the table began to break up. Those not due to go on watch soon climbed into their bunks. Blow sent for Monkhouse.

"Go along to the fore-ends and see if they're cleared up yet," he told the messman. "If they are, tell Tom Titt I would like to see him."

Monkhouse was back within seconds. "He says they're just finishing off. He'll be along in a minute."

Blow had got out the medical manual once more and was browsing through it when Titt appeared. He closed the book and put it down.

"How's Mitch, Tom?" he asked.

Titt rubbed his face. "Well, you know, he doesn't look all that good. I don't think he's any worse, but I wish he would eat something. But all he ever asks for is a glass of water. He should eat."

"I see. Well, I'll be along later to see him. I want to take his temperature and pulse. Jimmy'll be with me."

"Jimmy?"

"What's the matter? Have you got a few bottles of rum stashed away that you don't want him to see, eh?"

"I wish to Christ we had. No, I just wondered, you know."

"Okay then, Tom. If Mitchell's still awake tell him we'll be along. If he isn't, don't bother."

It was an hour before the coxswain and the first lieutenant ducked through the doorway of the fore-ends and made their way to Mitchell's hammock. Both men wore jackets and caps to stamp the visit as official.

The fore-ends was very quiet. From the mass of hammocks swinging from the deckhead, a dull animal sound of breathing rose and fell in a cross pattern of rhythms. With only a couple of small lights switched on, the compartment looked cold and cheerless.

Mitchell was sleeping, but he woke as the coxswain shook his hammock. Blow asked a few questions before taking the seaman's temperature and pulse. Brangwyn stood by and waited. Only when Blow had finished did he speak to Mitchell. He asked him how he felt. Mitchell was obviously embarrassed by the presence of the first lieutenant and mumbled a reply that he was all right. The visit was over. Both men ducked under the hammocks and crept quietly out of the fore-ends. Neither of them spoke as they walked the length of the passageway as far as the control room. Blow waited for Brangwyn.

"Well, I know it's easy to say, but he didn't look too bad, coxswain, did he?"

Blow blew his cheeks out and clasped his hands behind his back. "Mmmm? I don't think he is that bad, sir, though he's bound to be pretty weak, him not eating. But I don't think he's well enough to think about watchkeeping yet."

"No, of course not, coxswain. I wasn't thinking of that. How was his pulse?"

"Up a bit, sir, but fair."

"And temperature?"

"Same again, sir, fair. It's up—99.5. A slight rise since I last took it four hours ago."

"I see." Brangwyn nodded slowly. "Well, now, coxswain, what do you think is the matter with him?"

"Well, I wouldn't like to say at the moment, sir. I'd only be guessing."

"Have you any ideas at all? The captain is anxious to know, coxswain, as you can well imagine."

"Of course, sir, but it could be so many things. At a rough guess I would say it's some sort of infection."

"Infection, eh?" Brangwyn pondered. "What exactly do you mean, coxswain? What sort of an infection?"

As the two men continued to discuss Mitchell's condition in low-pitched voices, Cadbury, on one of his periodic prowls, caught sight of them. Like some small inquisitive animal he peered around the corner of the bulkhead. So they were at it again. Another secret discussion. What was going on? What was Jimmy saying to the coxswain? Was he putting him on oath? He nipped back into the pantry as he saw the first lieutenant prepare to leave. Holding his breath, he waited for him to pass. Blow was still in the control room having a word with the P.O of the watch. A few seconds later Cadbury heard his foot scrape the coaming of the bulkhead door. Cadbury sprang out of the pantry, nearly knocking the stocky figure over in his excitement.

"Watch what you're doing," gasped Blow angrily. "You want—" He stopped as he recognized the steward. "I might have known. What's all the bloody hurry about? Thinking about going ashore, are you?"

Cadbury stepped back, grinning and rubbing his hands on

his greasy trousers. "Hello, 'swain. All right, eh?" He cackled inanely, his head bobbing up and down. "Okay, eh?"

Blow's lips came together tightly as he measured the steward with a long look.

"Heh, heh, heh." Cadbury stopped rubbing his trousers and brought his hands up in front of him, wringing them together. "I saw you just now, speaking to Jimmy. Something good, eh? What was he on about? What's going on, 'swain?"

Blow took a pace forward and drilled the steward in the chest with his forefinger. "Listen, lad. What the first lieutenant has to say to me is no one else's business but mine. Understand? And if ever I catch you trying to listen in again you'll get my boot up your arse, so watch it!"

Cadbury giggled and twisted his legs. "I wasn't listening, 'swain. I wouldn't do that. I just happened to see you talking and wondered, that's all."

"And that's another thing. There's far too much talk going on about what we're supposed to be doing and where we're going and all that. Somebody keeps spreading buzzes. If I catch the bugger at it he's in for the high jump."

The steward's eyes shaped themselves into large O's. "Buzzes? It's not me, 'swain, straight up. Don't think it's me. I don't spread any buzzes."

"No? Well, just let me catch the bugger and he'll be sorry." Blow stomped off, leaving the steward grinning fatuously to himself. Back in his own mess, Blow slipped off his jacket and plumped himself down on the bench. He sighed heavily. He felt dead tired and would have liked to lie down for a week. Wearily he glanced up at the clock. Titt would soon be taking over the watch from Bain in the control room. That meant he had a little more than two hours before relieving Titt. He decided to have a cup of cocoa before turning in. He was sitting at the table sipping the scalding liquid gently when Bain arrived.

"Still up, Bill? I thought you'd have turned in by now."

"If I'd any sense I would have. I'm all in, after today."

Bain slumped down on the padded bench. "So am I. I'm

absolutely sold out. Thank Christ we don't have to go through a minefield every day. I don't think my nervous system would stand it. Must be getting old."

Blow put down his cup. "Nobody ever gets any younger, Jock. Funny when you're young. You look at your grandparents as if they'd been that age all their life. You can't imagine them as young folk, any more than you can imagine yourself as old. But it comes to all of us—and a damn sight sooner than you think."

Bain stopped rubbing his eyes. It wasn't often the coxswain spoke in this vein. He must be feeling it. "What was Jimmy on about, by the way?" he asked, changing the subject. "He looked as if he'd something on his mind."

"Oh, nothing. Just having a word about Mitchell. He came along to see him tonight. That's a good cup of cocoa on the galley. You should have a drop. Helps you sleep."

"Oh, he was, was he? What's this? Second opinion, eh? Or was he just making sure he wasn't swinging the lead?"

Blow frowned. "You haven't forgotten that Mitchell's the sight setter on the gun's crew. The first lieutenant's every right to feel worried. Wouldn't you if you were in his shoes?"

"Steady on, Bill. I was only joking."

Blow got to his feet. "It's not much of a joking matter. I don't mind telling you the old man's quite worried about it. Here we are on the billet and we're a man short. It's no joke. . . . Anyway, I'm turning in." Blow slipped off his white rollneck jersey and shoes and hoisted himself into his bunk. He pulled the quilt over himself as he turned to face the bulkhead. In a few minutes he was snoring softly.

Bain sat at the table, too tired to move, debating whether to have cocoa or not. Finally he made his mind up and grabbed a mug. He walked to the galley, thinking. Poor old Bill. He must be feeling the strain all right to go on like that. He shouldn't be at sea. He'd done more than his whack already. How many patrols had he done? Damn near thirty, was it? That was more than enough. Anyway, a submarine was no place for a man over forty. Bain stood in the passageway by the galley and finished off his cocoa, then went to turn in.

The night passed slowly. It was still bitterly cold. The wind had come up again, showering the bridge with a biting spray as the breaking wave crests were swept up in a million particles. The coast of Norway was only fifteen miles off to port, but the submarine was drawing away from land and heading toward the northeast. The strong wind had gathered a good deal of cloud and was piling it up in to the Skagerrak and the North Sea. The sea had become ugly and black, but occasionally a scattering of lighter patches could be glimpsed as the waves reared and broke into fungus-colored froth. Cheney had taken a number of star sights before the cloud had moved up and was able to pinpoint his position accurately. For long spells he remained on the bridge, only going below to consult the chart and help himself to coffee from the pot that boiled all night long on the pantry hot plate.

Throughout the night the steady waspish drone of aircraft could be heard. Everyone on the bridge asked himself the same question: Were the aircraft searching for them?

Cheney paced the bridge restlessly. There would be no sleep for him until they dived just before the first light of dawn. Now that they had arrived on the billet he was beginning to work himself up into a highly charged nervous state—like a professional fighter before an important fight. He felt supremely confident. Equipped with all the ingenious weaponry that science could devise to kill, he had become the most potentially dangerous killer of all—man!

For the hundredth time since he'd arrived on the bridge, he turned to scan the thickening night. It was unfortunate that at that moment he caught the starboard lookout in the act of yawning. The barest fraction of a second before Cheney had turned around, able seaman Moore had lowered his binoculars to wipe the spray from the lens. Weary to his bone marrow, he had allowed himself one tiny, half-stifled yawn.

Cheney was on him like a tiger.

"What the devil do you think you are doing, lookout? You're supposed to be doing a job—do it!" Cheney exclaimed savagely.

Moore jumped. "Sorry, sir. . . . I was just—"

"I don't want to listen to any of your excuses. Just get on with it," the voice snapped viciously above the wind.

Moore shut up instantly. It was futile to try to explain. A choking sensation gripped him by the throat as the blood rushed to his face. Of all the rotten bastards. Christ, he'd just put his glasses down to clean them. What was he supposed to do, let them get dirty? They'd be a lot of good then. Of all the green rubs. You strain your fucking guts and eyeballs out for night after night, through all the shit, muck and perishing cold, and the minute you stop to clean your glasses the skipper gets the boot in. Bloody old bastard! Just like the rest of the pigs. That's all the thanks you got for doing your best. . . .

Moore had cause to feel angry and humiliated. In addition to his gift of extraordinary good vision, he was probably the most painstaking and conscientious lookout in the three watches. Time and again he'd demonstrated his powers, spotting objects long before the O.O.W. or the other lookouts had. And now here was the skipper handing him out a first-rate bollocking and in front of that little shit Joyner, who would be sure to make the most of it. Moore choked back his anger, forcing himself to concentrate. His humiliation turned to bitterness. Christ, no one had need to tell him the importance of keeping a good lookout. He knew only too well what could happen if he got careless. He'd learned the hard way. Once you'd been rammed by a destroyer you didn't easily forget it.

The first faint streaks of dawn at last came after the long night. It was only the barest spill of light that rimmed the horizon, but it was the signal to dive. Cheney ordered the hands to diving stations and, pressing the klaxon, took the boat down to 60 feet. They would remain at that depth until there was sufficient light to use the periscope.

Two hours later the crew had just finished breakfast and were clearing up. Blow went along to see Mitchell. His condition was much the same. Neither his pulse nor his temperature had gone up further. But he still had not eaten, and he looked weak. He also complained of a slight pain, low down in the region of his stomach. Blow left. For the first time since Mitchell had been excused duties, he felt vaguely worried. But he dismissed the thought. Mitchell would be up and about in a few days, he assured himself.

Lacey, the gunlayer, had just come off watch as the coxswain was leaving the fore-ends. He stepped aside to let him pass.

"What was he after, then?" he asked Hollingsworth, the telegraphist, as he stepped into the mess.

"The 'swain? Oh, he was just having a look at Mitch."

Lacey wasn't really interested but asked: "What did he say?"

Hollingsworth yawned and scratched his head. "He didn't say anything. Just took his temperature and pulse and left." He leaned over and called softly in the direction of Mitchell's hammock: "Hey, Mitch? What did the 'swain have to say?"

There was no answer.

Hollingsworth shrugged. "He's sleeping. And that's where I'm heading. See you." He climbed up on the table and hoisted himself into his hammock.

Lacey sat down. He looked idly at the shambles about him, but it didn't register. He was trying to make up his mind whether to have a cup of tea before he turned in. The rest of the watch would be in at any time. If he started making tea now he would have to make enough for all of them. He didn't fancy that.

Young Kennedy was the first to come through the bulkhead door. He grinned cheerfully at the gunlayer, his fresh face looking almost healthy in the dim lighting. Kennedy could afford to grin. This was his first patrol. With the resilience of youth he'd shaken off the effects of the bombing and the passage through the minefield. As yet he hadn't had to take any prolonged physical or mental batterings. There were no lines of fear etched indelibly around his eyes or the corners of his mouth.

"Hiya, Guns," he greeted. "Fancy a cupper before turning in?"

Lacey looked up suspiciously. "Who's going to make it?"

"I'll make it. I was going to anyway."

"Oh," said Lacey, suddenly affable. "Goodo, mate. Great idea.

I could do with a cupper now that you mention it. But you'd better shake it up—the others will be here in a minute."

Kennedy looked at him in surprise. "Well? I'll make enough for all of us—I don't mind." He whistled softly to himself as he collected the teapot and made his way over to the copper.

Lacey watched him, a half-amused, half-contemptuous smile on his face. Let him do it while he's willing. He'll learn soon enough that it's every man for himself in this lot. He leaned back and made himself comfortable, not even bothering to help by getting the cups out.

Crabbe and Moore were the next to come in the mess. They were followed shortly by the two stokers, Micky Rafferty and Henry Ford. Mulholland also appeared, dragging himself out of his hammock. He was due to relieve Barbour in the tube space.

"Somebody making char?" he asked.

Lacey jerked his head in the direction of Kennedy.

"Goodo. I'll have a drop before I go on watch." He nipped forward to tell Barbour.

Moore got the cups out and sat down. A moment later Kennedy, cheeks puffed with the effort of carrying the giant teapot one-handed, returned. The muscles in his forearm straining, he eased the pot down onto the table.

"Christ," said Mulholland, "you've got enough there for the ship's company of the *Nelson*. How much did you make?"

Kennedy flushed with embarrassment, as he always did when he became the focus of attention. "Well, I didn't know how many there was going to be," he said.

Lacey laughed patronizingly. "Never mind him, Tosh. You're doing all right."

Kennedy poured out the tea, filling his own cup last. He sat down beside the others.

"What's the latest?" Crabbe said once everybody had settled. "Heard anything yet?"

Mulholland rose to his feet. "Yeah, the skipper's got another minefield lined up for us tomorrow."

Kennedy momentarily paled but quickly recovered as Mul-

holland took out a copy of *Good Morning* from his overalls pocket. "If you don't believe me," he said, "you can read it
for yourself. It's in the papers." He picked up his cup and made
his way forward, climbing over the heaped-up pile of gear
that cluttered the compartment.

"Here," said Rafferty. "Why are you asking us what the latest is? We're only stokers. You're seamen, aren't youse? You get
all the buzzes that are going. Us, we're up to our necks in those
bloody pumps half the time. Anyway, the last time you said the
Jerries were packing it in, didn't you? What's happened? Have
they changed their minds now?"

"I didn't say that," protested Crabbe. "It wasn't me. All I
said was I thought there was something up this patrol." He appealed to Lacey. "Didn't I, Trapper?"

"How the hell should I know what you said or didn't say?"
replied Lacey sourly. "Everybody keeps shooting their mouths
off about where we're going and all that balls. Me? I'm interested in one thing only—when we're going to get back up the
Clyde. I've got a nice little party all lined up in Glasgow"—he
pronounced it *Glassgay*, thinking that was the way the Scots
did. "Her old man's in Burma, or some bloody place, shooting
Japs." He grinned evilly. "I'm keeping his side of the bed warm
for him coming back."

"You want to watch out he doesn't catch you, mate," said
Rafferty. "If he's a pongo you might get a dirty great bayonet
up your arse."

Lacey made a derisory sound. "That'll be the day a squaddy
catches me, I can tell you. Anyway, he ought to be glad his wife's
not going short of her rations." He nudged Moore with his elbow
and winked. "What do you say, Pony?"

Moore gave him a cold look. "I got no time for a bloke who
fucks about with another bloke's wife—or party—when he's
away. They deserve all they get."

They all looked at Moore, surprised by his intensity of feeling.

"What's the matter with you, then?" said Lacey, needled by
the unexpected and unwarranted censure. "What's all this stuff

you're giving us? Don't come it. If you could get your feet up, you would, just like the rest of us. So don't give us any of your old ab-dabs."

Moore got up. "If I was away and came back and caught somebody fucking about with my missus, I'd shoot the bastard."

An embarrassed silence fell over the group. No one expected Moore to take the gunlayer's boastful remarks seriously. Moore went to turn in. There was a long pause before anyone spoke again.

"What's the matter with him, then?" Barbour was the first to break the silence.

"Somebody's been mucking about with his old lady, by the sound of it," said Rafferty.

"He's not married, is he?" asked Barbour.

Lacey sneered. "Course he's not."

"Well, what's he on about, then? Some pongo sleeping with his mother?"

Lacey made a sign to keep their voices down. "I've noticed he's been a bit funny lately. I mean, look at that just now. All I do is to mention I'm up homers with this party and he dives off the deep end."

Kennedy's eyes switched from speaker to speaker, not knowing what to make of the sudden development. He looked up to Moore, as an old hand, in much the same way he idolized Titt and the T.G.M. He wasn't all that fond of Lacey, but in a way he envied the swashbuckling, tough-guy attitude that the gunlayer adopted. There was a kind of gangster-romantic appeal about it. Since joining the Navy, and especially the submarine service, Kennedy had been imbued with the idea that the harder and tougher you were the more manly it was. You got drunk, you held the other services and *all* civilians in contempt, you didn't give a damn for anybody and looked after number one, and the first bloke that looked at you sideways you clobbered. That was the philosophy of life on the lower deck of the Navy. Pony's open and flat contradiction of the gunlayer's views seemed to deny this. It was part of Kennedy's youthful ambivalence that while he was able to accept the moral anarchy of people like Lacey, he also found strong sympathy for the views on social behavior implicit in Moore's reaction. Unfortunately, owing to his immaturity, the person who spoke to him last tended to make the greatest impression, but early in his naval career one particular impression had stamped itself firmly on his mind, coloring all his thinking with the indelibility of a powerful dye. It had been shortly after he'd finished his submarine training in Fort Blockhouse. Sporting a brand-new submarine rollneck sweater and a glittering H. M. Submarines cap tally on his cap, he had swaggered into the "wet" canteen with his equally young and inexperienced "oppo." They had got themselves a couple of pints and looked round for a place to sit. No one moved to offer them a seat at the tables. Miserable and unsure of themselves among all the battle-hardened, tough-faced veterans who sat drinking beer, they tried to brass it out. They had no idea they looked such obvious rookies. One glance (without even bothering to look at the features) at the new jerseys and cap tallys told all. Ignored, they found themselves forced into the far corner of an L-shaped recess. It was an unpopular place because of its distance from the bar and the air of isolation it created.

They found a seat and were drinking their pints when an old three-badger carrying a couple of pint glasses came up and gestured to them to move over. They moved along the bench, trying hard to give the impression that they didn't have to if they didn't want to.

The three-badger sat silently knocking back his beer. When he'd finished it he started on the other one without pause. Draining it off, he rose and went to the bar for another two. Halfway down his fourth beer, he turned to Kennedy.

"Finished your training, then?"

Kennedy stammered and blushed. Frightened and thrilled at the same time by the massive figure with flat lips and face like a boxer, he nodded dumbly. He'd hoped they might have been taken for crew members of one of the submarines that lay alongside the jetty. That afternoon he and his mate had been down at the pier. A submarine from the flotilla at Algiers had entered the tiny inlet, her Jolly Roger fluttering proudly. All the base had turned out to cheer her in. Kennedy had looked wonder-eyed at the faded blue paint and the patches of rust on her superstructure. She looked as if she'd come from the ends of the earth. The tan-faced men on the bridge and the casing, sporting their white caps, had looked like descending gods. Later Kennedy had had the idea of getting hold of white caps for that evening. With himself and his mate wearing them, they would bear the unmistakable stamp of having returned from foreign service. And now the very first person who had spoken to them had rumbled them immediately as a pair of trainees. Kennedy tried to swallow his chagrin.

The old seaman laughed. "Never mind, son. Once you get a couple of patrols in you'll be able to go ashore and get drunk and bag off with the best of them."

They bought him a pint each the next time they went to the bar. It didn't seem right to get him just one.

The three-badger grunted by way of thanks, blew the froth off the top and nearly drained the first glass at one gulp. They sat there all night, buying him drinks and feeling secretly proud that they were drinking with an old hand. He told them all sorts of stories about submarines and foreign stations, but he never once bought them a drink.

The bell finally rang for last orders. The big seaman struggled to his feet. "Must go, lad. I've a watch to keep yet. Don't forget what I said. A couple of patrols and you'll be all right. A pair of right stroppy little bastards you'll be then." He suddenly became loquacious in a friendly way. "Yes, I can see the pair of you pissed up to the eyeballs, staggering off from a run ashore, collars torn and spewing your rings up—a right couple of skates."

The alcohol seemed to hit him as he gained his feet. He laughed drunkenly and slapped Kennedy on the back. "Nev' mind, me lad. Don't worry. They're all the bloody same when you're three sheets in the wind."

Kennedy and his mate were feeling the effects of the drink themselves. They wanted desperately to get out in the fresh air. But the big three-badger held his hand up. It flopped about as though it were broken at the wrist.

"Just listen to what I tell you. They're all the bloody same.

Black, brown, white or yellow—no difference, and the best of
the lot's the Chink—I should know, I've had the lot." He
leered, a slack-mouthed alcoholic grin. "And I'll tell you something else. I've had a dose from the lot—'cept the Chink. So
don't listen to what they say. They're all right. Do your dobeying, too—five minutes, five bloody minutes—press a suit of
number one whites in five minutes. 'Ould you do that?" He
belched. Suddenly he straightened up and shook his head as if
trying to clear it. The next second he'd lurched off as if he'd
never seen or spoken to the pair of them before.

Kennedy had been a bit shocked at first by this crude exposi-
tion of naval philosophy. But subtly, by degrees, as he became
more and more accustomed to hearing it expressed, he grew
to accept it. If you wanted to "qualify" in the Navy, become one
of the lads, a proper Jack-me-hearty, you had to be able to get
drunk out of your head, use the most foul kind of language, express contempt for every living soul, and sleep with every bint
you could get your hands on—young or old, black or brown, fat
or thin, it didn't make any difference. It wasn't love you were
after—that was sloppy and feminine. No, they could keep that,
you were a kind of social privateer, and every woman was a po-
tential target. And supposing you got a dose of clap, like the
old three-badger? Well, all you did then was to stick your chest
out manfully and boast that it was part of your kit anyway.

Admittedly this, the last part of Jolly Jack's dictum, troubled
the young seaman. It could still send shivers up and down his
spine when he thought of it. For this reason he could never bear
to go near the V.D. mess on board the parent ship, where all the
currently afflicted were gathered together at the far end of the
messdeck in a corner euphemistically referred to as Rose Cottage. The name, adopted by generations of sailors, had become
traditional and was in fact a "magical" device used to mitigate
the serious nature of the disease.

Parallel, and paradoxical, to this playing-down effect circu-
lated a number of grisly stories which concerned themselves
with the treatment of the affliction. These stories, invariably
peddled by ex-inmates of Rose Cottage, had an exhibitionist

purpose insofar as they were intended to show up the teller in a tough-guy light.

The first man Kennedy had ever heard these stories from was in fact sitting right next to him now: Lacey the gunlayer. Kennedy had listened in wide-eyed horror as the older man had described with sickening detail the alleged method of treatment. According to Lacey, before treatment with antiseptics, a bougie would be inserted in the diseased organ. Once it was in position, the medico would press a plunger which caused a number of fine needles to sprout from the tube like porcupine quills. The bougie was then forcibly withdrawn, ripping and tearing open the sensitive tissue. Only then was the antiseptic introduced. Kennedy had come near to being sick while the gunlayer, a grin creasing his leathery-skinned face, recounted the story.

As his mind raced on, an awful thought struck Kennedy. Caught up in the excitement of his first patrol, he'd half forgotten about it, half pushed it away

It now struck him like a blow from a clenched fist.

He stared at Lacey with hate-filled eyes as he illogically linked his predicament to the gunlayer, in an association of ideas. Before rejoining the boat after his last leave he had decided to spend a night in Glasgow. He had booked in at the Y.M.C.A. When he'd paid for his bed he counted what he had left. Ten bob, plus the two quid his mother had given him. He was rich. On his own he set out. He roamed the center of the city, going from bar to bar and getting a kick out of it as he noticed people's eyes lighting up with respect as they caught sight of his H. M. Submarines cap tally. He wished he could also have worn his white rollneck submarine jersey, but they were forbidden ashore.

In a pub near the Scotsman's Umbrella he met a couple of young R.A.F. blokes, looking clumsy and ill at ease in their stiff uniforms and heavy boots. They teamed up and for the rest of the night knocked back pints together. He shot them a right old line. Everyone seemed to be curious about submarines and, in between asking questions, swore they wouldn't go down in one for a fortune. Did they breathe oxygen when they dived?

Did they ever get the bends? What was it like to be depth charged? Was it as bad as it looked on the films? Could they see fish when they were below? Kennedy answered the two R.A.F blokes' questions with the assurance of an old hand. He left his two drinking companions at Central Station where they had a train to catch. Feeling big, bold and adventurous, he staggered down the steps into Argyle Street and picked up a tart who was hanging about. She was much older than he was, but he was so excited he hardly noticed. Together they walked all the way to Glasgow Cross. The trams were too crowded to board, but he didn't mind. Subconsciously and despite his air of bravado, he didn't want to be seen with his companion.

He spent the night with her in a house somewhere on the fringe of the Gorbals. Next morning, feeling dreadful and scared out of his wits, he got up hurriedly, shocked at the sight of the old woman who had called him "dearie" the previous night. He flew back to the Y.M.C.A. and collected his kit. He couldn't get out of Glasgow quickly enough.

As he crossed over on the boat from Wemyss Bay it was his avowed intention to make straight for the sick bay once he got back on board the parent ship. No sooner was he back, however, than he was detailed off for duty, and by the afternoon he was slotted back into the familiar routine. He tried to push the whole horrible episode from his mind. But for the next few days, before they sailed, he was in a state of near terror, rushing off to the heads every odd minute to examine himself. Nothing happened, and caught up in the excitement of preparing for sea, he'd been able to push the matter temporarily out of his mind.

His recollections had stirred up a train of thoughts, and in an unguarded moment the thing that he was trying to suppress had leaped out of his unconscious like a wild animal from a cage.

With a flush of dread he realized he'd felt a slight itching in the region of his genitals in the last few days. He'd put it down to "dobey rash" (it was the cause of all itches in the Navy). Dobey rash? Oh, my God! What had he done? The first signs were supposed to show up in ten days, weren't they? He made a quick calculation. It was exactly eleven days since he'd returned off leave. Feeling hot and cold all over, he got to his feet. His legs were trembling and his heart palpitated. The urge to scratch his genital region was almost unbearable.

Lacey hadn't missed the strange look Kennedy had shot him. He was quick to ask: "What's the matter with you, tosh? Don't tell me you're feeling sick an' all. We'll be working two watches at this rate."

The others looked up. To Kennedy's hypersensitized mind they seemed to stare accusingly. He was sure his guilt showed in his face. He swallowed nervously. "I-I'm all right. Just felt a bit queer for a moment."

Lacey gave him a hard look. "What is it? Is it your guts?"

"Mebbe he's got Cupid's measles. Eh, son?" Barbour suggested with a horrible grin.

Kennedy nearly fell down in fright. His heart gave a painful thump. He opened his mouth to reply and the words tripped over each other. "I-I-I'll," he stammered, "I'll have to go." Unable to face them any longer he turned and fled. He heard them laugh as he ducked through the bulkhead door. The gunlayer's voice, rising above the rest, seemed like an indictment: "He's got gyppo gut, that's what's the matter with him."

There was another sally of laughter.

His head spun as he entered the passageway. What was gyppo gut? He'd never heard the expression before. It seemed horrible and foreign and somehow connected with the dread disease. He stopped himself in time as he realized he was close to running the passageway in a blind panic. He tried to get hold of himself. What was he going to do? They said it was a lot worse if you tried to hide it and didn't go for treatment right away. What would happen now? Would he go blind and die? God, what was he to do? Tell the coxswain? The thought of confessing to him was unbearable. What would he think? And what would Wells think? They'd probably have to isolate him like they did on the parent ship—in the tube space? He'd be the object of everyone's derision and be treated like a leper. How could he possibly tell anyone he thought he'd caught the boat up? That had been one of Lacey's favorite expressions. The tough-guy way of putting it. It sounded horrible now. How could he ever have found it laughable. Supposing he told Titt? He could trust him. But Titt would only tell him to go and see the coxswain. Worse, he'd insist that he did. He began to wish he'd never left home. Home where it was safe and sound and comfortable. Where nothing like this ever happened. But how could he go home now in his condition even if it were possible? What would his mother think? With final horror it occurred to him that his condition had been "paid for" with the money she had given him.

Kennedy had wandered up the passage as far as the P.O.'s' mess. He stood outside the doorway, some instinct warning him he should see the coxswain. The velvet curtain whipped back and Monkhouse appeared, carrying a tray. The coxswain, the chief stoker and the E.A. were grouped at the table. They glanced up at Kennedy.

Blow noticed the look on his face. "What's up, lad?" he asked. "Did you want me for something?"

Kennedy's mouth opened and shut, but his vocal cords seemed paralyzed.

"Speak up, laddie. I won't bite you. What is it?" Blow encouraged.

"Probably wants to go ashore." Preece's lips curved into their familiar sneer. "Fed up, son? Want to go home, do you?"

Kennedy reddened in anger and embarrassment.

"Well, tell the coxswain. He'll fix you up. What have you got, crabs or constipation?"

Blow made an angry gesture to the chief stoker to keep silent, but it was too late.

Kennedy had been on the point of asking him if he could see him in private. He shut up. It would be too humiliating to ask with the chief stoker sitting there leering. The grinning face would uncover his secret the moment he spoke.

"It's—it's nothing, 'swain. Nothing at all."

Blow scanned the pale face searchingly. Kennedy was hiding something. "You sure, son?"

"No, it's all right. It's okay." Kennedy wheeled about stiffly and before Blow could stop him he'd gone.

"That little bugger had something on his mind, Bill," said Bissel.

Blow rubbed his smoothly shaven chin. "Yes, I know. And if it hadn't been for Harry here and his wisecracks he would have told me."

Preece laughed scornfully. "The bugger's got crabs. That's what it is, I'll bet. I've seen them before, hanging about like wet dreams frightened to own up. They're worse than wrens with a round up the breech."

Blow was annoyed. After twenty-five years in the Navy he had seen all the ugly things there were to see. He was neither prudish nor squeamish, but there were times when Preece could make him feel just a trifle sick. He got up from the table angrily, making a mental note to have a word with Titt about Kennedy. "Well, I just hope, Harry, it was nothing serious young Kennedy wanted to see me about. I'm turning in." He made for his bunk.

Four minutes after leaving the P.O.'s' mess, Kennedy arrived in the motor room. He'd walked the whole length of the boat and was making for the heads. Rigid with fear and shame, he looked like a man about to commit suicide. Thornley, who had the watch in the motor room, had retired into a mood of brooding isolation since his encounter with Titt. He barely noticed Kennedy.

Kennedy slid back the door of the tiny compartment. He closed it behind him, taking care to see that it was latched properly. In the confined space of the heads he began to sweat. His insides had turned to water. Twisting his body, he struggled to slip off his overalls. Spurred by fear and anxiety and a sudden need, he wriggled out of the upper half of his suit. He began to undo the buttons of his pants. Before sitting down, his nervous, fluttering hands found a familiar shape. He gave the wheel a quick wrench.

In the fore-ends they were putting the cups away and clearing the table. Someone dropped a cup and the dregs spilled over the deck. No one attempted to wipe it up. The deck was already soaking wet.

"What's the time, Guns?" asked Crabbe, unable to see the compartment clock from his position.

Lacey jerked his arm up. He consulted the big flashy watch strapped to his wrist. He waited till the second hand hit twelve. "It's exactly half past the hour," Lacey announced.

"Is it that time?" Crabbe said unbelievingly. "Here—I don't know about you, but I'm off to kip."

Only Bissel remained awake in the P.O.'s' mess. He sat at the table, the light from his bunk spilling over his shoulder as he thumbed through the manual on the Sperry gyroscopic compass. He yawned and stretched his long limbs. It was difficult to read the small print. He put the manual away, slipped off his jacket and shoes, and rolled over into his bunk. Reaching up, he switched the light out. Only the pilot light burned. A small blue glowworm that gave off just enough light to enable hurrying men to find their gear without cracking their heads or shins.

In the control room, Joyner was O.O.W. He had the periscope up. The blue watch squirmed in apprehension. They were sure the periscope was sticking up out of the water like Nelson's column. Titt, on the afterplanes, squirmed with the rest of them. His reasons were twofold. Not only had Joyner's clumsy use of the periscope set him on edge, but he also needed to go to the heads. He hated having to ask permission from the "ticket collector," knowing he'd make a great fuss about it. He kept putting it off, but his need was becoming urgent.

No one had noticed Kennedy come through the control room. Joyner had had the periscope up at the time, and the watch had been far too concerned with his antics to pay attention to anything else.

Only one man, Thornley, knew that Kennedy was in the heads, but even he had half forgotten.

Titt reached a decision. He waited for Joyner to put the periscope down. He just couldn't wait any longer. Stanley, the control room messenger, could take over the afterplanes for a spell. Joyner could go and get stuffed.

Kennedy was feeling sick. His examination of his person seemed to confirm his fears. The area around his genitals was red and itched madly. In vain he tried to convince himself that he'd caused this himself by persistent scratching, but that line of reasoning only led him to ask why he should scratch at all unless there was something wrong.

Engrossed in his examination and oblivious of his surroundings, he sat in abject misery. All the warnings he'd received from Wells about submarines being inherently dangerous went unheeded.

Just above his head, and unknown to him, the needle indicator on a pressure gauge jerked ominously.

In the submarine, compressed air was used to blow the waste matter from the heads overboard. Not a great deal of pressure was required—about 20 to 30 pounds per square inch. But first the ambient sea pressure had to be overcome. At periscope depth approximately 30 feet) the pressure of the surrounding water was about 15 pounds per square inch. Thus a total pressure of 35 to 45 pounds was required to operate the system and successfully discharge the waste matter. For this purpose a reservoir bottle was fitted to the bulkhead and connected up to the main, compressed air line, an arterial complex which ran the length of the submarine. When the bottle was charged to the required pressure from the main line, the inlet valve would be shut. The system would then operate independently from the reservoir. Flushing was achieved by means of a lever at the side of the pan.

Three things were important in the operation: first, the pressure in the reservoir had to be sufficient to overcome sea pressure; second, when the tank was blown, it was essential that the discharge to sea valve be fully open; third, the manipulation of the lever that controlled both the blowing system and the operation of a nonreturn flap had to be carried out in a strict sequence of movements. Failure to do this could result in the contents of the pan being blown back in the face of the operator. At pressures ranging from 30 to 100 pounds per square inch (depending on the depth) this could be not only embarrassing but painful.

Some of the hands, on entering the heads, would immediately crack open the valve from the main line. By the time they had finished their business the reservoir would be charged. It was a practice frowned upon. All it achieved in the long run was the saving of a few seconds. But with some of the hands it was a kind of show-off trick like riding a bicycle with no hands.

Kennedy, always anxious to be up with the others, had adopted the practice. When he sat down to use the heads he acted from habit and cracked open the valve from the main line.

Two things went against him that day, however. Because of his suspected condition he spent more time in the heads than he would have normally. And unknown to anyone, the relief valve on the reservoir was jammed solid.

Kennedy had gone in the heads at twenty minutes past the hour. By the time the hands in the fore-ends were turning in, the air pressure in the reservoir had reached 80 pounds per square inch.

A few minutes later it had crossed well into the treble figure mark.

By 10:45 the needle had plunged into the red and stuck. It was no longer capable of registering the enormous pressure in the bottle.

Joyner had finished with the periscope. Titt could contain himself no longer and asked permission to be relieved. The "ticket collector" hemmed and hawed before reluctantly granting Titt's request. Stanley moved over from the telephone exchange to take his place on the planes.

"Jesus," groaned Titt as he stood up, "I'm absolutely bursting."

"Well, don't burst here," said Stanley. "Old Joyner'd do his nut."

Joyner half turned. "Is there any need to carry on a conversation, Stanley? Just relieve leading seaman Titt and get on with it."

Stanley, screened from Joyner's view by Titt, smiled cheekily and gave the "ticket collector" the two-finger sign. Renwick, on the foreplanes, nearly doubled up.

Titt felt stiff and cramped. Walking was painful as he threaded his way along the catwalk of the engine room. He took a note of the time on the engine room clock. Better not be too long or Joyner would spend the rest of the watch moaning at everybody.

In the heads Kennedy had just pulled up his clothes and was reaching for the phone to ask permission from the O.O.W. to blow the heads when the already strained reservoir bottle gave up. With a deafening roar it disintegrated like a fragmentation bomb.

Kennedy was killed instantly.

Titt, his foot poised on the coaming of the motor room bulkhead door, was picked up by the blast and flung halfway down the engine room. His head struck the engine guardrail.

A hot white light burst in his head, as if a searchlight had been thrust in his face. He crashed to the catwalk. Pain tore at his skull. He felt as if his eardrums had been blown out. Dazed, he lay sprawled out on the metal plates, unable to move. Gritting his teeth almost to a powder, he waited for the dreaded sound—the inward rush of cascading water. *I've had it, Ruth,* he mumbled to himself in his head. *This is it, this time. . . . we've hit a mine.* Thoughts, last-minute desires and regrets whirled in his mind. His senses began to reel and the terror gave way to feelings of infinite sadness.

Nothing happened. There was no torrent of water.

Unbelievingly Titt forced his eyes open. Blinking and shaking his head, he staggered to his feet. It was impossible, but there might be a chance yet. From the direction of the motor room he could see nothing but a white swirling fog that blotted out everything. Thornley must have been able to shut the bulkhead door, he thought. Perhaps there *was* a chance yet? But he'd have to make sure about the door. The door would have to be shut at all costs. It was the inexorable rule, the rule for survival. Shut bulkhead doors!

Reeling like a drunk, and unaware that the trouser legs of his overalls were in ribbons and flapping about his feet, he staggered aft in the direction of the door. He was on the deck again when his legs buckled under him.

He took a deep breath and like a wounded bull dragged himself to hands and knees, inching forward. There was a terrible unnatural silence. He couldn't understand it. And then it came to him that his eardrums must have been blown out. The muscles in his neck and face stood out like cables as he urged himself on. He shook his head. His sight had begun to fade; odd shapes and lights flashed in front of his eyes. But he was heading the right way. The door couldn't be all that far now. Just keep going . . . keep going. . . .

He was still crawling blindly toward the door when the rush of bodies overtook him and dashed into the motor room. It took two stokers to hold him back. They shouted at him that it was all right, but he didn't seem to hear and kept going blindly.

His outstretched hand had reached the coaming of the door before he collapsed in an inert heap.

Chapter
Seven

Titt came back to consciousness to find the coxswain bending over him. He blinked hard, trying to focus his sight. A stabbing pain shot through his head, causing him to gasp involuntarily.

"Are you all right, Tom?" Blow was asking.

Titt groaned and tried to prop himself up on one elbow.

"Steady, now," Blow warned.

Titt's head buzzed. It felt split in two halves, and everything seemed disjointed and out of place. Where was he? What had happened? There was a puzzling familiarity about his surroundings. His hand, exploring underneath the blanket which covered him, contacted leather. He twisted around. From his position he could see a table at eye level. On the opposite side of the table, covered by a blanket, a figure lay stretched out on a bench locker. It came to him that he was lying in the P.O.'s' mess.

He tried to raise himself on both elbows, but Blow pushed him back gently. "Easy, now, till we have a look at you."

Titt tried to open his mouth but a pain knifed his head. He closed his eyes again. Around him he could hear the low murmur of many voices. The air was heavy with the sharp, pungent smell of antiseptic. For some illogical reason he was reminded of a funeral. His thoughts were all jumbled up. He didn't seem to be able to think clearly. There was something about a door? A door? That was it. He'd tried to shut the motor room bulkhead door after the explosion when they'd hit the mine. His features twisted, following the pattern of his thoughts.

But if they'd hit a mine . . . how could he . . . With an effort he forced his eyes open. His voice, which didn't sound like his voice, croaked: "What happened, 'swain? How did we—"

"Just lie still, Tom." Blow's hand pressed gently but firmly on his shoulder.

Titt lay back. Something must have happened. The coxswain's ruddy cheeks looked as if they'd been daubed with white powder. And why were they all speaking in such grave whispers? Was he imagining things or had that been Jimmy and the captain in the background? In God's name, what had happened? Were they keeping something from him? A shock of horror hit him. He stretched his hand down his side. For an awful moment he thought he'd lost a leg and they were frightened to tell him. Sweat beading on his forehead, he tried to raise himself up again. The faces in the mess swam crazily in front of his eyes like a series of pictures pasted on a spinning roulette wheel. The coxswain's eyes, the dimpled chin of the first lieutenant and the great beak nose of the captain all merged into one and then with a kaleidoscopic twist sprang apart into a myriad of shapes and colors. His senses began to slip away again. Before he lost consciousness he had the crazy idea that he'd been drugged. Something terrible must have happened and they were trying to hide it from him. . . .

Ten minutes later, when he came to again, his head had cleared. It still throbbed violently, but he was beginning to piece together what had happened. He forced himself up into a sitting position, supporting himself with braced arms.

"Titt—" Blow, bending over the figure on the other side of the mess, turned angrily.

The deckhead swam crazily. Titt put his head between his raised knees.

Blow started to come around the table but Titt signaled him back with a wave of his hand. "I'm okay, 'swain." He slipped his legs off the bench and onto the deck, groaning as the pain hit him again. "My bloody head."

"I should bloody well think so," said Blow. "What do you think you're up to? You should be lying down."

Titt clutched his head, shaking it. "No, I'm all right—there's nothing broken." He put his hand up to his head, his mouth jerking open with pain as his probing fingers discovered the raw edge of a wound. He sucked in his breath.

"Don't touch it now," Blow cried. 'You've got a nasty gash there, so don't go pawing about with your grubby hands."

Titt felt the wound gingerly and removed his hand. "It is a bit, isn't it?"

"Leave it alone. I'll probably have to stitch it before you lose any more sawdust out of that thick head of yours."

Titt looked up at the coxswain questioningly. "What happened, 'swain? I mean, I was just going aft to the heads when I heard this bloody great explosion and the next thing I'm on my back. I thought we'd hit a bloody mine."

Blow shook his head. He was silent for a second. "No, it wasn't a mine. The heads blew up."

"The heads?" Titt echoed in disbelief.

"Yes. The safety valve on the reservoir must have jammed with the valve from the air line open." He shrugged his shoulders. "The bottle couldn't take it and exploded. That was your mine," he added grimly.

Titt's eyes had widened in horror. "No," he gasped. "Good Christ! Was there anybody in—" He stopped, his eyes swiveling toward the figure stretched out on the other side of the mess.

Blow caught the glance. "No, he's all right. Like you he was knocked out by the explosion. He's in one piece, though God knows how."

Titt looked relieved. "Christ, it's a good thing there was nobody in the heads at the time. I could just. . . ." His voice trailed away as he saw the stiff expression in Blow's features. "But how could . . . I'd just left the control room . . . nobody had—"

"Kennedy was in the heads, Tom," Blow interrupted. "He must have been killed right away."

Titt was numbed with shock. "Oh, God. Poor little bastard. Was he—did he?—"

"He was blown to bits. He couldn't have known anything about it," said Blow, unable to keep emotion out of his voice and feeling a massive weight of guilt bow him down. If only he'd insisted on Kennedy's telling him what had been on his mind when he'd come along to the mess it might never have happened. The delay could have saved him. Unless—unless Kennedy himself had opened the valve. He, despite all warnings against the practice, could have done it. He bit into his lip. What was it the young seaman had wanted to see him about? Had the chief stoker's crude guess been right? Bloody man. It was he who had been responsible for Kennedy's scurrying off as he did. If he hadn't— Blow caught himself in time. It was no use blaming anyone else. The responsibility was his, no one else's. He should have been more considerate and not pushed the matter to one side.

Blow straightened up. This would get him nowhere, and there was work to be done.

At that moment Bain came into the mess. He carried a bolt of canvas underneath his arm. Titt wondered what the hell he wanted canvas for at a time like this. And then it hit him. He felt like being sick.

"All right, Jock?" said Blow.

Bain nodded grimly. His face had the appearance of a death mask. "Yeah, I'm all right, Bill. Might as well get on with it."

"I'll see about getting you some help, Jock. Hang on here and I'll nip up for'ard."

"I'll give him a hand," Titt cut in quietly. He knew what Bain would have to face in the motor room. He'd helped dig enough bodies out after the bombing raids on Portsmouth to know what it was all about.

Blow stopped suddenly. "You?"

Titt had risen to his feet and was leaning on the table. "I'll be okay, 'swain. Don't bother to ask them up for'ard. It's— well, it's just better that I give Jock a hand, that's all."

Bain and Blow exchanged glances.

"You're sure now?" said Blow. "You know what you're going into back there?"

Titt nodded slowly. "I'll be all right."

Blow pressed his lips together. "Okay, then." He turned to

Bain. "You'll have to hang on a bit, Jock, while I have a look at this bugger's head. It's a good thing it's solid bone." He gestured to Titt. "Sit down, you great oaf."

Titt sat down.

Before examining the wound Blow had another word with Bain. "While you're waiting, Jock, it might be a good idea to nip along to Steve and tell him we'll need all the hot water we can get. Get him to boil pans and see that they switch the copper on in the fore-ends at the same time."

Bain put the canvas down and made to go.

"Oh, and another thing, Jock, when you're at it. Get some buckets from the fore-ends."

Bain stopped and turned to look at the coxswain. His mouth opened and snapped shut again.

He went out.

Titt thought he was going to be sick when he entered the motor room. The compartment looked like a scene of mass butchery. Someone had sprinkled disinfectant all over, but it didn't kill the smell. Unspeakable objects littered the deck and clung to the bulkheads. There was blood everywhere. Standing by the bulkhead door, head poking out into the engine room, the motorman on watch retched.

Bain was the first in. He turned to Titt, his eyes burning with revulsion and yet steady. "You be all right, Tom?" he asked.

Titt couldn't speak. He nodded, choking back the wave of nausea that churned his insides over. He put the buckets he carried down on the deck.

Silently, the two men got to work.

Two hours later they'd cleared up all they could.

Titt got out his sailmaker's needle and palm, and as Bain held the edges of the canvas together he began stitching up the awful bundle.

M'Guinness, who now had the watch (the motormen were doing half-hour spells), turned his head away. "Jesus, Mary and Joseph," he whispered in a low sobbing voice, repeating the words over and over again.

Titt put his needle away. He had finished. The bundle was

secure now. He straightened up, getting to his feet in slow motion.

"Okay, Tom," said Bain huskily. "We'll nip along and tell Bill we're through."

Both men made to go through the bulkhead door. M'Guinness grabbed Titt by the arm. The motorman's face was haggard and grooved.

"You're not going to leave me here on me own with . . . that there?" he protested in a plaintive screech. "In the name of God, man. . . ."

Bain gripped his arm. "We won't be long. We're just going along to see the 'swain. We'll be back as quick as we can. Some of the others'll be along in a minute too. We'll have to scrub the compartment out." He let go of his arm. "Just you hang on, mate. We won't be long."

They left M'Guinness looking in horror at the canvas sack and muttering "Jesus, Mary and Joseph," to himself as if he were praying.

Blow poured out two large measures of rum.

"Here," he said, "knock that back. You've earned it."

Bain and Titt took the glasses and drained them. By the look on their faces they might have been swallowing poison.

"Well done," said Blow quietly. "You did a good job." He poured out another two measures of rum. "Have a seat. I'll go and get the scrubbing-out party organized and see about removing Kenn—" He stopped suddenly. "Well, we'll get the motor room cleared. There's plenty of space in the engine room."

In the fore-ends the crew sat stunned by Kennedy's death. When they spoke it was in whispers. It was hard to believe he'd been alive a few hours ago. Not only his death but the way in which it had happened had unnerved them. Death in itself was not a wholly unfamiliar thing. Most of them had lost friends and shipmates at one time or another, and all had experienced the sense of chill horror creeping over them when the B.B.C. announced in sepulchral tones that another submarine was long overdue and must be considered lost. But in a way they had been conditioned to accept this. There was even some comfort in the knowledge that if they "bought it" they would all "buy it" together. When submarines went down they invariably went down with all hands. It was this individual death that shook the crew and posed them a problem. It wasn't even as if Kennedy had been engaged in a foolish (or so they thought) or heroic act. He'd just died as a result of an accident, like a man being knocked over in a street. It seemed wholly unfair to them, a cheap trick that was against all the rules. Like somebody whipping out a knife in a fistfight. It hadn't even been a clean death. To be splattered about the motor room in little pieces was an ignominious thing. Human remains wrapped up like a parcel of garbage were an intolerable insult to the living. A man should at least be able to die in one piece. To be reduced to scraps of flesh like the animal remains that cluttered the chopping blocks of butchers' shops was an insufferable humiliation to all. That this happened daily in the battlefields and bombed cities was beyond the compass of their experience. Their war was a war of sudden merciless attack and equally merciless attrition as the enemy launched his thunderous patterns of depth charges.

No one had ever seen the results of his work at close hand. If he had, it was doubtful if he'd be able to carry on with what he was doing.

Persistent, like a heavy fog, a strange unnatural air hung over the fore-ends. The crew felt apprehensive and ill at ease, as if Kennedy's death had been an omen. No one really wanted to speak about Kennedy, and yet it seemed almost sacrilegious to speak about anything else. It would be different when the patrol was over and they were back on the parent ship or home on leave. It would be possible to speak freely about it then. Some would even enjoy speaking about it. To be exposed to such horrors would generate feelings of sympathy and elevate the stature of the teller in the eyes of his audience.

Mitchell had to be told. He'd heard the voices, the whispering frightened tones. It was impossible to keep it from him. Titt, back in the fore-ends to muster volunteers to scrub out the motor room, told him. Mitchell made no comment when Titt had finished. He just lay back in his hammock and stared at the deckhead, his head rocking slowly from side to side.

Renwick, Stanley, Corr and Mulholland volunteered for the scrubbing and cleaning party. Rice had wanted to volunteer, but when it came to it he just couldn't find his voice. Armed with mops, pails, scrubbers and more disinfectant, the four men left for the motor room.

When they'd gone, Titt asked some of the hands seated at the table to rise. They got up to allow him to get at Kennedy's locker. Titt pulled the dead man's spare clothing and effects out and put them on the table. The crew sat looking on silently. The papers, paybook and letters Titt put to one side to be handed over to the coxswain. He made a list of the items of clothing. When they got back to the parent ship the clothing would be put up for auction and the monies received sent to the dead seaman's next of kin. It was part of the tradition and a way in which shipmates and friends could materially express their feelings. A collar or an old pair of trousers might fetch as much as ten or twenty times its original value. The buyer seldom wore the articles he'd bought. More often than not they would be stuffed away at the bottom of his kitbag and forgotten about till the next time he had occasion to empty out his kit.

This was the longest day the crew had ever experienced. It dragged on and on. Though hidden out of sight in the engine room, Kennedy's remains drew the thoughts and feelings of the men like a magnet. Round-eyed, they kept staring into the compartment, unable to help themselves. For the second day in succession they prayed for night to fall, when they could surface and be rid of the monstrosity that lay silent in the engine room.

Everyone in the control room looked up as Cheney came in. The lines at the side of his face seemed deeper and his eyes were like pieces of coal. Brangwyn had the watch. Cheney gave him a curt nod and motioned to the stoker on the periscope control. In the silent control room the big periscope seemed to hiss malevolently as it rose out of the well. Cheney carried out this usual methodical survey and went over to the chart. Five minutes later he told Brangwyn that they would surface in half an hour.

As the submarine went deep again, Cheney went back to his cabin and slowly began dressing for the bridge. It was raining up top.

When he'd fully clothed himself, he lay down on his bunk and adjusted the red goggles over his eyes. When he got up again, it was time to surface. He made for the door but paused. He'd nearly forgotten one item. Returning to his locker he opened a drawer and extracted from it a small Bible. He put it in his pocket.

They were ready to surface now.

Back in the control room he spoke to no one, signaling his instructions to Brangwyn with his hands. He brought the submarine up to periscope depth for one last precautionary look around. There was nothing to report from asdics.

Cheney ordered main ballast tanks to be blown. The air poured into the tanks with a roar. Like a steel coffin the submarine with its corpse rose from the sea.

Once on the surface the control room bustled with activity as the crew secured from diving. The telegraphs clanged noisily, and seconds later the engines coughed once or twice and sprang into life.

Bain and Titt, immediately on surfacing, had gone into the engine room. Both men were dressed in clean white sweaters and wore caps and oilskins. As they reappeared, half-carrying, half-dragging their bundle, the crew stepped hurriedly aside as if fearful of contagion. Brangwyn motioned the two men to wait by the foot of the conning tower. He went over to the voice pipe and called up the bridge. A moment later he was back. His eyes met Bain's.

"All right," he said, coming erect and speaking in a heavy solemn voice. "Please carry on." The crew, most of whom had mustered in the control room, came to attention as the two men grabbed hold of the canvas.

Titt hooked one arm into the ladder and heaved. Their faces

glistening with sweat as they struggled to manhandle their awful burden, the two pallbearers inched their way up into the conning tower. Blow came up behind them.

The ceremony was short and without frills. Bareheaded, the rain running down his face, his hair brushed stiff by the wind, Cheney read the service. ". . . we do now commit his body to the deep. . . ." Cheney tucked the Bible under his arm and stepped back.

Blow signaled to Bain and Titt. They grabbed the sack as Beer whipped away the ensign which had covered the body. Beer tucked the ensign away safely behind the periscope standard and returned to help. As the three men launched the sack overboard, the submarine rolled heavily to starboard. The saddle tank came out of the water, and Kennedy's remains hit the glistening wet metal with a nauseating thud. A look of horror and revulsion came over the faces of the small gathering. Cheney gripped the bridge capping as Bain made to climb down onto the tank. Even as he swung his leg over the gunwale, the submarine rolled over to port, submerging her exposed tank in a swirl of angry water. For a moment the dark-gray blob seemed to cling longingly to the submarine before it was engulfed in the waves and sucked into the black depths of the sea.

Scorpion's first casualty had been decently buried.

Chapter
Eight

It was their sixth day in the Skagerrak and the thirteenth day since they had left the parent ship, back in the Clyde. Penetrating deep into the Skagerrak, they had gone north as far as Bohus Bay and the lower reaches of Oslo Fiord. Though they had scoured the whole area with the aid of high-powered binoculars, periscope and asdics, they had seen nothing. The seas were as deserted as the Bering Straits.

With the passing of each day Cheney became more and more restless. He spoke little, and only to give orders or instructions. The last time he had spoken at length was at the inquiry following Kennedy's death. It hadn't lasted long, as it was obvious that the cause of the accident was the failure of the safety valve on the reservoir to function when the bottle was charged beyond its normal capacity. Whether this was a result of Kennedy's carelessness or not was never concluded, but Cheney used the incident to blast everyone about the need for vigilance.

From then on he'd shut himself off in a mood of smoldering intensity. Day and night he paced the bridge or the control room, his shoulders hunched and his eyes glowing darkly. His temper, never very good, worsened daily, and the slightest error or mistake sent him into a towering rage.

Most of the crew suffered from his tongue-lashings and as a result carried out their duties nervously. Their overcautious manner inevitably led to further mistakes and exposed them to yet more blistering attacks. They became jumpy and irritable, snapping at each other like dogs. Though they spoke little of the accident, they had been deeply affected by it. Every visit to the heads was a reminder of the dead seaman. At one time the tiny compartment had also served as a kind of reading room where a man could peruse his personal mail in privacy. But now no one stayed for any length of time. The sight of the scarred bulkheads and the canvas screen that now covered what was left of the doorway were antagonistic elements which made them feel uneasy.

Harassed by Cheney and then by the first lieutenant, the crew suffered. Brangwyn, as next to Cheney in the hierarchical pyramid of naval authority, was the first to feel the effects of his wrath. Reacting dutifully, he expressed, at the same time as he assuaged his temper, the tenor of the captain's feelings to those next down the line. In turn, and imbued with an equally strong sense of duty, they lashed out at those underneath them. A chain reaction had been set up, in which everyone began to hate everyone else.

Miserable with the endless succession of watches and the long days dived, with nothing to relieve the tedium of their existence, the crew shuffled about wearily. It was a life in which it seemed they did nothing but sleep and eat and go on watch. Only half alive, lacking enthusiasm for the job they were supposed to be doing and plagued by the officers from the captain downward, they grumbled incessantly and had only one thought in mind—to get back home.

The only possible relief for their boredom would be found in action, but this was too drastic an alternative to contemplate seriously. Relations in the fore-ends became more and more strained. The conditions of their daily existence had a number of built-in stress factors, all of which were guaranteed to produce feelings of frustration and despair. Friction was an inevitability. Searching about to relieve their tensions, the crew were continually on edge. Small things affected them deeply. A man biting his nails or scratching his head could create for himself half a dozen enemies. Even the simple and familiar act of eating would disclose a habit repulsive to others. Best friends turned on each other. Sensitivities were aroused, nerves were bared and tempers boiled to volcanic heights. Renwick had developed a habit of smothering his food with sauce. To a number of the crew members this appeared an act of the utmost depravity, and they would suddenly stop eating, knives and forks raised, to stare at Renwick with hatred.

The personal habits of each man became focal points of unhealthy attention, and no one was entirely free from this form of censure. It was a situation in which violence—even murder —became feasible. The death of Kennedy, Mitchell's illness, the unknown nature of the patrol, and the splenetic behavior of the captain did nothing to allay the explosive situation.

During the afternoon of their twelfth day at sea, when the hands were having tea, an argument broke out between Thornley and Rice. No one really knew what it was about. It was just one of those things that seemed to have its own laws of development.

Rice had been talking to someone in his usual pedantic and slightly insistent manner when Thornley broke into the conversation sneeringly: "Aw, why don't you stow it, Ricey? You don't half go on, do you? Half the time you don't even know what you're talking about."

Rice, sitting opposite the big seaman, heard the remark and did the worst thing possible—he deliberately ignored it and went on talking.

Thornley's nostrils flared and his eyes narrowed. "Here," he said, "I was talking to you, Ricey. I asked you a question." Rice stopped this time and looked around, hating Thornley at the same time he was afraid of him. He tried to keep his voice under control: "A question? What about?"

"Never mind the what about stuff. Don't give me any of your sea lawyer's bullshit. I was speaking to you and you bloody well answer."

Rice flushed. He didn't know what to say. Thornley kept looking at him. The silence grew.

"Well? What about it, Ricey?"

Rice was puzzled. What was it he wanted? Why didn't he just shut up and leave him alone? Thornley continued to stare at him. "I'm sorry, I don't know what you mean," Rice tried to reason.

"You don't know what I mean." Thornley mimicked the high-pitched voice. "Course you don't know what I mean. You don't know anything, do you?"

Rice shrugged resignedly. There was no point in trying to deal with such oafish stupidity. He looked at the others in mute appeal.

"Never mind them," Thornley sneered. "I asked you the question. Are you going to answer it or are you just going to shut up, Ricey?"

Rice colored heavily at the insulting tones. Apart from that, he didn't like Thornley's calling him Ricey. He stifled his anger and tried to think the thing out logically. What did you do with a man who tried to provoke an argument? You held onto your reason, kept calm and tried to placate him.

"I don't know about any question. But if you have one, I'll be glad to try and answer it." Unfortunately the tone in Rice's voice made it sound as if he were dealing with a fractious child.

The muscles in the big seaman's jaw went rigid. "Hey, don't you start telling *me* what to do and what not to do. You're not talking to some bloody goon out of training school. So just watch it."

Thornley's threatening attitude caused Rice to lose his head momentarily. "Oh, for heaven's sake, Thornley—" he blurted out in exasperation.

Thornley leaned forward across the table, big and menacing. "Just watch it, tosh."

Rice threw reason overboard. "Just you leave me alone, will you? Just keep to yourself and leave me alone." His voice rose to a thin petulant shriek.

Thornley grabbed him by the sleeve of his overalls. "Another word out of you and I'll do you. Keep your trap shut."

Rice hated anyone to touch him. He lost his head completely, his fear of Thornley overcome by the rage that burned inside him. He sprang to his feet, an insane light in his eyes. "You keep your hands to yourself, Thornley, if you know what's good for you—or you'll find yourself in trouble."

"Trouble?" Thornley's lips curled back to expose his teeth. "Trouble? Why, you syphilitic little twit."

Corr, who had been watching closely, silently got to his feet. It was about time somebody screwed Thornley once and for all. He had just stepped clear of the table when Rice said something in his girlish voice about Thornley being nothing but a bullying storm trooper.

It was just what the big blond seaman had been waiting for. Quick as a flash he rose and lashed out with both hands. There was a sickening sound of a hard object meeting flesh. Rice went backward over the bench locker. His eyes began to purple where he'd been struck.

With a roar Corr was across the table, scattering cups and mess gear. His lowered head caught Thornley high up in the chest, slamming him back hard against the torpedo rack. There was no room to use fists or the knee. He grabbed Thornley's arm and with a violent wrench forced it up his back.

The noise wakened Titt. He leaped out of his hammock in time to prevent Corr from butting Thornley in the face. Savagely he tore the two men apart. Thornley tried to swing a punch at Corr, but Titt flung him back forcibly against the rack again.

"Cut it out!" he yelled. "Cut it out, you bastards!" Corr lowered his fists. The three men glared at each other, panting heavily.

"Right, that's enough from the pair of you. One word and you'll both be in the rattle."

Someone had helped Rice back up on the bench. A dry sobbing sound came from his half-opened mouth. Titt pushed his way through the crowd.

"Let's have a look," he said to Rice, who sat covering his face with his hands.

"Leave me alone, will you?" sobbed Rice, his shoulders shaking with pain and humiliation.

"Don't bugger about, Rice. I said let's have a look."

Rice drew his hands away from his face and looked up miserably. Both eyes were bright red, and the surrounding flesh was swollen and purple. Titt whipped around.

"All right," he said with quiet fury, "who did it? Who was it?"

Everyone looked at Thornley.

"Is this your work?" asked Titt.

Thornley stared sullenly and ran his fingers through his long hair. He squared his shoulders defensively. "Well," he began, "it was his own fault. He asked for it. He—"

"Okay, Thornley, that's enough. Get your cap." Titt took Rice's arm. "You'd better come along, too. I want the 'swain to have a look at those eyes of yours."

Rice shook his head.

"Come on, mate." Titt eased him gently from the bench. "You'll feel better when the 'swain's had a look at you."

Rice got to his feet. As Titt released his arm he started walking slowly toward the door. Titt waited till he saw he was all right, then turned to face the mess. His eyes were cold with anger.

"Ready, Thornley? You, too, Jock."

"Me?" gasped Corr indignantly. "Ah was only—"

"Never mind what you were only—you, too. We'll get this little lot straightened out once and for all, I can tell you something right now, and this goes for the lot of you." His eyes swept the ring of silent faces. "I'm not having any fighting in the fore-ends. If you want to thump somebody save it till we get back to Dunoon. There's plenty of wide open spaces there and you can thump away to your heart's content—but not here, not on board ship. The next bloke that steps out of line will find he's enough trouble on his hands to make him wish he'd never been born. So get the idea fixed into your thick skulls. Remember you're on board ship, not in a dockside boozer."

The crew shuffled their feet and looked embarrassedly at the deck.

Titt gestured to Corr and Thornley. "All right, then. Let's get going." Rice was waiting by the doorway. The four men headed toward the P.O.'s' mess.

Most of the petty officers had finished tea and returned to duty, but a few sat around the table in the mess. They looked up as Titt knocked and pulled back the curtain.

Blow was there. He gave one look at the expression on Titt's face and got to his feet. "What's up, Tom?" he asked.

In a few short sentences Titt told him what he'd seen. Then he stepped back out into the passageway and ushered Rice in.

There was a gasp of astonishment from the men seated at the table. Blow was livid.

"Okay, Tom. Get those two along to the engine room and wait for me. I'll be along in five minutes after I've seen to Rice." Titt made to go, but Blow clutched his sleeve. "And, Tom, keep them apart. I don't want them slinging any more punches. Remember, no talking, nothing—just keep them apart."

"Don't worry. I'll see to it," Titt said.

The watchkeepers squirmed around in their seats as the three men entered the control room. Robinson had the watch. He looked at the trio disapprovingly. The crew stared, wondering what was going on. Titt hurried through the control room. He didn't want to have to answer any of Robinson's questions.

In the engine room Titt led Corr aft and told him to stay there while he himself remained with Thornley on the for'ard part of the catwalk by the condenser.

A few minutes later the first lieutenant arrived with the coxswain at his heels. Blow had the ship's charge book tucked under his arm. Both men looked grimly severe. They halted on the platform. The coxswain came to attention and opened his book. Thornley was ushered forward and the charge read out. Standing stiffly at attention, his cap under his arm, Thornley pleaded provocation by way of defense.

"All right, coxswain, call the first witness," Brangwyn instructed as Thornley stepped back.

Rice, who had been waiting in the control room, came in. His face was almost unrecognizable. The flesh surrounding his eyes was discolored and badly swollen. He said what he had to say. Then it was Corr's turn.

Titt wasn't called, as he hadn't actually witnessed the blows being struck. But as he'd preferred the charges, his presence was required. As for the incident between Corr and Thornley, he'd decided to let it go. No matter what his intentions might have been, Corr hadn't actually struck Thornley. He made no charge against Corr.

The proceedings were over in a few minutes. Brangwyn wound up by reminding everyone of the serious nature of the offense. He put Thornley in the captain's report. The men were dismissed but warned to hold themselves in readiness should the captain want to see them right away.

When they'd gone, Brangwyn dropped his manner of severe officialdom. "This is a shocking business, coxswain," he led off worriedly. "Heaven knows what the captain's going to have to say about it."

Blow made no comment.

"Did Titt have anything to say?" Brangwyn went on. "I mean, apart from what he told you about the actual incident, did he suggest in any way there might be something behind it?"

"Titt only told me what he actually saw, sir—nothing else."

"I see." Brangwyn pulled at his lower lip. "There's nothing you can add that might be of help? Is there bad blood, for instance, between Thornley and Rice? Have they been quarreling?"

"If they have, Titt hasn't said anything about it to me, sir."

"Hmmm. Very well, coxswain. I'm going along to see the captain now. It shouldn't surprise me if he'll want to deal with this right away—it's a very serious matter."

Blow's face was expressionless.

"That's all, then, coxswain. I'll send for you when I've seen the captain."

Blow came smartly to attention. Clutching the charge book tightly under his arm, he ducked through the bulkhead door.

Brangwyn remained behind. He stood in the engine room deep in thought, reluctant to go and rouse Cheney. The captain would hit the roof when he learned of the fight in the fore-ends. The incident would give him ample opportunity again to sound off about the sloppy discipline and loosening of morale. Brangwyn groaned inwardly—as senior executive officer he was going to be held partly responsible. In God's name, why did they have to start fighting among themselves, of all things? Thornley should have known better. He was a regular after all, not like Rice or Corr, who were "hostilities only" ratings. But what had caused them to come to blows? Had it been Rice with his persistent grating logic who had finally angered Thornley so much that he'd lost his head completely and lashed out? It was unforgivable, if understandable. It was easy for a man like Rice to get on one's nerves with his sea lawyer's arguments and his ability to quote King's Regulations and Admiralty Instructions at length. Not that he was disrespectful to his superiors, but underneath the aloof pedantic manner there was a bit of the Bolshie hidden. No doubt he was spreading his pernicious propaganda all over the fore-ends. Fortunately most of the men were too sensible to be taken in by it, but it was easy to see how that sort of thing would anger Thornley. It would go on and on like the steady dripping of a tap until finally something would break. And now Thornley would have to pay a heavy penalty for his lapse. The captain would have no option but to put him on a warrant charge. His two good conduct badges would help to take some of the sting out of the sentence, but he was almost bound to get cells when they got back to the parent ship. Brangwyn bit his lip. It was a damned shame, and worst of all it would reflect on the command of the ship. The Admiralty took a very severe view of this sort of thing. The incident wasn't going to help Cheney in his situation at all. Brangwyn groaned again. The next few minutes were going to be most uncomfortable. He braced himself and squared off his cap. Better get it over with.

Cheney wasn't asleep. He called on Brangwyn to enter. Brangwyn pulled aside the curtain and entered the cabin. Cheney lay on his bunk. He looked like a man in the throes of a fever. Deep lines ran down the side of his face, and his eyes were puffed and heavy. A blue-black stubble covered his chin.

"What is it, number one?" asked Cheney, his voice seeming to come from a hollow cavern.

Brangwyn took a deep breath and in a tumble of quick sentences told him of the fight in the fore-ends.

Cheney's eyes seemed to burn in his head. The veins in his

neck swelled, and the jaw muscles rippled under the cheek-bone. "Muster them in the engine room—immediately," he said in a terrible voice when Brangwyn had finished. Rising gauntly from his bunk he reached for his cap and jacket.

Brangwyn screwed up his courage. "Sir?" he said.

"Yes, number one?" Cheney's voice boomed like that of an angry prophet's acting under the guidance of the Lord.

"Thornley, sir. I think he was genuinely provoked by Rice." Cheney stared at him.

"I know it was terribly wrong, sir, what he did, but—well, sir, he has a bit of a temper, but he's a good seaman and—I think he lost his head momentarily and—"

"Go on!"

"I just wanted to say, sir, there are mitigating circumstances. Thornley has a good conduct record and—well, I'm certain he's as sorry as anyone that it happened—"

"Is that all, Brangwyn?"

Brangwyn nodded lamely.

Cheney put his cap on. "I'll be in the engine room, number one." He glanced at his watch. "Have them mustered within two minutes," he said in a voice of iron.

In the engine room Cheney treated the small group to an exhibition of cold rage. He was openly contemptuous of Rice, listening to his story in critical silence, and he railed at Corr and Titt, treating them almost as if they'd been party to the assault. Thornley was trembling inwardly by the time it came his turn. Cheney showed him no mercy. He lashed into him venomously, like a high court judge dealing with a psychopathic murderer. Thornley was placed on a warrant charge and had all privileges stopped. Not that this meant much aboard ship—there were few privileges to be had anyway—but his rum was automatically stopped.

After the men had been dismissed, Cheney, still in a tower-ing rage, hauled Brangwyn back into his cabin. The emotional current that Cheney had managed to generate sparked about the first lieutenant's head.

"I warn you, Brangwyn," Cheney thundered, "as I've warned

you before, that I won't have it. Discipline aboard this vessel
has become a disgrace. The slightest sign of more trouble in the
fore-ends and I will stop every man's rum issue and cancel all
patrol leave. You're going to bear down on them, Brangwyn—
and you're going to bear down hard. There's to be no more
of this slackness in the relief of watches. In the future every man
will take over his watch on time—I will accept no excuses for
lateness. And another thing, Brangwyn—there's to be no more
cluttering up the control room when we surface. If the men
want to smoke they'll just have to take it in turns, but I won't
have them jamming up the control room. From now on, apart
from watchkeepers, only two men will be allowed in the control
room at a time."

Brangwyn listened and swallowed hard. He reflected how easy
it was to find fault if you went out of your way to look for it.
But he held his tongue, realizing that in Cheney's present in-
flammatory mood anything he said would only provoke further
recriminations. At last Cheney came to the end of his tirade.
He dismissed Brangwyn with a wave of his hand.

"That's all for now, number one. You can let chief petty officer Blow know that from now on the slightest infringement
will be dealt with severely. One way or the other, Brangwyn,
I am going to have a tight ship. You understand?"

Brangwyn nodded, not trusting himself to speak. He turned
to make for the doorway.

Cheney stopped him. "There's another thing, number one,
that I might mention, seeing you're here." He threw his senior
executive officer a dark glance. "Were you aware of the fact that
able seaman Mitchell had been ill prior to joining this ship?"

Brangwyn frowned, wondering what was coming now. "Yes,
sir. I seem to remember something about it in his medical record, sir. He was sent over to Haslar Hospital from Fort Blockhouse, but as far as I remember it was nothing serious, sir."

Cheney's eyes narrowed. "I also had a look at his medical record, number one. Mitchell was diagnosed as suffering from a
condition known as tachycardia. The diagnosis was made by
his family doctor, while he was on leave."

Brangwyn's frown deepened.

"On his return from leave," Cheney went on, "he was sent to Haslar for observation. According to the records, they could find nothing wrong with him."

"I remember now, sir," said Brangwyn.

"Good. Well, you'll probably also know that tachycardia is one of those impressive medical terms that mean nothing more than an increased rate of heartbeat. In Mitchell's case the condition didn't appear to last long after his return from leave. He was released and returned to duty from Haslar within a day or two. Shortly after that, as you know, he was drafted up to the Forth and joined us."

Brangwyn's eyes widened as the captain's meaning became clear to him. "Surely you don't mean, sir—"

"I mean nothing, Brangwyn. I merely recount the facts." He paused. "I think, however, this should be borne in mind when it comes to the matter of diagnosis and treatment of his present condition. Are you with me, number one? Have a word with the coxswain, and you'd better have another look at Mitchell yourself."

"Very well, sir," replied Brangwyn. "I'll go along when we surface tonight." He excused himself hurriedly and slipped out of the cabin, his thoughts a confused jumble. He just couldn't bring himself to believe that a crew member was malingering. The idea was preposterous. His doubts began to spread. Was the captain right after all? Was discipline, in fact, going all to pieces? His thoughts broke off as he spotted the small scurrying figure of Cadbury in the passageway. For a moment his features clouded suspiciously, but he had too much on his mind to give much attention to the steward and his odd activities. His voice drew Cadbury up in his tracks.

"Steward, go along to the petty officers' mess and tell the coxswain I would like to have a word with him.'

An expression of relief spread over the steward's face. For a moment he thought he'd been caught eavesdropping. He bobbed obsequiously. "Right away, sir."

Brangwyn, engrossed in his own thoughts, did not notice the

steward's look. He went into the wardroom and sat down to await the arrival of the coxswain. A few minutes later Blow appeared. A vague sense of unease gnawing at him, Brangwyn questioned Blow closely about the sick seaman.

"And you're quite sure about the temperature, coxswain?" Blow stiffened perceptibly. "Quite sure, sir," he replied with emphasis. "The last time I took it—only a few hours ago—it was 100.2 degrees, sir. His pulse was—"

"Yes, yes, yes, coxswain." Brangwyn waved his hand impatiently. "I just wanted to be quite sure about his temperature. And you say he hasn't eaten for some time now?"

"That's correct, sir."

"Mmmm. Well, I think I'll come along with you tonight when you go to see him."

"Just as you wish, sir," Blow answered stiffly.

Brangwyn looked up sharply. "The matter of Mitchell is of some concern to us all, coxswain. Particularly the captain. I don't have to remind you that with"—he hesitated, for some reason not wanting to mention the death of Kennedy directly—"Well, with two men short it places quite a strain on the watches."

"I realize that, sir," Blow answered levelly.

"Very well, then, coxswain. We all understand how important it is that Mitchell should be returned to duty as soon as possible."

"Of course, sir. But the man is ill and until—"

"I'm not saying he isn't," Brangwyn broke in irritatedly. "But we must try and establish the nature of his condition—you agree? Very well, then. I would suggest we go and see him shortly after we surface tonight."

"As you say, sir."

"That's all then, coxswain." Brangwyn got to his feet and glanced at his watch. "Shall we say 2200 hours, then."

After Blow had gone, Brangwyn sat down again. He was annoyed with himself. He'd been rather unfair to the coxswain. It must have seemed as if he were casting doubt on the man's judgment. No wonder he'd looked displeased. After all, as ship's medico, Blow carried the main burden of responsibility toward the crew's health. Perhaps it would have been better to come out with it and state frankly that the captain suspected Mitchell of malingering. No, better to have another look at Mitchell first. After that, if there was any doubt, he could inform Blow of Cheney's views. It would also be a good time to raise the question of discipline and morale. He glanced at his watch again, feeling himself yawning. He got slowly to his feet and with tired movements took off his jacket and shoes. He climbed into his bunk and switched the light off.

The solid mass of hammocks in the fore-ends lurched from side to side in a wide cumbersome arc as the submarine rolled heavily. Shortly after surfacing, most of the hands had turned in again. Usually about this time at least half of them would be awake and yawning around the table, but this night the fore-ends had fallen into a mood of quiet brooding after the earlier eruption of violence.

Able seaman Moore, like the rest of them, was dog tired, but he found it impossible to sleep. His thoughts kept returning to the letter he had received from Alice. Every sentence, every word on each page, was now indelibly committed to memory. He heard the two men enter the fore-ends, soft-footedly pick their way through the unholy chaos of the compartment and make for Mitchell's hammock. Moore sat upright. In the dim light he could just make out the figures of the coxswain with the first lieutenant trailing behind.

Above the dull rumble of the engines and the creaking of the hammocks, Moore tried to hear the low whispered tones. He sat upright, craning his head forward, but he couldn't make out a word. A long time seemed to elapse before the two men left. After they'd gone, Moore lay back again, trying to stem the torrent of thoughts that ran through his mind. It was hopeless. He cursed softly to himself and got up. Groping under his pillow, he found his shoes. Forgetful for a moment, he clambered down off the table, shoes tucked under his arm. His stockinged feet hit the wet deck, soaking up the cold water like pieces of blotting paper. He shut his eyes in enraged agony, standing stock-still as his lips fashioned a stream of silent oaths. He hoisted himself back on the table and glared malevolently at the two figures who lay sleeping on the bench lockers. He would have to wait until dinner was up and they were roused before he would be able to change his socks. With a final curse of despair, he pulled his shoes on over his wet feet. Pausing only to check that both the letter and his tin of tobacco were in the top pocket of his overalls, he groped his way through the dimly lit compartment and headed for the bulkhead door.

Donahue was salting trays of meat and vegetables as Moore came along the passageway. Already beginning to sweat in the tiny galley, Donahue mopped his face. "What the hell are you looking so cheery about?" he asked as he caught sight of Moore. His big beefy arms waved about. "Just look at this lot. If you had to feed a bunch of howling, hungry bastards you'd have something to moan about."

Moore grimaced.

Donahue's big red face cracked in a smile. "What's up then, Pony? Feeling a bit chokker?"

"Chokker? I'm two bloody blocks. I'm brassed off to the teeth with the whole bloody issue. I wish to Christ we'd get our recall and go back home."

The cook patted him on the shoulder with an enormous hand. "Never mind, mate, you'll be finished your twelve soon. And you can always sign on again if you don't like it outside," he said, lifting the meat trays off the top of the stove and crouching down to open the oven door with his knee.

"Big laugh," Moore replied sourly. "Here, how about a cup of char, Steve?"

Donahue straightened up. "Tea?" he panted. "You'll be lucky. Do you know what time it is? If you want a cupper go along and see Cadbury. He might have some on the go."

"Cadbury? Do me a favor, will you?"

The cook shrugged his massive shoulders. "Well, it's up to you. Beggars can't be choosers." As he spoke, Donahue was busy emptying out tins, testing the hot plates and jiggling his pots and pans around. "Here," he said, suddenly changing the subject, "I see old big-mouth Thornley got it. Imagine thumping Rice. The bastard wants to pick on someone his own size. Well, he'd had his little lot now. I heard the old man just about did his nut—what do you think he'll get?"

"He'll get chokey, for sure. Twenty-eight days—mebbe fifty-six."

"Fifty-six days over the wall." Donahue wagged his head. "Well, that'll take some of the stroppiness out of him, eh?"

"Better him than me," said Moore, stretching his arms and yawning. He tapped the top pocket of his overalls. "Well, I think I'll nip along to the control room for a smoke."

"Okay, mate. And if you see that twit Cadbury, tell him I want a cup of tea or there'll be no grub for his lot tonight."

"I'll tell him," promised Moore and sauntered off.

Farther along the passageway he stuck his head in the wardroom pantry. Donahue had been right—Cadbury was sipping a cup of tea. Moore passed on the cook's message. Cadbury seemed to find it funny. "Hee, hee, hee," he giggled, "no dinner for the wardroom. That would be a laugh. I can just see old Jimmy's face if I told him there was no scran tonight." He poured out a cup, topping it up with condensed milk. "Fancy a cupper, Pony?" he asked.

Moore hesitated as he eyed the steward's long black-rimmed fingernails.

"Go on," said Cadbury, pouring out another cup. "It'll do you good." Before handing it to Moore, he gave the cup a rub with the cuff of his grubby white jacket.

Moore took the cup, careful to drink from the side opposite where the steward had rubbed it. Reaching up into his top pocket he pulled out his tobacco tin. Something fluttered for a moment and fell to the deck. In a flash Cadbury swooped down and picked it up.

"Yours, Pony?" Cadbury asked, showing his spongy gums in a fatuous smile.

Moore nearly dropped his tea as he saw the piece of folded

paper in the steward's hand. "Here, give me that!" he cried in alarm.

"Heh, heh, heh," cackled the steward. "Secrets, eh, Pony? What's this you're hiding from your old mate?" He waved the grease-stained letter in front of Moore's face.

Moore made a grab at the letter, spilling his tea. "Give me that, will you!"

Cadbury leaped nimbly back. He waved the letter tantalizingly.

Moore put his cup down on the pantry draining board. "If you don't hand over that letter," he hissed between clenched teeth, "I'll do you."

Cadbury rolled his eyes. "Letter, eh? O-ho, what's all this, I wonder?"

Moore took a pace forward, balling his fist.

"Now, Pony," Cadbury warned, pointing his finger, "you want to be careful. You know what Thornley got for thumping a bloke."

Moore's hand shot out and grabbed the lapel of the steward's jacket.

Cadbury squealed in alarm. "Okay, okay, okay," he spluttered. "Just let me go. I was only having a joke."

Moore snatched the letter from him. He put it back carefully in his upper pocket. "I don't like those kind of jokes, Cadbury. You'd better be careful in the future." He picked up his cup and with another glare at the steward stomped off.

Titt was in the control room, standing behind the helmsman. He was clad heavily in duffel coat and seaboots. Moore stepped over the coaming of the bulkhead, cup in hand.

"What's this then?" said Titt. "Where's all the char coming from? You got friends on board or something?"

Moore grunted.

"Got a widgy on, then?" Titt asked.

Moore muttered something unintelligible.

"What was that?" asked Titt.

"I said it's that bloody steward. Honest to Christ, I'll do him one of these days."

"What's he been up to this time?"

Moore shook his head. "Oh, nothing. He just gives me the shits, that's all. He's a bloody menace. How he ever got in boats I don't know."

Oak, who was helmsman, swung round. "I thought he was a great mate of yours, Pony," he ribbed.

"Piss off. Great bloody mate of mine. The bastard's round the bend, so he is. I don't know how the old man stands for him."

"He just gave you a cup of tea, didn't he? He didn't give us a cup, did he, Tom?"

"So that's where you got the tea. I thought you might have got it from the chef—did you happen to notice when you came by the galley what Steve's got on the menu tonight, by the way?" Titt asked.

"Some kind of stew, I think," Moore grunted.

"Not again," complained Oak. "That's all we ever get these days, stew. Stew, stew, stew. Somebody wants to tell the chef we're not all from Liverpool."

"Stop dripping and keep your eye on the wheel." Titt nudged Oak in the back. "You want to think yourself lucky. We'll be out of fresh meat in a few days, and it'll be corned beef and tinned bangers for the rest of the patrol."

Oak eased the wheel over, his eyes fixed firmly on the compass strip. "Rest of the patrol? It's beginning to get on my wick, so it is. What the hell are we supposed to be doing up here anyway? Does anybody know? I wish some bastard would tell us—I'll bet we're the only boat in the home fleet that's at sea. We're always getting browned off for some shitty job."

"You'll get browned off in a minute, mate, if you don't keep on course," Titt warned.

The three men fell silent. Moore walked over to the exchange and put his cup down. He came back to stand beside Titt. Titt glanced up at the control room clock.

"Okay, mate," he said to the helmsman. "Five minutes are up. Alter course now."

Oak swung the wheel over. The numerals on the compass strip spun across the narrow face of the visor, slowing down as the helmsman put on opposite wheel to check the swing of the bows. The submarine settled on her new course as she zigzagged her way northward.

Moore swayed and grabbed the back of the helmsman's chair to steady himself as the submarine began to roll more heavily on her new course. Regaining his balance, he straightened up. Making sure the letter was still there, he removed his tobacco tin from his top pocket. He opened the tin, fished out a paper, and spilled a little tobacco into it. With a quick, practiced darting movement of his tongue, he licked the gummed side of the paper and rolled it up into a neat tube. The straggly ends, where the strands of tobacco pushed out, were nipped off with his finger and thumb and dropped back carefully into the tin. The flick of his lighter briefly illuminated his gypsylike features in the dim red glow of the control room.

Titt turned away, shielding his eyes with his hand. "Christ, what's that you've got there, a flamethrower?"

Moore flipped the lighter in the air and caught it deftly. "Made it myself when we were in dock at Devonport," he said with some pride. "We were all at it up in the engineer's shed. Making lighters and those little submarine brooches, you know."

"Lucky for you, mate. Nothing else to do but bugger about making lighters. How long were you there?"

Moore grinned one of his rare grins. "Near six months. It was great. Living ashore in digs an' all. Proper barons we were."

"Six months. How did you manage that? What were you on?"

"The *Walrus*. We were there for near the whole summer."

"Lucky bastards. How come you got six months' docking?"

"Well, we got rammed in the Med. Took the periscopes away and half the bridge—right bloody old mess it was. So we got sent home."

Titt stroked the bristle on his chin. "I remember. I was out in the Med then. You were on one of those ferry runs from Alex, weren't you?"

"Not then we weren't," Moore said. "We were on patrol,

mate. We didn't just do ferry runs from Alex, you know. We did our share of patrols."

At that moment Cadbury popped his head into the control room. He waved to Titt and Moore, grinning all over his face.

Moore took one look. "I'm off to the heads, mate," he said to Titt and stomped off.

Cadbury stepped over the coaming of the bulkhead. "Hello, Tom," he said breezily. "Bit nippy tonight, eh?" He pointed to Titt's duffel coat. "Still, you won't feel it with all that on." He rubbed his hands together. "What's happening? Anything doing up top?"

"No, just a couple of battlewagons and half a dozen cruisers buzzing about, that's all," said Titt laconically.

The steward's eyes rounded for a second. "A couple of battle—" He broke off and started grinning again. "Ah, you're kidding me on, Tom. For a moment I almost believed you." With a lightning change of expression he grabbed Titt's sleeve. "Here—" he began earnestly.

Titt shut his eyes and took a deep breath. "Yeah?"

"How would you like a cup of tea? I gave one to Pony. There's still some left. I'll go and get you one if you want."

For a moment Titt debated the question. Like Moore he wasn't sure if he wanted a cup of tea from the steward. "Okay," he gave in, "but make that two—one for Oak here. He doesn't deserve it, but you'd better give him one an' all."

Cadbury held up his hand officiously. "I'll do that, Tom. Don't you worry. Just you leave it to me." He shot off.

Titt stood for a moment wondering if there was anything behind the steward's offer. He didn't generally offer cups of tea around unless he was after something. A clattering sound came from the direction of the conning tower. He looked in time to see the captain clambering down the last few rungs of the ladder. Cheney pushed back the hood of his bridge coat and, blinking once or twice, walked to the chart table. A couple of minutes later he switched off the light and pulled the weighted canvas cover back over the chart. Making for his cabin he met Cadbury as the steward was ducking through the bulkhead door. Cadbury spilled some of the tea from the cups he carried.

For a moment Titt thought Cheney was going to say something, but he swept past Cadbury, pausing fractionally to shoot him a cryptic glance.

Titt took the cups from Cadbury and handed one to the helmsman. "Here you are, mate, and I hope it poisons you."

Oak thanked him and took a cautious sip. Cadbury stood aimlessly for a moment. Titt hoped he wasn't going to have to listen to the steward's inane drivel, but Cadbury, complaining of the cold, soon left.

Titt shook his head, unable to fathom the steward. He sipped at his tea. It wasn't bad. At least that was something Cadbury could do. Apart from that he was the weirdest bugger Titt had ever met in submarines. In fact, Titt reflected, he was one of the weirdest buggers he'd met in his life. Moore was right. It was a mystery how the steward had ever got into the submarine service. Had he volunteered, or had he been drafted in as so many of the crews were now? Either way the man should never have been allowed to enter a submarine. He was half around the bend. Titt sipped at the scalding liquid, feeling a glow of warmth spread through his body. But maybe they were all half around the bend if it came to it. Certainly there was an odd atmosphere in the boat that hadn't been there on previous patrols. It wasn't just that they were all on edge and screwed up. That happened anyway, whether you were in action or not. If you put twenty-odd men in a space that would have been too small for six and shut them up there in a cold and damp atmosphere for the best part of three weeks you couldn't expect anything else. Living in the fore-ends at sea was a miserable existence, but you learned to live with it. What was it then? What was so different about this patrol? What was this odd feeling that seemed to be affecting all of them? Look at Moore. That was a good example. Goes about for days shut up like a clam and suddenly starts spouting as if he had to get it off his chest. And then there had been the punchup. Kennedy, poor little bugger, was dead, and Mitchell was lying ill. But there was more to it than that. That was only part of it. There was a strange air about, as if a ghost were haunting the fore-ends.

Suddenly it dawned on Titt.

Nobody's heart was in the patrol, that was it.

Not that anyone ever looked forward to the idea of going on patrol. You'd have to be out of your head to feel like that. But somehow they did it, and it could only be because deep down they believed there was no alternative to what they were doing. You'd never get anyone to admit to it, but it was what most of them felt. Now, for some reason, they'd lost their basic beliefs, and without that they weren't much more than mercenaries, irrespective of how unwilling they felt.

Titt turned, his thoughts breaking off, as he heard someone come up behind him. It was Moore, back from the heads. Neither man spoke, but Titt saw Moore glance at the cup. Crazily, he was almost on the point of explaining to Moore that he hadn't asked the steward for tea, but he checked himself in time. He was getting as bad as the rest.

"You know where we are?" Moore broke the silence. He made it sound as if the question were suddenly important.

"Well, at this rate of knots, and on this course, we should be getting near the foot of Oslo Fiord," Titt answered.

Moore seemed to digest the information carefully. Then he jerked his head in the direction of the bridge. "Who's got the watch up top, Jimmy?"

"No, Robinson."

"Hmmm. Just as long's it's not the bloody ticket collector."

There was another silence.

"Bloody cold, isn't it?" Moore rubbed his shoulders through the meager covering of his overalls.

"I'm not surprised, the way you're dressed. Why don't you put something warm on?" Titt asked.

"Nah. I'm going for'ard in a minute. Where'd you say we were?" But before Titt could answer, Moore had wandered off toward the chart table.

Titt wheeled to face him. "What are you doing?"

Moore flipped on the light above the table.

"Hey, watch it," Titt called out to him. "The skipper's on the prowl."

Moore waved his hand as he withdrew the canvas cover. "It's all right, mate, don't panic. I'm just having a quick gander."

"Pony," Titt called out again across the intervening space. He was about to take a stride forward when he heard a warning cough from Oak behind him. He turned in time to see Cheney step into the control room. It was too late to warn Moore.

Cheney, his goggled eyes giving him a sinister appearance, was halfway toward the conning tower when he saw the figure bent over the chart. He froze in his tracks. Titt held his breath.

Cheney came to life. A couple of giant strides took him across the control room. He stood towering above the unsuspecting Moore.

"You there!" his voice thundered, rising above the drumming of the diesels. "What the blazes do you think you are doing?"

Moore jumped and spun. He saw the red-goggled figure, lips drawn back in a snarl, standing above him. "I-I-I," he stammered in shock. "I-I was just—"

Cheney's fist came down with a crash on the chart table. "Silence, man. I don't want to hear your excuses. Who gave you permission to look at the chart? What do you mean by it?"

Moore's dark features had turned white. "I-I was only—"

"Silence, I said," trumpeted Cheney again. He pivoted gauntly.

Here it comes, thought Titt. He waited for the onslaught.

"Leading seaman Titt."

Titt stepped forward. "Yes, sir?"

"Is this man on watch?" Cheney snarled.

Titt hesitated. There was nothing he could do to help Moore now, the bloody fool.

"Well, have you lost your voice—is he?"

"No, sir. That is—" Titt felt his anger rise as he answered the captain. Cheney knew damn well Moore wasn't on watch. It was bloody obvious. But to insist on an answer to the obvious was just another one of those humiliating tricks used by the officers to make you out as a fool. "No, sir, he isn't on watch," he replied between tightened lips.

Cheney leaned forward. "Very well, Titt. Get him out of the control room—now, this minute," he hissed threateningly.

Titt flushed. More bloody humiliation. Why doesn't he just tell him to go himself? But, no, that would be too bloody easy. He wants to make both of us jump through the hoop. Titt drew in his breath, but Moore didn't wait to be ordered. Before Titt had a chance to open his mouth, Moore had hurried out of the control room.

Cheney wasn't finished yet. His breath audible as it whistled through his nostrils, he stepped closer to Titt. "You are supposed to be petty officer of the watch, aren't you, Titt?"

Titt felt a tightness in his chest and a burning sensation in his throat. They weren't just satisfied with plunging the knife in—they had to twist it around and around. "I am, sir," he said huskily.

Cheney drew himself up to his full height. "Very well, Titt. In the future I will expect you to carry out your duties in a proper manner—under no circumstances do I ever want to see anyone, except the officers, at the chart table again. Do you understand, Titt? Well, do you?"

Titt swallowed hard. "Yes, sir."

Cheney stood for a moment, his head rocking back and forward stiffly on his shoulders as he glared at Titt, before striding off toward the conning tower. Hoisting himself up the ladder, he vanished from sight.

"Whew," breathed Oak, when he'd gone. "I'm glad it wasn't me that copped that lot. Suffering Jesus. . . ."

Titt's eyes were narrowed in anger. "Shut up and watch your ship's head," he snapped at the surprised helmsman. Oak glued his eyes to the compass and held his tongue.

Ten years in the Navy, half of them in submarines, Titt's thoughts raced angrily, and you could still be treated like a half-witted dolt or a naughty child. The officers held all the tricks. Treat the men with contempt, dress them up in comic-opera uniforms, surround them with caste barriers and taboos, and after a while they would really begin to believe they were inferior beings and an officer a direct descendant of the Almighty. Christ, look at the treatment just handed out to Moore, as if he'd been caught in the act of nicking the wardroom silver, and all he'd wanted to do was to have a look and see where they were. And why the hell shouldn't he? He was a member of the ship's company. He ran the same risks, shared the same hardships and would have to sink or swim with the rest if it came to it. But you'd have thought he was a spy the way Cheney had carried on. What was so secret about a chart anyway? Everyone knew they were in the Skagerrak. But that was it—the men weren't supposed to know about charts and plots and things like that, or they might get uppity. Charts were a bit of the officers' magic, and you'd better not go mucking about their altarplaces with your grubby fingers or you might get them chopped off by way of ritual punishment.

Moore had gone back to his hammock. He covered himself with the stiff wet blankets and lay back staring at the deckhead. The evening meal would soon be ready, but he didn't want to eat. Slowly the mess was becoming alive. The bulge of hammocks shook as figures leaped out and landed on the table with a drumming sound that echoed through the fore-ends. There was a noisy rattle as mess gear was sorted out, and sleepy voices could be heard conversing in low tones. Moore felt like screaming. A long, wild, desperate shriek that would clear away all the muck and filth and the crazy system that was screwing him down.

Every muscle in his body wound up tight as a spring, he lay on his back, his eyes fixed on the dripping wet deckhead above him. Two hours later, long after the evening meal was over, when the control room messenger came to rouse the watch, he was still awake, staring at the deckhead.

At the messenger's call, Moore forced his protesting body out of his hammock. Wrapping an old scarf around his neck, he trudged along to the control room. A bridge suit lay draped over the afterplanes stool. Moore picked it up. It was damp and cold, as stiff as cardboard. An arid expression on his face, he clambered into it. It seemed to chill him to the bone the moment he put it on. Shivering, he looked at the control room clock. Not even time for a quick smoke before going on the bridge.

Bain, who was P.O. of the watch, gave him the thumbs-up

sign to indicate it was all right to go ahead and relieve the star-board lookout. Moore grasped the rungs of the conning tower ladder and heaved himself up. The enormous rush of air cre-ated by the hungry diesels drummed against his clothing and made his ears sing. He fought his way up the tower. His mit-tened hands, already chilled, found the coaming of the upper hatch and he pulled himself out onto the seesawing deck of the bridge. Instinctively he looked up. The sky had again been cleared by the wind, and a great shimmering moon circled above the swaying periscope standards. In the sharp air the stars and heavenly bodies were needlepoints of brilliant light spanning the vast arch of the sky. Moore looked seaward. The water sparkled and shone, waves seemingly frozen in serrations of crusted ice. The bridge glinted with a cold metallic sheen. In the distance to the north and east a jagged, alien coastline appeared. It was a beautiful night, but Moore was too en-grossed in his own misery to appreciate it.

He slapped his hands together and drew up his shoulders. By the forepart of the bridge, deep in the shadow cast by the periscope standards, there was a glint of reflected light from the O.O.W.'s binoculars. He stepped forward.

"Permission to relieve the starboard lookout, sir," he said.

The first lieutenant half turned. The wind whipped his words away, but acquiescence was only a formality. Moore crossed the bridge and tapped the starboard lookout on the shoulder.

Able seaman Barbour unslung his binoculars with a sigh of relief. "Thank Christ you've arrived." Barbour blew on his hands. "It's perishing up here—freeze the bollocks off a brass monkey, it would."

Both men ducked instinctively as a shower of stinging spray, whipped up by the wind, cascaded over the bridge and landed on the deck like a fall of shot. Barbour's binoculars were soaked. Moore took them. Cradling the glasses in his arm, he reached inside his suit for a piece of dry periscope paper. He dried the lens carefully before he raised the binoculars to his eyes. He thumbed the focal adjustment screw.

"Seen anything about?" he asked in a low voice.

"Not a thing. Every bastard's got his head down but us, by the look of it," replied Barbour.

"I hope you're right. They'd see us for miles in this."

Brangwyn's voice rose sharply above the wind. "Just relieve the lookout there, Moore, and carry on with your watch. There's no need to have a discussion about it."

Moore stiffened and bit his lip. "Okay," he said to Barbour, "I'll take it now—off you go."

Barbour went off to report to the first lieutenant. Moore settled himself firmly against the bridge rail and began scanning the horizon. One quick sweep around, then a bit-by-bit inspection, then another quick sweep. Behind him he heard a muffled scraping sound as Barbour lowered himself down the hatch, and then, except for the sound of wind and water, there was silence.

Moore tried to put everything else from his mind and concentrate on searching the horizon. Ignoring the demands from his body for warmth and rest, he swept his binoculars back and forth in an arc of 180 degrees.

The sea was completely empty, stretching to the north and east like a polar icefield. The scene was desolate and hostile. Moore had a sense of utter loneliness.

Chapter Nine

Donahue had begun to prepare breakfast. He'd started shortly after diving. It wasn't an easy job to fry bacon, eggs and tomatoes for something like three dozen people on a stove not much bigger than an ordinary household model. The eggs were the biggest problem. Even using his largest pan, he could only fry six at a time. Consequently he had to repeat the operation six times. By the time the last batch was fried, the first had gone hard and rubbery. The last lot of eggs he'd collected from the parent ship were the worst he could remember in a long time. It wasn't just that a fair proportion of them were bad, but no matter how carefully he cracked them the yolk would break and run into the white. Some of the crew liked their eggs sunny side up, others preferred them turned, but they had one thing in common—they wanted to see the yolk whole and intact.

Donahue threw a whole lot of eggs away in disgust before he decided to break them in a saucer first and not directly into the pan. The mushy ones he saved to make puddings and an occasional fancy dish. Omelettes were out. The officers would have eaten them, but the crew, conservative as they were in many things, viewed them with suspicion. Muttering to himself, Donahue filled a tray with strips of bacon and popped it into the oven. He'd wait a few minutes before he began frying the eggs.

Steward Cadbury was up and about. Scurrying in his pantry like a small animal, he got out plates and cutlery. Switching his hot plate on, he headed for the wardroom. The first lieutenant lay awake in his bunk, but the only other occupant, Joyner, was asleep. Cadbury knocked and pulled the curtain aside. From the direction of the galley farther up the passageway a delicious smell of cooking invaded the wardroom.

"How long, steward?" asked Brangwyn, his nostrils wrinkling.

"Only a few minutes, sir," Cadbury replied, starting to grin for no reason at all.

Brangwyn pursed his lips. "Very well, steward. Tell Lieutenant Robinson I'll relieve him as soon as I've had breakfast."

Cadbury's head bobbed. "I'll do that, sir. Right away, sir." He shot off. Brangwyn glared after him.

The few minutes turned out to be nearer twenty. When Cadbury eventually served the breakfast, the eggs were hard and the bacon as dry as toast. The first lieutenant had roused Joyner. Both men were looking forward to breakfast with considerable pleasure. Cadbury put the plates in front of them. Brangwyn stared at his with disgust. If he'd told the steward once that he didn't like tinned tomatoes he'd told him a thousand times. He absolutely loathed the things, and it wasn't as if he could just push them to the side of his plate—Cadbury had seen to that. The bright red pulp swamped the whole plate. Brangwyn glared malevolently at the steward and silently salvaged two strips of bacon. The egg was untouchable. He had to finish off his breakfast with nothing but marmalade and a few slices of the brown concrete Cadbury served as toast. The coffee that followed was hot, but it had a strange oily taste. After a few sips Brangwyn pushed the cup aside. To add to his chagrin, Joyner was eating away steadily in obvious enjoyment. The "ticket collector" had cut his slice of bread into small squares and was using them to mop up the gravy, and he was so absorbed that Brangwyn felt he was watching a cat eat. Staring at the top of Joyner's head with a feeling of the utmost revulsion, he had the mad desire to hit him with something.

A knock on the paneling brought him back to his senses. He looked up guiltily toward the curtain which framed the doorway. It was the steward again.

"What do you want, Cadbury?" he barked. "I'll ring when I've finished breakfast."

The steward made a little ducking motion with his head. "It's the captain, sir. He'd like to see you in his cabin, sir, after you've had breakfast—with his compliments, sir," he added as if suddenly remembering the bit of rigmarole.

"Very well, steward." He waved his hand over the table. "You can remove some of this while you're here." He watched Cadbury's expression closely as he pushed his barely touched plate forward, but the steward portrayed no sign of having noticed anything unusual. His features remained as bland and idiotic as ever.

Brangwyn waited until the steward had backed halfway through the curtain, and then he snapped out: "Cadbury? How often have I told you that I don't like tinned tomatoes?"

The steward's eyes rounded in wonderment. His mouth dropped open. "Eh? What was that, sir? Did you say tomatoes, sir?"

Brangwyn drew a deep breath and covered his face with his hands. He counted up to five and withdrew his hands. "I said, how many times have I told you I do not, repeat, *not*, like tomatoes?"

"Oh," exclaimed Cadbury, apparently in complete surprise. "Did you, sir?"

Brangwyn winced and gave up. He waved his hand wildly. "Never mind, just get this cleared away, will you? Mr. Joyner will ring for you when he's finished the rest of his breakfast." Something in Brangwyn's voice made Joyner look up for a minute, but he quickly resumed eating.

Cadbury backed out with a little half bow and vanished from sight as the curtain fell back. When he'd gone, the first lieutenant lay back on the bench, breathing heavily as if he'd just undergone a strenuous physical ordeal. God, how he loathed the steward and that doltish manner of his. His glance strayed toward Joyner, who was finishing off his coffee. Brangwyn was filled with such a deep feeling of revulsion that it frightened him. These bouts of hatred seemed to become stronger with the passing of each day. He'd have to watch himself; his nerves were obviously strained. But it was this damned patrol. Everything seemed to be going wrong, and Cheney was getting to be more bad-tempered than ever. What they needed was to find a target. To engage the enemy in action would release the captain's pent-up energy and help to mop up some of the tensions that were steadily developing among the crew. In the circumstances, action would be a welcome therapy. Wondering what the captain wanted this time, Brangwyn got to his feet and reached up into his locker for his toilet bag. He'd feel better able to face the captain when he'd had a wash. He made his way along to the officers' heads. The door was stiff, and he had to put his shoulder to it. Another one of the many things on the boat that were crying out for attention. They were badly in need of a spell in dock.

Squeezing into the heads, he wedged his knees against the lavatory bowl and ran some water into the tiny handbasin. He wiped over his face and neck with a damp cloth and inspected the stubble on his chin. He really should shave. Deciding against it, he ran a comb through the jungle of his hair. He had one last look in the mirror and left. Back in the wardroom he slipped on his jacket, squaring it off and patting down the lapels which tended to curl in the damp atmosphere.

Feeling a little refreshed, he headed for the captain's cabin. At his knock Cheney's voice answered immediately. Brangwyn pushed open the door and went in. The cabin was littered with books and papers. Cheney had a chart spread out in front of him on the small folding table. The chart spilled over the table and ran up the bulkhead. Cheney reached for the pilot and began flipping over the pages. He motioned to Brangwyn to draw closer. Brangwyn took a pace forward, his curiosity aroused. Peering over the captain's hunched shoulders, he was able to read the legend on the chart.

He drew in his breath. It was a large-scale projection of Oslo Fiord, liberally marked with the familiar red crosshatching which indicated the presence of known minefields.

With a growing sense of uneasiness he waited for Cheney to speak.

Cheney straightened up and closed the pilot book. Brangwyn noted the purple shadows under the eyes and the tightness of the skin over the cheekbones.

At last Cheney broke the silence. "I've been having a look at the fiord, number one," he began, tapping the chart with his finger. "As you know, most of the U-boats are concentrated at the head here"—his finger traced a line—"at Bunde."

Brangwyn's brow ran into creases. Bunde Fiord? The captain couldn't be serious. They would have about as much chance of penetrating that fiord as a U-boat would the Manchester canal. It was unthinkable.

"However," Cheney went on, "they are very much out of reach there, but down here, farther south at Bogen"— Brangwyn's eyes anxiously followed the captain's stabbing finger—"at the head of Tonsberg Fiord, they have set up an asdic station. The whole thing is very probably like our own affair at Loch Goil. The U-boats will lie off shore, secured between buoys, and run their main motors and auxiliary machinery while dived. The chaps ashore will listen in and see if they can spot anything that might be a bit noisy. After that the boats will more than likely run up and down the sound—you can see there's a bit of water here—to round off the whole thing." Cheney paused to rub his eyes.

"More than likely this is the last stage in their working-up trials. In a word, we can rest assured that most of the boats there are, as near as damn, ready to put to sea. . . . That's the general picture." He picked up his pencil and ran its point down the narrow tongue of the fiord. "As one might expect, the waters are heavily netted, but they have a boom here. Given a chance, we should be able to breach it without much difficulty." Cheney leaned back in his chair.

Brangwyn bent forward to study the chart more closely, and his frown deepened. Just above the 59th parallel where Bohus Bay narrowed to join Oslo Fiord he picked out the port of Bogen near the head of Tonsberg Fiord. The Germans had chosen a good spot for their operations. The U-boats would be well protected by a complex of islands which formed an almost unbroken ring seaward. Between the islands the channel waters would be strung with antisubmarine nets and heavily mined. A frogman would have difficulty getting through. That left the opening to the south. It was impossible to breach the boom. They would have to wait until it was lifted to allow entry to some vessel, then slip through in its wake.

Worriedly Brangwyn took note of the features of the fiord. It looked like a death trap. Even if they did manage to slip through the boom when it was raised, they would be entering an area which would be stiff with listening devices. The station at Bogen would be able to pick up the faintest whisper. Brangwyn experienced a fluttering sensation in his stomach. Breaching the boom would be hazardous enough, but to get out again. . . . Once detected in the confined waters they would never break free. They would be trapped.

"You think we might be able to get through the boom, sir?" he asked, trying to calm his feelings and survey the situation objectively.

Cheney bit softly into his knuckle. "We'll get through the boom all right, number one. It may take a little time, but we'll get through. There's bound to be some traffic, even if it's only a small supply vessel. We should be able to slip in behind her when they raise the boom." Cheney began tidying up his papers.

Doubts clawed at Brangwyn's mind. The operation looked extremely hazardous. Could it be that Cheney was allowing his personal considerations to outweigh his better judgment?

Cheney rolled up the chart. He turned round and fixed Brangwyn with a stare. "You seem to have some doubts in your mind," he said in an ominously quiet voice.

Brangwyn felt himself color slightly. It was his duty to back up the captain all the way, and yet, despite his feelings of loyalty, he felt unhappy about the plan. Submarines had slipped through boom defenses before and gotten away with it. There was a risk, of course, but you couldn't fight a war without taking risks. It was all a question of whether the risk was justifiable in the precise circumstances you were dealing with. In the end the problem resolved itself into a question of probabilities; certainties seldom existed. There was also the question of personalities. If you were a gambling type you gambled; if you weren't, you didn't. Because of the position Cheney had been placed in, would he now take chances that he wouldn't have taken before? Gambling in any form was a dangerous pursuit. The man who gambles temporarily detaches himself from reality and is really only able to exercise discrimination within the rules of the game itself. To Brangwyn, a gambler was a man suffering from a form of mental aberration. He hoped Cheney had not fallen into the temptation.

"Well, sir," he began circumspectly, "I must say at first glance there appear to be a number of hazards—" He hesitated, wondering how far he could go. "It's not so much the boom but the listening station at Bogen that worries me. They'll be able to pick up and classify every sound within miles. If we were to get caught in the sound by a destroyer or an A/S trawler, well—well, we'd have to be lucky to get away with it."

Cheney's eyes narrowed. "I don't believe in luck, Brangwyn," he said coldly. "Things don't just happen—you make them happen. Luck is for the indecisive and the weak-willed."

Brangwyn flushed. "I was merely pointing out, sir—"

"You were pointing out the difficulties. I am aware of them and they can be overcome." Cheney paused as if searching for his next words. When he spoke his voice was low and vibrated with intensity. "Number one—the object of our patrol is to discourage the enemy from making a break for it should the German High Command throw its hand in." He took a deep breath. "The best way to obtain that objective is to sink a U-boat. Anything else is only a half measure. Hit them and hit them hard. That's the only thing Jerry will understand." Cheney thrust the rolled-up chart into Brangwyn's hands. "Study that chart, number one. Go over it with the navigator. I want you both to familiarize yourselves with every single marking. Have you got that, number one? Put Joyner in the picture, too—it might be helpful—but above all, I want you and Robinson to study that chart so that you will be able to read it in the dark if necessary. Once we're in the sound we must act with certainty and in a very limited space of time."

Brangwyn made to go.

"There's one other thing, before you go—how is Mitchell?"

The sudden switch of subject caught the first lieutenant on the hop. "Mitchell, sir? Oh . . . well, he seems to be pretty much the same since I saw him last. The coxswain in fact tells me that his temperature has come down a fraction, but he now appears to be complaining of a pain in his stomach."

"I see." Cheney stared for a moment at the top of the folding table. He looked up quickly. "What is your opinion of his condition, number one?"

Brangwyn weighed the question carefully before answering. He stroked his chin thoughtfully. "Well, sir, I don't think there's much doubt about it, sir. His illness appears genuine enough. What it is I have no idea, but the coxswain—"

"It's your opinion I am concerned with for the moment," Cheney cut in.

"Well, sir, as I said, I don't think there's any question that he's not genuinely ill."

"Very well, Brangwyn. Tell the coxswain I want to see him in here, in my cabin, at 2200 hours. The officers will meet in the wardroom at 2230. Arrange it so that Joyner has the watch on deck then. That will be all, Brangwyn."

When the first lieutenant had gone, Cheney put the rest of his papers away, stowing them neatly in the bottom of his locker. Removing his half boots, he stretched out on his bunk. Despite the fact that the next day would see the beginning of May it was still freezing cold in the submarine. Shivering slightly, Cheney pulled a blanket over himself and closed his eyes.

The *U-4117* had left Kiel the previous day to make her way up to the new U-boat base in Oslo Fiord. She was one of the very latest type of XII boats and was fitted with a snorkel device which enabled her to run on her diesels while submerged. Ten days before, she had rested on the slipways at Kiel. With furious energy the crew and dockyard workers had labored day and night preparing her for sea. Leaving the slipway, she'd done her first dive, run her engines, tested her motors, swung compasses and been degaussed, all within a period of 72 hours. She had left Kiel unescorted and threaded her way through the narrow waterways separating the islands of Denmark. Reaching the Skaw at the Baltic entrance to the Skagerrak she had dived and proceeded northward to Oslo Fiord.

Following behind her and traveling on the surface under heavy escort was her sister ship, the *U-4118*. Both submarines had come off the slipway within hours of each other. The *U-4118* was making passage on the surface because of a fault in her snorkel tube. But because of the heavy and constant bombing raids on the yards it was important to get her north to Bunde as soon as possible. Apart from her normal complement she also had on board two dockyard workers who were to attend to the faulty snorkel when they reached base.

The vessels were separated by no more than 60 miles. Underneath the water the *U-4117* was making ten knots, while the *U-4118* proceeded at a brisk eighteen.

As Lieutenant Brangwyn left Cheney's cabin to return to the wardroom and despatch Cadbury to fetch the coxswain, his counterpart, on watch in the control room of the *U-4117*, was disturbed by the approach of the engineer officer. Lieutenant Heideger listened as the engineer informed him that the snorkel had developed a fault and wasn't breathing properly. They had begun to ship a great deal of water through the induction valve. Heideger immediately sent for the captain. Lieutenant Commander Grueber joined the two men in the control room. Together the three men discussed the situation. It was eventually decided that if the intake of water could not be checked they would blow main ballast and continue their passage on the surface.

When Heideger resumed his watch, the *U-4117* was no more than a few miles away from the *Scorpion* and overhauling her on a parallel course. Grueber had gone over to the plot to check his position. He returned a few minutes later to order the periscope to be raised. Carefully he searched the waters in which he might have to surface. He'd received a signal to the effect that a British submarine had been sighted in the entrance to the Skagerrak, and though no further sightings had been made Grueber decided to act on the assumption it was still in the area; Grueber was not a man to take unnecessary risks. Ordering his first lieutenant to keep a sharp periscope watch, he had the chief hydrophone operator relieve the man on watch as an extra precaution. With the diesels running and creating a background of sound, only an expert could hope to pick up alien hydrophone echoes.

A worried frown on his square features, Grueber rejoined his engineer on the for'ard platform of the engine room.

On board the *Scorpion,* Rice was on duty in the asdic cabinet. Day after day now he and the other operators had strained their ears in an effort to pick up the slightest hydrophone echo. Keyed up to a high pitch, their performance curve had begun to fall off as the days reeled off with nothing to report. Failure to find anything had dulled the edge of their keenness.

Rice was methodical, but he lacked experience and imagination. Unlike Winch, he hadn't developed any intuitive sense. But then Winch seemed to possess quite extraordinary powers. It was almost as if he were able to sense the approach of a vessel even before the first muffled *swish, swish,* of her screws could be heard. The asdic unit was no more than a nervous extension of his own sensory system.

Slowly and painstakingly Rice carried out sweep after sweep. He tried hard to concentrate. Once he thought he'd picked up something and he swung back on the bearing, his ears cocked as he strained to listen. But there was nothing. He wondered if his mind had begun to play tricks.

The minutes in the control room ticked away. Robinson, the O.O.W., was having difficulty with the trim and continually admonished the two planesmen. At near-regular intervals he would raise the periscope and search the horizon. And each time he drew a blank. Apart from the ragged coastline of Sweden which lay partially obscured by the early morning haar the seas were empty.

Rice suddenly jerked upright.

A faint sound gnawed at the outer edge of his senses. Was it real or imaginary? He craned forward in his seat, cocking his head instinctively to one side.

Swish, swish, swish. There it was again. He checked the bearing carefully, noting it in his head, and made a quick sweep through 180 degrees before coming back to it.

There could be no doubt about it. He had an echo!

Trying to control the flutters in his stomach, Rice focused his receiver on the bearing for at least ten seconds. He felt as if someone had stuffed his mouth with cotton wool as he sought to find his voice.

"H.E. bearing red 170," he called out nervously to break the drowsy silence of the control room.

Robinson spun around. "What was that, Rice?"

Rice's voice seemed to crack as he repeated the bearing. Robinson ordered the periscope raised, pouncing on the handles and flicking them down as it slid out of the well. He searched the horizon carefully. The early morning haar had lifted off the water. Robinson whipped the periscope into high power. There was no sign of life anywhere.

He frowned. "Are you sure you have an echo, Rice?"

Rice listened again. "It's very faint, sir. It's difficult to tell at this range. It could be diesel."

"What is the bearing now?"

"Bearing red . . . red 169, sir."

Robinson had another look. Unhurriedly he searched the horizon, inching back and forth over the angle of bearing. He signaled the periscope down. With a precautionary glance at the bubbles on the inclinometers to check the trim, he walked over to the asdic cabinet.

"You still have an echo, Rice?" he asked, his voice expressing disbelief.

Rice didn't answer immediately. He concentrated, then straightened up. "There's something there, sir," he replied earnestly. "The range appears to be closing. There's some distortion from fresh water layers, but it does sound like diesel, sir."

"Hmmph." Robinson pursed his lips and went back to the for'ard periscope. For the third time he scanned the bearing. After a long search he ordered the periscope down, shaking his head.

"There's nothing there, Rice. Are you quite sure—"

A noise startled everyone.

Cheney burst into the control room in his stockinged feet. He brushed Robinson aside as he ordered the periscope up. His lips drawn back in a snarl, he squatted low on the deck to grasp the handles as they cleared the well.

"Bearing now, Rice?" His voice whipped out like a lash.

Rice, taken aback by Cheney's sudden and dramatic appearance, hesitated.

"The bearing, Rice?" Cheney roared.

Rice jumped in his seat. "R-r-red 166, sir," he blurted out.

Cheney trained the big periscope on the bearing. For a split second he remained frozen, and then the handles snapped together with startling abruptness. His voice rang out with the shock of an electric discharge.

"Pipe diving stations, Robinson. Attack team close up at the double. We might have a U-boat."

His hand shaking with excitement, Robinson unhooked the Tannoy. Within seconds the quiet calm of the control room was shattered. The compartment began to fill with urgent hurrying figures as the attack team took over from the watch. Winch's two-hundred-pound bulk burst through the doorway. Cheney grabbed him, hurried him toward the asdic cabinet, and stood over him as Winch slipped into the operator's chair and took the headphones from the bewildered Rice.

Winch fiddled with the dials. Cheney's hands gripped the back of the chair until his knuckles showed white.

"Have you got her, Winch?" he breathed tightly.

Winch nodded calmly. "Bearing 163, sir. Sounds like a diesel . . . about 230 revs . . . range closing."

Cheney leaped back to the for'ard periscope. He whipped it up, but the surface of the sea was still empty. "Right," he called out. "Start the attack. The target is a U-boat."

Robinson, closed up at his action station, began to feed information into the fruit machine. Inwardly he cursed himself for his error in not making the instant deduction that the captain had—a positive echo with nothing visible on the surface had to be a U-boat using her snorkel.

"Port ten . . . steer 315. Set all torpedoes to run at twenty-five feet. We'll fire by asdic."

A viselike tension gripped the attack team as the range closed and they neared the point at which they would fire.

Winch's voice shattered the silence: "Sounds like she's blowing her tanks, sir," he cried warningly.

Cheney dived for the periscope.

As the lens broke clear he saw the glint of sunlight on the U-boat's upper structure as she climbed slowly out of the water.

"What speed does the plot give, Robinson?" he yelled.

"Ten knots, sir."

"Group up . . . half ahead both . . . port ten . . . steer 300. . . ." Cheney rapped out the string of orders.

He was too late.

As he helplessly watched the surfacing U-boat, the space between her periscope standards narrowed and seemed to merge into one solid column as she put her helm over to go about on a reciprocal course.

Lieutenant Commander Grueber had decided to return and pick up the convoy.

An animal cry seemed to tear itself loose from Cheney's throat as he saw his intended victim turn. He flung the handles of the periscope together with a vicious crack.

"Call off the attack. Watch diving," he snarled at Brangwyn in a barely recognizable voice. For a moment he stood gazing unseeingly at the spot where the periscope had vanished down the well. Then he stalked, hunch-shouldered, out of the control room.

The hours passed, stretching wearily across the day. The sighting of the U-boat and the abortive attack had caused a ripple of excited conversation to spread through the submarine. But as watch followed watch in boring monotony the crew fell back into a mood of dull lethargy.

Shortly after retiring to his cabin Cheney had sent for the first lieutenant. Brangwyn had never seen him so angry. Thumping the table Cheney told him that in the future any hydrophone echo, no matter how insignificant it seemed, was to be reported to him immediately and without fail. Brangwyn went back to the wardroom with his ears burning. Smarting under the lash of Cheney's tongue, he made it clear to Joyner and Robinson what was expected of them in the future.

Robinson was the most deeply affected. He tried to talk himself out of the guilt feelings that assailed him, but he couldn't disguise the fact that he'd made a blunder. In an effort to relieve his conscience he shifted some of the blame to Rice. It was because of the asdic rating's hesitant and indecisive reporting that he'd failed to take action more quickly. Already Robinson had succeeded in pushing out of his mind the fact that he had virtually taken no action. Despite this, his brash self-assurance had taken a knock.

The crew had just finished tea. Winch wiped the crumbs from the corner of his mouth and hitched up his trousers over the immense bulk of his girth. A cup of tea in his hand, he went to relieve A.B. Gwynn on the asdic set.

The "ticket collector" had the watch in the control room. Everyone else on watch had been worked up into a sweat by his antics in trying to keep a trim. They kept glancing at the clock, counting the minutes until they would be relieved.

Winch crossed the deck of the control room and made for the cabinet.

Joyner spotted him. "Are you relieving the asdic operator, Winch?" he asked peevishly.

Winch's huge bulk swung around. "I am, sir."

"Don't you know that you should report to the officer of the watch first?" said Joyner, his lips a thin line.

Winch shrugged resignedly. "Sorry, sir."

"Very well, Winch. Just remember it in the future, will you?" Joyner turned away.

Winch smiled to himself. He found it difficult to take the sub-lieutenant seriously. Amused, he went over to the cabinet and signaled Gwynn out of the chair.

Adjusting the earphones on his head, he twirled the asdic directional dial through an arc. The smile on his face died. He spun the dial again. No sound. He made a complete sweep and stopped.

His sixth sense told him that there were surface vessels about.

Stoker Ford, manning the telegraphs, had been idly watching Winch. He straightened up from where he was leaning as he saw the change of expression. He'd seen that look on Winch's face before. Within seconds and without saying a word he'd managed to communicate the knowledge to the rest of the watch that Winch was hot on a contact.

Joyner, unaware of what was going on, leaned against the for'ard periscope.

"H.E. bearing green 175 . . . mushy, but sounds like a number of units," Winch's voice rang out.

Joyner jerked upright, stumbling as his foot caught the rim of the periscope well. "What's that, Winch? H.E.—" he gasped.

"H.E. bearing green 175," repeated Winch with invincible calm.

Joyner felt his heart start up like a trip-hammer. A paralysis gripped his limbs. His voice squawked out as he ordered the periscope up. Halfway to reach for it, he remembered the first lieutenant's instructions from the captain. Trying to keep the nervousness out of his voice he called out shrilly for the captain in the control room.

Cheney was out of his cabin and along the passageway in an instant.

Joyner had forgotten he had the periscope sticking out of the water. "Winch has an echo, sir," he said as Cheney came tearing into the control room.

Cheney glanced at the unattended periscope. He shot the

"ticket collector" a burning-eyed glare as he thrust him aside. He grabbed the handles and swung the periscope in a circle.

"Bearing, Winch?" he cried.

"Green 174, sir."

Cheney leaned on the handles and heaved around. A faint tissue of smoke hung on the horizon to the south.

They were in contact with the approaching convoy.

The water danced and shimmered in the bright rays of the afternoon sun. A freshening breeze had raised sea horses to frolic about on the running tide. Despite the bright sun it was still very cold.

Lieutenant Commander Dortmann, on the bridge of the *U-4118*, neither felt the cold nor enjoyed the beauty of the spring day. He was anxious to get to Bunde Fiord, complete his working-up trials and get to sea again. On the aftermost part of the bridge, standing clear of the lookouts, were the two civilian dockyard workers. They had asked permission to be allowed up top for some fresh air. To their surprise it had been granted. Both men were thoroughly enjoying the day. It was a sheer pleasure to be away from the bomb-stricken dockyards. Unlike Dortmann, they weren't aware that a British submarine had been reported in the Skagerrak. Grinning at each other they sucked in deep lungfuls of the sparkling air.

Dortmann wasn't particularly worried about the alleged presence of the British submarine. In fact he considered it more than a possibility that the sighting had been an error. It wasn't the first time the Luftwaffe had made such errors, and with half the planes manned by youngsters fresh from training school the number of false alarms had greatly increased. In addition, Dortmann considered himself amply protected by the two modern destroyers and half-dozen E-boats which were to see him safely as far as the boom before making their way back. Dortmann's worries were centered on the problem of completing his working-up trials and getting his new command out to sea as quickly as he could.

Leaning over the bridge, he raised his binoculars and

watched one of the E-boats cut close to his sister ship, the
U-4117, which had taken up station at the rear. He swung his
glasses and gazed westward toward the gateway of the Skagerrak and the opening to the North Sea, or the German Ocean,
as he called it. A knifelike edge cut into the perimeter of his
lens. The port wing destroyer had come around hard on the
opposite leg of her zigzag. A great white bow wave flew up from
her stem and her starboard guardrails were nearly under water
as she heeled sharply on her turn. The dockyard men nudged
each other as they gazed admiringly at the graceful power-
packed lines.

A pattern of events had slowly begun to develop.

Dortmann, unaware that his movements and that of the convoy were being plotted on a tiny computer, saw the bows of his
vessel come around as the helmsman automatically altered
course in accordance with the zigzag pattern. The whole progress of the convoy formed an intricate design with the two
U-boats as the central point of the motif.

Nearly five miles away it was Cheney's task to unravel this
complexity of motion and place his ship in a position to fire her
torpedoes. A host of considerations were involved. A few simple facts formed the basis of his calculations. From these a number of deductions pyramided upward in a rise of probabilities.
Cheney knew his own course and, making allowances for wind
and tide, his own speed through water. Subject to the same considerations, he also knew the speed at which his torpedoes
would travel. The enemy's relative bearing was a fact also
known to him. But the speed, course and range were only probabilities and, furthermore, were subject to change.

The problem was further complicated by the approach of a
2,000-ton destroyer bearing down on him with the speed of
an express train.

With snap sightings from the periscope, Cheney began to
build up the picture. The chessboard pattern of the convoy began to resolve itself. Cheney now awaited one vital piece of information from the fruit machine before he could fire.

"Up periscope . . . steady now!" Cheney sprawled across the deck to seize the handles as they cleared the rim of the well. The periscope rose, dragging him to his feet. A bright shaft of sunlight pierced the control room as the periscope broke the surface of the water. Cheney glued his eye to the lens, and with a twist of his wrist flicked the instrument into high power.

The approaching destroyer looked as big as a battleship. Shutting its presence firmly from his mind Cheney forced himself to concentrate on the nearest U-boat in the convoy.

The noise of the destroyer could now be clearly heard. The crew felt the grip of tension. This was always the worst moment in an attack—as they slipped through the destroyer screen.

"Down periscope . . . what's my D.A.?" Cheney's voice vibrated in the churchlike quiet of the control room. "Right. Up after periscope." He turned quickly to Brangwyn: "Watch the trim, number one," adding almost as an afterthought, "the destroyer is going to come quite close to us."

He had one quick look through the after periscope and returned to the big attack periscope. It hissed out of the well. Cheney grabbed it. Quickly he brought it to bear on the target.

"Right . . . put me on green 10."

McLintock, the E.R.A., squeezed around. His eyes fixed steadily on the bearing ring, he locked his calloused hands over Cheney's to steady him on the bearing.

Like a lantern slide projection drawn slowly across a screen, the bows of *U-4118* nosed into the lens of the periscope and drew toward the hairline sight.

"Fire one!" roared Cheney. There was a dull thud, and the boat lurched in recoil as the torpedo was expelled from the tube.

The noise of the destroyer was ominously loud.

"Fire two!"

"Fire three!"

The destroyer was practically on top of them now. The crew crouched involuntarily and held their breaths as the control room seemed to reverberate to the thunderous sound.

"Fire four!" Bissel on the firing panel was unable to hear and had to lipread the order.

Clungk, clungk, clungk. The churning propellers of the destroyer beat the water in an ear-piercing plangency.

"Flood Q's . . . eighty feet," Cheney yelled as the destroyer passed over the conning tower with feet to spare.

Horror-stricken, Brangwyn watched the bubble begin to slide forward. Bain had the foreplanes hard to dive, but the sudden loss of weight caused by the discharge of torpedoes had lifted the bows.

Cheney pounded Bain on the shoulders. "Get her down, man! Get her down!" he screamed. One glimpse of his periscope standards and the destroyer would warn the U-boat. The attack would be ruined.

Both needles on the depth gauges hung up at 26 feet. Cheney's knuckle was jammed into his mouth. Everyone in the control room seemed petrified. The needles flickered uncertainly, then with a little jumping motion swept in an accelerating arc as the effects of flooding Q tank were felt.

"All torpedoes running, sir," reported Winch from asdics.

Cheney swung to Bissel, who stood with stopwatch in hand. "How long, Bissel?"

"One minute forty-five seconds, sir," the E.A. replied.

Cheney bit into his knuckle. More than a minute and a half to wait before he knew whether his attack was successful or not. The muscles on his face stood out like cables.

On the bridge of the U-boat the O.O.W. put his hand to his mouth to stifle a yawn. Night life in the battered city of Hamburg still held attractions for those willing and able to pay for it. He wondered how Norway would be. Behind him the dockyard workers beamed and sniffed the salt air. The breeze was freshening, but within a few hours they would be in the sheltered waters of the fiord. Next day they would be back at work.

Dortmann, a scowl on his face, eyed the two men bleakly. He'd decided they'd had long enough up top. He resented the way they laughed and grinned at each other. In his fanaticism, their action seemed to him almost a dereliction of duty to the fatherland.

Down below, the crew of the *U-4118* went about their tasks. Some of them whistled as always happens among a crew as they near port. Even some of the older hands who had gone through the winter battles in the North Atlantic appeared cheerful. They sensed that the war was nearly over for Germany and they were glad. No more long patrols; no more depth charges; no more bombs. All they wanted was to get home again and see what they could save from the wreck. In the seamen's mess the men off watch played cards and wrote letters to post when they reached their new quarters. Their conversation was lighthearted, almost bantering.

Two polished steel missiles slammed into their hull and exploded violently.

Mercifully the crew were knocked senseless by the cataclysmic release of energy. Then their bodies were smashed and torn into unrecognizable pulp as the hull broke up and the water rushed in.

On the bridge four men saw the blinding, unbelievable flash. Its meaning was understood instantly by Dortmann just before his body was catapulted upward to smash against the periscope standards with back-breaking force. For a moment his inert figure hung between the standards like a pitiful broken doll. The U-boat, her hull mortally ruptured, rolled over, taking her captain with her.

A few minutes after the explosion, all that remained of the *U-4118* was a slick of oil, a few bits of wood and an odd article of clothing.

Chapter Ten

At 120 feet the pressure hull trembled with the shock of exploding depth charges. Reeling from the colossal blows, the submarine shook from stem to stern. A rain of moisture-absorbent cork showered down from the deckhead.

For the past three hours the destroyer, aided by the E-boats, had kept up an insistent attack. After the sinking, the *U-4117*, escorted by the second destroyer, had raced for the sanctuary of Oslo Fiord.

Able seaman Stanley, the exchange operator, licked his pencil, noted the time and logged the depth charge pattern. According to his tally the number of depth charges stood at 68.

"H.E. bearing red 160 . . . closing," Winch reported.

The destroyer was coming in to attack again.

Anxious looks were exchanged by the crew as they listened to the high-pitched tapping sound bouncing off the hull. The relentlessly probing asdic beam from the destroyer had found them again. Like a bony finger scraping along a window pane the sound persisted. Cheney altered course.

With a mad roar the destroyer swept overhead, its depth charges launched in advance. Somewhere above the heads of the crew the explosive canisters were sinking slowly. The tiny metallic clicks of the pistols cocking were clearly audible. The pattern was falling dangerously close.

Kkkrruuump! Kkkrruuump! The charges exploded.

The control seemed to quiver like a giant tuning fork. There was a sound of glass breaking. All the lights went out. From somewhere in the mass of piping on the deckhead, a joint in the high-pressure air line screeched off like a steam whistle. A fountain of oil gushed out from the blowing panel. Fuses exploded like hot firecrackers as they blew out of junction boxes.

Amid the din Bain called out: "Foreplanes out of control, sir."

"Foreplanes in hand!" Cheney yelled to Stanley on the switchboard.

An emergency light flickered and blinked on. The control room crew surveyed the scene in shocked silence. Bits of glass were strewn all over the deck, wallowing back and forth in a pool of oil and water. From the bulkheads, pipes and cables sagged drunkenly. The dial on the foreplane depth gauge was shattered and the needle twisted into an unrecognizable shape. Even the dimness of the emergency lighting couldn't disguise the chaotic disruption.

Cheney surveyed the wreckage unemotionally, as he awaited reports from damage control. In a few minutes Dinsdale, the engineer officer, came back from a hurried tour of the boat. Incredibly, the pressure hull had remained intact under the enormous stress of the explosions. One or two rivets had sprung, but Dinsdale had no serious damage to report.

For the next hour the destroyer and the E-boats remained in close contact. Pattern after pattern of depth charges erupted. Quite suddenly the terrifying clamor ceased. And though the crew strained their ears, they no longer heard the ghostly tapping on the hull.

Unable to believe the attack had been called off, the men waited in fear and apprehension, but the only audible noise was the steady ticking of the control room clock.

The explanation came soon. The submarine began to plunge rapidly. They had found a freshwater layer, and it was distorting the high-frequency asdic signals from the destroyer.

"Two hundred feet, sir." Bain's voice reminded the crew they were still plunging downward.

Brangwyn ran both ballast pumps to gain buoyancy. The bows were down at a steep angle, and they still continued to descend. At 250 feet Brangwyn looked appealingly at Cheney. They would have to blow main ballast if their rate of descent was to be checked.

Three hundred feet. Going down. Brangwyn shot Cheney another worried glance. Cheney didn't speak but shook his head. To blow main ballast would betray their position to the searching destroyer. All eyes were now glued to the afterdepth gauge. The thick glass cover had starred, partially obscuring the figures on the dial, but it was clear to everyone that the indicator needle had began to edge into the forbidden red sector.

They would have to blow main ballast.

At 350 feet, with the hull groaning and creaking in protest, they hit salt water again. The submarine gained buoyancy almost immediately and leveled off at 375 feet. It was the deepest they had ever been.

In the fore-ends Wells and his crew sweated to operate the foreplanes on manual control. Their combined efforts hardly moved the heavy brass wheel.

"It's no good—the bloody thing's jammed," panted Mulholland.

Wells stood back for a second, breathing heavily. He spat on his hands. "Come on. Let's have another go," he said, grabbing the wheel and putting his back into it. "Right then . . . one . . . two . . . six . . . heavy!"

The three men threw their weight on the wheel. It moved an inch before jamming up solid. All their efforts refused to budge it. Wells straightened up and clambered over to the phone. Calling up the control room, he reported the foreplanes jammed.

"That's it, then," he said, coming back to rejoin Mulholland and Barbour, who had flopped down on the deck exhaustedly. "No bloody foreplanes, what next?"

Mulholland grinned sourly. "Well, at least old Bain'll be glad. Nothing to do now but sit on his arse."

Wells gave the peak of his cap a twist. "Well, you're not Jock Bain, you miserable gett, so you'd better rise off your backside and start clearing some of this shambles up."

Mulholland and Barbour groaned in unison. Even in the emergency lighting it was easy to see the mess the compartment was in. Bits of broken glass and crockery lay everywhere. Oil, spurting from loosened glands in the telemotor line, had spilled on the deck and floated on top of the inch pool of water that slopped around. A food locker had somehow burst open, scattering tea, sugar and milk about in sticky confusion.

"You, Sweeny," Wells spoke to Barbour. "Get some spare bulbs and see if the lighting's working. They should have the fuses back in by now. Let's get some light on the subject for a start."

Muttering protests, Barbour got to his feet. "Why did I ever join this outfit?" he moaned.

"No, you should have joined the wrens. You'd have made a fine officer's groundsheet," Mulholland said.

Wells jerked his hand. "Come on, you two. Let's cut the cackle and get on with it."

Mulholland eased his long frame from the deck as Barbour went to break out bulbs from the spares locker. Greasy strands of hair fell over his eyes. He tossed his head angrily. "Where the hell do we start?" he asked despairingly.

Wells held up his hand. "Shh. Just a minute. What was that?"

Both men listened. A faint groan came from the direction of Mitchell's hammock.

Wells ducked under the bulge of the hammocks and worked his way over to the far side. He climbed up on the locker, pushing the empty hammocks out of his way. Mitchell was tossing about and groaning softly. In the dim light his face was no more than a swatch of gray.

"What's the trouble, mate?" Wells queried. "What's up with you?"

Mitchell answered by groaning again. His hands clutched his stomach. "I feel awful, chief," he said, his eyelids cracking open. His voice was weak and tremulous.

Wells leaned closer. "What is it? Is it your stomach? Are you in pain?"

"Aaaagh," Mitchell groaned again. His head nodded. "I

feel sick." His legs came up as he pressed his hands tightly to the region of his stomach.

"It's a pain in your stomach?"

Mitchell nodded weakly. A fresh glow of light came from somewhere. Barbour had managed to replace the broken bulbs. Wells examined the drawn features of the sick seaman closely. Mitchell looked ghastly.

"Easy on there, son. Is there anything I can get you?"

Mitchell's knees jackknifed nearly to his chin as he retched. The spasm stopped. "Water . . . can you get . . . water . . . a glass of water. . . ."

Wells looked at him anxiously for a second before jumping down off the locker.

"What's up with him, chief?" Mulholland asked, seeing the worried look in the T.G.M.'s eyes. "Is he feeling dicey?"

Wells ignored the question and took Mulholland by the arm. "Phone up the control room, Scouse," he said in a low voice. "Tell the 'swain to get along here. He'd better have a look at Mitch. Tell him I said so if anyone asks. Okay?"

Mulholland hurried toward the phone as the T.G.M. went to fetch water.

Oak had taken over the exchange. Stanley had volunteered to clean up some of the mess in the control room. Oak flicked down the tab and picked up the phone as it rang. "Control room," he answered.

"Hello, hello. Control room?" Mulholland's voice crackled tinnily. The line was wild with static.

"Control room, control room here," Oak repeated.

Cheney swung around impatiently. "What in heaven's name's going on, Oak?" he snapped.

"I think it's the fore-ends, sir. I can't—"

"Never mind that. Ask them what they want, man, and get on with it."

Oak jiggled the key. Mulholland's voice came through again: "What the hell's going on there? Is that the control room?"

"Control room here," Oak repeated desperately. "Hullo, hullo. . . ."

"Thank Christ for that," Mulholland snorted as the line cleared. "Listen, Stan, tell the coxswain—"

"I-it's not Stan. It's me—Gospel," Oak broke in for some reason.

"For God's sake, man," Cheney roared, "will you find out what they want!"

In his nervousness Oak found the wrong key and cut himself off. He could feel Cheney's eyes burning into the back of his neck. He tried again and got through to the fore-ends. "Fore-ends . . . fore-ends . . . what is it you want?"

Mulholland took off. "I want to go ashore. That's what I bloody well want. What the hell's going on there?"

In his confusion Oak nearly repeated Mulholland's words. He stopped himself.

By this time Cheney was in an absolute fury. "Oak," he screamed, causing everyone in the control room to jump, "find out what they want in the fore-ends! At once! Do you hear—at once!"

Oak spoke into the mouthpiece again. "What is it you want?" his voice pleaded in despair.

The line crackled again. Mulholland's voice came through faintly: ". . . the coxswain. Tell him he's wanted. . . ."

Oak covered the mouthpiece with his hand as he turned to Cheney. "It's the coxswain, sir. He wants the coxswain."

Cheney exploded. He beat his fist into his palm.

"*Who* wants the coxswain? *What* do they want him for?" he roared.

Oak flushed a deep red. Cheney turned to Brangwyn. "Get that man off the exchange at once," he said.

With the captain screaming at him from one side and Mulholland from the other, Oak lost his head. He pressed the wrong tab again and got through to number two main vent station up forward by the P.O.'s' mess. Speaking in a wholly unnatural manner as Monkhouse answered the phone, he said: "Please state your reason for wanting the coxswain. . . ."

Monkhouse looked at the phone as if it had gone crazy and hung up.

The exchange began to buzz angrily. A pair of lights flashed on. Somebody else wanted the control room. Unable to decide which call to answer first, Oak panicked. Stanley arrived to solve his problem. He tapped him on the shoulder. "Okay, mate, move over. I'll take it." His face hidden from the officers, Stanley was nearly doubled up with laughter. He squeezed into the exchange and grabbed the phone. By this time everyone in the control room was craning to witness the melodrama. His face a fiery red, Oak slipped away.

Squawking sounds were heard from the line. Everyone waited on tenterhooks as Cheney, white-faced with rage, glared over at the corner. Stanley swung around.

"Mulholland, sir. Says the T.G.M. wants the coxswain to go along and have a look at Mitchell." He flicked off and took the next call that was waiting to come in. Hardly able to keep his face straight, he answered briefly and hung up.

"Well?" snapped Cheney.

Stanley didn't dare look at the captain as he answered. "No. Two main vent station, sir. Wanted to know why we were calling them up."

Cheney wheeled on Brangwyn. "Have the coxswain relieved, number one—that's if you can find anyone capable of taking over the afterplanes," he added viciously.

Brangwyn swallowed hard and beckoned Titt.

Blow slipped out of the stool as Titt grabbed the control bar.

"Go forward and have a look at Mitchell, coxswain. It seems the T.G.M. is a bit concerned about him."

Blow had heard every word that had passed, but he gave no sign as he listened to the first lieutenant's instructions. "Very well, sir," he said and marched off. The stoker on the periscope control lever opened the bulkhead door for him. Blow ducked through and into the passageway.

Cheney glared around the control room in a cold rage. He faced the asdic cabinet. "Anything yet, Winch?" he asked brusquely.

A few seconds of silence as Winch completed a sweep. "Nothing, sir. No H.E. anywhere," Winch reported.

Cheney strode over to where Dinsdale and an E.R.A. were working on the leaking blowing panel. "How long, chief?" he said.

Dinsdale straightened up and wiped his hands on his white overalls. "Hmmmm? Shouldn't be long now, sir. Ten minutes or so and then we can get around to having a look at that leak in the prop shaft gland."

"I want you to have a look at the foreplanes first," Cheney said. "As quickly as you can."

Dinsdale frowned. "We're taking quite a bit of water aft, sir."

"I know, but I want you to deal with the foreplanes first, chief," Cheney said curtly.

Dinsdale looked as if he might argue for a minute. He stole a glance at Brangwyn. The first lieutenant looked away. Dinsdale nodded. "Very well, sir."

Cheney swung back to face the planes. He watched the bubble carefully for a few seconds. "Take her up to one hundred feet, Brangwyn."

Brangwyn ordered the pumps started. With no foreplanes to help, the submarine rose clumsily. He had to pump out quite a lot of water before she began to shift from her depths. Once started, she came up like a lift to 6o feet. Brangwyn had to flood hurriedly again. At last he got her trimmed at 100 feet.

Cheney looked at the aftergauge critically. "Anything?" he called over his shoulder to Winch.

"No H.E. to report, sir," came the reply.

"All right, Brangwyn—periscope depth. We'll have a look."

Brangwyn bit his lip. He was having a hard enough job keeping her at 100 feet, where a few feet either way made little odds. But at periscope depth, a few feet out and you were blind or had the periscope sticking up out of the water like a flagpole. He took a deep breath and gave the order.

The light was beginning to fade. Poking the periscope up, Cheney saw nothing but a rolling mass of gray water. The wind had come up again, and fighting the flood tide, it had created a stiff choppy seaway. He searched the horizon carefully. The destroyer and the accompanying E-boats were nowhere to be seen. The sea was empty. No sign remained of the forty-odd men who had gone to their deaths only a few short hours before.

Cheney put the periscope down.

"Eighty feet, Brangwyn," he ordered. "Fall out diving stations. Go to watch diving. We'll surface in two hours."

Brangwyn picked up the Tannoy as Cheney went over to Dinsdale. Clearing his throat, he made his announcement. The submarine seemed to come alive as if waking from a dull stupor. The tense atmosphere that had settled over the compartments like a thick fog seemed to dissipate as the bulkhead doors were opened up and the ventilation blowers started.

Once again they had survived. Thankfully the crew breathed a huge sigh of relief. But they were bone-weary and running out of reserves of nervous energy. Only Stanley appeared as indestructibly cheerful as ever as he grinned elfishly all around.

With Dinsdale at his side, Cheney stopped to have a word with the first lieutenant before going to inspect the foreplanes. "Start the men on clearing up right away, Brangwyn. Get a party in the fore-ends. We'll reload torpedoes tonight."

Everyone groaned at the news. Reloading at sea was a major operation. It would take hours. There would be no sleep for them that night. Every single piece of equipment, stores and movable gear would have to be stripped out and piled in the passageway before they would be able to rig the torpedo rails. Dinner would have to be eaten standing up or squatting on the deck. And with the state of the galley it looked like cold beef and pickles.

The crew prayed for heavy weather. In anything of a seaway, the rolling and pitching of the boat made it impossible to reload.

Feeling beaten and miserable, the fore-ends party shuffled forward to report to the T.G.M.

Mulholland and Barbour had already started to unsling the mass of hammocks. Mitchell was a problem. They decided to put the sick seaman in the P.O.'s' mess. Bodily, hammock and all, he was carried gently and laid out on Bain's bunk. He looked fevered and his eyes were unusually bright. With Mitchell out of the fore-ends, Wells got the hands cracking. Titt was in charge of the working party in the passageway. They started piling the gear up as it was passed through the bulkhead doorway. An hour later only the mess table and the lockers remained to be cleared from the fore-ends. Titt nipped forward to see Wells.

"What's your trouble?" the T.G.M. asked, rubbing a greasy hand over his brow.

"I was thinking we might have a cup of char first before we shifted the table," Titt suggested. "We could do with it."

Wells didn't seem sure. "Okay," he said finally, "but you'd better get a move on—we'll be surfacing soon. Get one of your blokes to make it. If I let one of this lot out of the fore-ends I'll never see them again. Away you go then and chop-chop."

Titt hurried aft to organize the tea. He bumped into the coxswain in the passageway. Blow looked worried. Titt sensed it had something to do with Mitchell. "How is he, 'swain?" he asked.

Blow looked as if he hadn't heard the question. He came to himself. "Mitchell? Hmmm? He's not so good," he said gruffly, squeezing past Titt and heading down the passageway toward the wardroom.

Brangwyn rose to his feet as the coxswain appeared in the doorway. "Ah, there you are, coxswain. Come in. It's about Mitchell, I suppose. I was just wondering . . . the T.G.M.'s not the sort to get in a flap—" He broke off as he saw the worried look in Blow's eyes. "Is there anything the matter?"

"I think Mitchell's very ill, sir," Blow answered gravely.

"He's worse then?"

"I'm afraid so, sir. His temperature and pulse have gone up quite a bit. He's not well at all, sir."

Brangwyn stroked his chin. "I see. That doesn't sound good, coxswain. And you still have no idea what it could be?"

Blow took a deep breath. "I think it's appendicitis, sir."

"You what?" gasped Brangwyn as if unable to believe his ears. "Did you say . . . good heavens, coxswain. You can't be serious."

Blow nodded firmly. "It looks like it, sir. I can't be sure, of course, but he has all the symptoms."

Brangwyn sat down. "My God, coxswain. Do you realize what you are saying? If it's appendicitis—good heavens, it doesn't bear thinking about," he said, shaking his head as if recovering from a blow.

Brangwyn got a grip on himself. He got to his feet. "I think I'd better come along with you and see him right away," he said, reaching for his jacket.

Monkhouse had just made a pot of tea. He was about to offer a cup to Blow when he caught sight of the figure of the first lieutenant behind him. Monkhouse didn't need to be told. He put down the cup, slipped out of the mess and drew the curtain behind him.

"When did you first feel the pain, Mitchell?" Blow asked after he'd taken the seaman's temperature and pulse again for the benefit of the first lieutenant. "Speak up, lad, we're trying to help you."

Mitchell licked his cracked lips. "I'm not sure, 'swain," he said weakly. "A few hours ago. It was when the destroyer—" He broke off, his features twisting in pain. "I was trying to get out of my hammock—"

"You were trying to get out of your hammock—why didn't you tell me this before?" Blow said in exasperation. "You should have sung out. Somebody would have heard you. What in God's name did you want to do that for?"

"I felt sick. I wanted to vomit. . . ."

"Go on. What happened then?"

"Nothing—nothing happened. I just couldn't. My arms. . . ."

Blow, his mouth in a tight severe line, shot the first lieutenant a glance. He turned to Mitchell again. "And that was when you felt the pain, was it?"

Mitchell nodded. "It was just after that."

"Now listen to me carefully. Did you wrench yourself when you tried to get up?"

"I think I might have, 'swain."

Blow took a deep breath. "Okay, son. Just take it easy now. Try and get some sleep. I'll be back later. And meantime if you want anything sing out—there'll be somebody about. Whatever you do don't try and get up again. You understand? Stay where you are and don't move."

Brangwyn waited until they got back to the wardroom before he spoke. "Well, he certainly doesn't look well, coxswain," he said, biting his lip. "Why are you so sure it's his appendix? Couldn't it be something else—some sort of bug or virus?"

Blow shrugged helplessly. "I can't be sure, sir. All I can say is that all the symptoms point that way." He held up his hand, ticking off the points on his fingers: "He's fevered; temperature and pulse are up; he feels sick and can't eat—hasn't for days— and now this pain in his stomach." Blow stopped to frown. "There's only one thing puzzles me, sir. . . ."

"What's that?" Brangwyn clutched anxiously at the straw.

"Well, sir, this pain. According to the book it should be a bit lower down." He saw the look in the first lieutenant's eyes. "All the other symptoms fit though, sir. And another thing, he tells me he's been bothered off and on with his stomach for the past six months. He's been off his food and gets these bouts of nausea."

Brangwyn made up his mind. "Very well, coxswain. I'll go and see the captain right away. He'll probably want to have a word with you. I'll send Cadbury along."

Blow made to leave. Brangwyn stopped him. "I only hope to God you're right, coxswain. You know what this'll mean?"

Blow flicked the curtain aside. "Yes, only too well, sir," he replied evenly and strode out of the wardroom.

Cheney leaned forward, his elbows on the folding table, his chin cradled in his hands as he gazed at the bulkhead.

With a little flutter of apprehension clawing at his stomach, Brangwyn awaited his reaction.

Cheney turned around with a bleak expression. "And from

what you say the coxswain thinks it might be appendicitis."

"That's what he said, sir."

Cheney picked up a pencil stub and played with it idly. "I suppose you realize, number one, that there are any number of cinditions that can cause an elevation of temperature and a high rate of pulse?"

"But the pain, sir—and he hasn't been able to eat."

"Yes, I know, Brangwyn. As you say, he hasn't been eating. Naturally he feels weak. In such a condition any sudden effort on his part—like trying to pull himself out of his hammock—could easily wrench a muscle." Cheney put the pencil down. "No, Brangwyn. I think the coxswain is wrong. I can understand his concern, but he's read too much into the symptoms. I'm sure Mitchell is ill, but it's not his appendix he's suffering from."

Faced with the captain's assured manner, doubts began to assail Brangwyn. "But supposing it is, sir? Supposing it is appendicitis?"

"Supposing? We must deal with facts. If we were to be guided by suppositions we'd never get to sea. Mitchell has a temperature, admittedly high, but you've known cases of—well, take sandfly fever, for instance. The temperature rockets up, but have you ever known it to be serious? He could be suffering from food poisoning, you know."

"But he hasn't eaten for days, sir."

Cheney scowled. "Very well, then, he hasn't eaten, but however you look at it the symptoms he portrays could be explained by a dozen illnesses or more—none of them necessarily very serious."

Brangwyn still wanted to be convinced. "Yes, sir, but—"

Cheney's manner hardened. "Number one," he said, his eyes narrowing, "I don't think you fully realize the importance of our mission. If we were to assume that Mitchell has appendicitis we would have to withdraw. Correct? Very well, then, shouldn't we be absolutely certain before taking such a serious step? Do you agree?"

Brangwyn felt trapped by the question. It was as if Cheney

had suddenly placed the burden of responsibility on his shoulders. He didn't know what to think. "I'm only saying what the coxswain—"

"And you would be prepared to call off the patrol on the basis of an opinion which, no matter how well meant, is nevertheless unqualified?"

Brangwyn was silent.

Cheney got to his feet. He glanced at his watch. "We'll be surfacing soon. How are they getting on in the fore-ends?"

"They've started rigging the rails, sir."

"Good. We must get the reloading finished as quickly as possible. The weather doesn't look too good, but we'll just have to keep the revs down and give Wells a chance. Make sure that *all* hands off watch are there to help him."

Brangwyn shifted his feet uncomfortably. "Very well, sir, but—"

"We'll keep a close watch on Mitchell during the night. You'd better send the coxswain along to see me. I'd like a word with him. All right, number one. And I shouldn't worry too much about Mitchell. He'll probably be over it in a couple of days, whatever it is."

Chapter Eleven

Titt took a deep breath and wiped his brow with an old piece of rag. Overhead the newly replaced bulbs glowed harshly, casting strong shadows. They were ready to load the last of the spare torpedoes. Four feet above the deck, supported in cradles on transverse rails, the bulky torpedo dominated the fore-ends. From the orifice in its tail a metal bracket protruded to which was secured a thin wire strop. The strop itself was hooked up to a tackle which ran forward into the tube space, the free end returning into the fore-ends where it was manned by the sweating and tired crew.

Occasionally, as the submarine took the brunt of the seaway on her quarter, the twenty-one-inch-thick monster strained threateningly in the cradles which held it.

T.G.M. Wells pushed his greasy cap back on his head and ran his fingers through his stiff red hair. His thumbs hooked into his belt, he eyed the torpedo respectfully. He beckoned to Titt.

"Sea's coming up a bit, Tom. I think we'd better rig extra tackles on this bugger." He struck the torpedo with the edge of his hand. "We'll pass a couple of strops around the middle and hook up tackles to the bulkheads. Okay?"

Titt shook his head worriedly. "Mmmm? Could do. But they'll never hold her in if she starts to roll."

"Nothing on God's earth will hold her if that happens." Wells put his hand on Titt's shoulder for an instant. "If it does we won't even have time to say prayers." He removed his hand.

"Right then, Tom. Let's get weaving when we've got the chance."

Titt leaned his weight against the long metal cylinder, sizing up the situation. He pursed his lips.

"Okay," he said. "I suppose it's better than nothing." He straightened up and called out across the compartment to Moore. "Pass me a couple of half-inch strops, Pony, will you? You can take the starboard side and I'll take the port. You know what to do, don't you?"

Moore grunted in reply.

Within a few minutes the pair of them had rigged tackles athwartships. The final operation was about to begin.

In silence and not without apprehension the crew waited for Wells to open the rear door of the torpedo tube. Titt, glancing about him to see what action he would take if things went wrong, noticed little rivulets of water running back and forth across the deck.

The sea was freshening.

Nervously the crew clung to the main tackle, their breathing momentarily held with each protesting groan from the transverse torpedo-supporting rails.

Like a slowly gathering electric storm, tension began to build in the compartment.

On the bridge Robinson, who was officer of the watch, barely noticed the approach of the heavy wave. Cheney did, and aware of the risks he was running in loading torpedoes in such weather conditions, his hands gripped the capping of the bridge until his knuckles showed white.

The submarine met the wave just as the warhead of the torpedo entered the tube.

In the fore-ends the deck began to tilt sharply as the bow of the submarine clawed its way up a wall of water. Cresting the wave, she hung for a second in indecision before beginning to race down the sweep of the trough. In her descent she heeled over at a severe angle to port.

The torpedo began to wobble in its cradles like an egg on a tilted spoon.

Titt's eyes bulged as he felt his purchase go slack. Sick with fear, the remainder of the crew held on blindly to the main tackle, unable to do a thing. The whole weight of the straining torpedo came on the starboard tackle.

With a crack like a circus whip that sent everyone's pulse soaring, the tackle parted and Moore catapulted backward into the scuppers.

Titt stared at the glistening nemesis which towered above him as the angle of the boat steepened. Paralyzed, his system shocked into immobility, he did the only thing he could—he prayed.

The torpedo wobbled and stopped on the point of balance.

It was as if a reel in a projector had suddenly broken, fixing the frame as a permanent record of an event and stopping all life and movement. The crew froze.

Wells was the first to move. He flung himself out of the tube space, his feet clawing at the tilt of the deck. With a shuddering movement the submarine began to climb back slowly erect, like a boxer shaking his head after a heavy punch.

"Start heaving on that rope," Wells yelled, grabbing hold of Mulholland and spinning him around as the seaman bent down to help Moore to his feet. "Never mind that. Grab the bloody rope, for Christ's sake." He seized the rope end himself, the veins on his big hands bulging. "Come on, now. Altogether— heave!"

Jolted into action by Wells, the crew began to haul away madly, frenzy giving them renewed strength. Titt dropped his own line to lend a hand. Inch by inch the torpedo began to move along the greased cradles again, creeping toward the empty tube like some prehistoric monster returning to its cave.

Only a foot or so to go now.

Mulholland dropped out of the line of heaving men and ran forward to remove the tail guard just as the deck began to tilt again. Their feet slipping on the greasy deck, the crew strained on the main tackle. The bar-taut rope quivered as beads of grease and moisture squeezed from its inner strands.

Mulholland wasted no time. Every second counted. He

whipped off the torpedo tail guard just as a fresh movement of the boat sent the angle of the deck skyward. The torpedo now threatened to slide backward into the fore-ends with the change of gravity, but the bow fell away again and suddenly it ran forward of its own accord. With a thud it came to rest on the tube stops.

Mulholland, with Wells shouting in his ear, struggled to unship the tackle from the tail of the torpedo. It seemed to be jammed. He tore at the stiff, unyielding wire rope. Blood suddenly welled from his hand as a frayed strand from the rope ripped open the skin. The sight lent desperation to his movements. In a moment he had freed the wire rope and with an oath flung it aside. Wells pounced on the rear door of the tube, swinging it shut with a clang.

The monster was safely imprisoned.

Titt, still trembling with fear, moved over to Moore, who was standing by the empty torpedo rack, rubbing his back.

"You okay, Pony?" he asked, making an effort to control his voice.

Moore's mouth twisted angrily. He nodded briefly without speaking.

"Did you hurt yourself?" Titt asked again.

Moore's lips curled again. "I'll live," he said curtly. Limping slightly, he turned away and walked aft.

Wells came over to Titt. He grabbed him by the arm. "Leave him, Tom. He'll be all right. We'll have a break for five minutes before we start clearing this lot up."

The crew didn't wait to be told again. With relief they squatted down where they could and began lighting up. No one spoke. They were too tired and still in the grip of shock caused by the near disaster.

Joyner, who was the torpedo officer, had remained in the background during the whole of the loading operation. He now frowned heavily. As officer in charge he resented the T.G.M.'s allowing a break without first asking permission, but he lacked the courage to challenge Wells directly. He said nothing but looked at his watch, noting the time carefully. Precisely to the second, five minutes later, he coughed meaningly. The sound was magnified in the dull quiet of the fore-ends as all eyes turned in his direction.

Joyner drew himself up nervously. His finger tapped the dial of his wristwatch. "Five minutes, T.G.M.—time's up."

The sound of someone licking the edge of a cigarette paper could have been heard. Wells stood for a moment rubbing the stubble on his chin. He looked at Joyner with scarcely disguised contempt. The crew removed their cigarettes from their mouths and waited for the explosion. Joyner's features began to color under the steady gaze of the T.G.M.

Wells spoke eventually. He measured out each word. "We're finished loading," he said in a wintry voice. "I think you can make your report to the first lieutenant now."

Joyner bit his thin lips. Inwardly his heart pounded with rage. He felt like screaming at the T.G.M. for daring to speak as he had. His fists clenched and unclenched. Struggling to control his voice, he said stiffly, "Very well, T.G.M.," conscious, even as he spoke, of the weakness of his reply. The ring of white stupid faces seemed to press in on him like a gathering of mocking clowns. Feebly he attempted to assert some of his vanished dignity and authority.

"You'll carry on clearing up," he said, trying to make it sound like an order.

Wells looked at him disdainfully, not bothering to reply.

Turning quickly on his heel, Joyner nearly ran from the fore-ends.

"What a right stupid, crummy bastard he is," Mulholland said when he'd gone.

Moore stuck his fag back in his mouth. He grunted sourly. "What do you expect? They're all bastards, aren't they? The whole shower of them. Pigs—that's all they are. Pigs!" He spat the words out.

"Yeah, but that one's not only a bastard but he's an inefficient bastard and they're the worst," Mulholland replied.

Stanley gave a whoop at this. "Inefficient?" he repeated. "Joyner doesn't even know his arse from a hot rock."

There was a faint ripple of laughter.

Wells didn't want the situation to get out of hand. He wasn't supposed to allow the hands to criticize the officers.

"Okay, lads," he said. "You've had your fun. Now let's get on with it, eh, and get this lot cleared up or we'll still be at it by the time we get back to Holy Loch."

There was a muttering of protests, but the crew got to their feet, shuffling around aimlessly before turning to. The compartment looked as if it had been swept by a hurricane. The atmosphere was thicker than ever with the smell of sweat and shale oil. Wearily they began stripping down the loading rails, handling the heavy bars carefully as the boat pitched and rolled wildly. Some of them stowed away the tools and loading gear and others began a general cleanup. Oil and grease covered everything, and with each movement of the heaving deck, water spilled out of the scuppers and ran about freely.

When they had got the fore-ends half cleared, someone began passing the hammocks back through from the passageway where they had been stored.

"Don't sling them up, lads," warned Titt as he saw what was happening.

The hands stopped. "Why not?" they protested in unison.

"Because the tiffys are going to be here any minute now to have a look at the foreplanes, that's why not," Titt explained. "There's no good in slinging your hammocks if you're only going to have to take them down again."

"Bollocks," swore Big Jock Corr, dropping his hammock on the wet deck. "I suppose that means we're not gonna be able to rig the messdeck table either?"

"Not until the tiffys are finished, you're not, Jock," Titt said.

Corr sat down heavily on an old tea chest. "That's just great, that is. Can't sling our 'mocks, can't rig the table. What are we supposed to do? Sleep and eat standing up? This bloody lot's beginning to get on my wick." He glared angrily around him.

Wells slipped quietly out of the fore-ends. It was Titt's pigeon. He'd have to sort it out himself.

The coxswain was in the P.O.'s' mess. Wells flopped down

on the locker bench and cradled his head in his hands. He felt very old and tired. At first he didn't hear Blow speaking to him.

"I said, are you finished in the fore-ends, Billy?" the coxswain asked for the second time.

Wells removed his hands from his head and looked up. "Finished? You can say that again. I'm bloody near all in."

"How did it go?" Blow asked, unconsciously shifting his glance to the calendar swinging on the bulkhead. "A bit rough, eh?"

"Rough?" the T.G.M. snorted. "I'll say it was rough. The last bloody kipper near came adrift. Talk about panic stations. I near shit myself. The bastarding thing was about out on top of us. Jesus, you'll never believe how close that was. I tell you I wouldn't want to do that again for all the crumpet in Kowloon."

Blow got to his feet, eyeing him for a minute. "Hmmm. I see," he mused, squaring off the lapels of his jacket. "Well, I'd better get along and tell Dinsdale. He'll be waiting to get his gang cracking on the foreplanes. He's been screaming at me every ten minutes since you started loading."

Wells tossed his head. "Has he? Well, I can tell you, him and his mob are not going to be very popular with the lads if he's going to start mucking about in the fore-ends now. They've just about had their lot."

Blow frowned and pulled at his ear. "Well, it's still got to be done. I know what you mean, but—" He shrugged. "I'm sorry. The lads'll just have to grin and bear it. The quicker it's done the sooner it's over."

Wells seemed to lose interest in the matter. He glanced away and suddenly caught sight of the sleeping figure of Mitchell, who lay in Bain's bunk. He jerked his thumb upward. "What's happening to him? It'll be hours before the fore-ends is cleared up. What are you going to do with him?"

"Well," Blow said, "I was thinking of keeping him in here for a bit, as a matter of fact. It'll be a bit of a squeeze, but we'll manage somehow. You don't mind, do you?"

Wells ran his fingers through his hair. "Me? I don't mind.

He'll be a bloody sight better off in here than he would be out there."

Blow patted down his jacket. "Well, in that case I'll get along and see Dinsdale and tell him he can get cracking." He picked up his cap and gave a final pull at the lapels of his jacket.

He caught up with the engineer officer in the engine room and told him that the torpedo loading was completed. Dinsdale rounded up the chief E.R.A. and a couple of stokers. Blow stood for a moment as he watched the little group, armed with tools, vanish at the double. Then he made his way back, first calling in at the wardroom.

The first lieutenant was awake and lay reading in his bunk. Joyner, the only other occupant of the wardroom, was already fast asleep. Brangwyn swung his legs out of his bunk at the sound of Blow's knock. "Come in," he said, stifling a yawn as he clambered down onto the deck. The coxswain pushed his way through the curtain and waited patiently while the first lieutenant searched for his shoes. He found them underneath the table. He slipped them on and sat up erect.

"Well, you'll be glad that that's all over, coxswain."

"I think everyone's glad, sir," Blow said evenly.

Brangwyn detected the acid note in his voice. His head came up sharply. "I've no doubt they are, coxswain—I've no doubt they are," he repeated, annoyed by the coxswain's tone. A pause followed. "You wanted to see me about something, coxswain?"

Blow clasped his hands behind him. "Yes, there was, sir. I thought we might—under the circumstances—issue an extra ration of rum to the hands, sir. They've all been hard at it and I think they deserve it."

Brangwyn rubbed his hand over his face, frowning. "An extra ration of rum, coxswain? Under what circumstances?" He pouted his lips and looked severe. "You know it's never been my practice to issue extra rum without due reason. I don't quite follow. I know the men have been working hard and no doubt they are tired, but once we start this sort of thing we'll be issuing rum every time they have more to do than usual. No,

I'm against it, coxswain. And I'm sure the captain would be too. . . . I'm sorry, but I can see no reason that would justify an extra rum issue."

"But, sir—" Blow began and stopped. "Very well, sir. Permission to serve spirits as usual."

Brangwyn inclined his head coolly. "Certainly, coxswain. Carry on."

Bottling up his anger, Blow turned, and sweeping aside the wardroom curtain, he stalked out into the passageway. He was livid. There weren't many occasions when he asked favors for the crew, but when he did ask them he expected them to be granted. It was one of the privileges of his position. Brangwyn's refusal was a near insult. Coxswains generally didn't ask for things and get refused.

Wells noticed the angry look as Blow came into the P.O.'s' mess. Not often did the coxswain allow his anger to show as it was showing now. The T.G.M. had another look and decided not to ask any questions. He had no desire to be told to mind his own business.

Meantime, Dinsdale and his crew had descended on the fore-ends. When Mulholland saw them enter with their bags of tools and looking as if they were about to take over, he flung down the tin of shale oil and rags he was using to clean up the deck. "That's it," he muttered. "That's my lot. I'm not doing any more if that crowd's buggering about in here."

The rest of the men looked at Titt. He was the senior hand and their spokesman in all matters connected with higher authority. They knew the planes had to be repaired, but they resented the way the engineer officer had just marched in as if it were no concern to the men who lived in the fore-ends. They couldn't help thinking what would have happened to them if they had trooped into the wardroom without a by-your-leave. So they looked at Titt, knowing that he couldn't do anything but hoping he would try anyway.

Titt resented the situation as much as any of them. He also felt that Dinsdale might have said something, made some sort of apology. The engineer officer, unaware of the feelings he had aroused, wasted no time but straightaway jumped up on a packing case and began his inspection of the deckhead where the foreplanes actuating ram was housed. Standing on tiptoes and flashing his torch about, he was wholly engrossed in what he was doing.

Titt approached him. The hands stopped what they were doing and watched.

"Excuse me, sir?" Titt had to repeat the question.

"What do you want? Can't you see I'm busy?" Dinsdale spoke over his shoulder, his voice muffled.

"We just wondered how long you're likely to be, sir. Is it going to take long to fix it?"

The torch was lowered slowly. The raised heels regained the packing case. Dinsdale turned slowly around and looked down at Titt. "What did you say?" he asked in an awesome tone.

"I asked if you could give us any idea how long you're likely to be, sir. I mean—"

"You what?" Dinsdale had a look on his face like that of a man stabbed in the back while having dinner. In a voice dripping with venom Dinsdale said: "Hadn't you better get on with what you are supposed to be doing? I'm sure you've plenty to do in here without bothering me with your questions."

Titt's mouth came down in a firm line; his jaw stiffened. "I only asked, sir, because we'll be having dinner soon and—"

Dinsdale nearly fell off the packing case. "I'm not the least interested in your reasons," he shrilled. "I suggest you get on with your job—whatever that is!" Turning to the chief engine-room artificer, Lithgow, who had come in with him, he said with an air of finality, "Chief, see that I'm not disturbed again, will you?" He took a deep breath and returned to his inspection of the planes.

Lithgow looked appealingly at Titt, who was standing with a wild look on his face, his fists balled. "Take it easy, Tom," he whispered. "Take it easy."

Titt bottled his anger and turned away. There was nothing he could do. One of the gods had spoken. He glared at the hands. For a moment he hated the very sight of them and their stupid silent faces. He couldn't see that in their mute expressions they were thanking him for having tried. He felt like shouting at them: *All right, you dumb bastards, just don't stand there like sheep. Say something. Back me up. We don't have to take this if we don't want to. Where's your bloody guts, you worthless lot?* But he didn't. They knew, just as much as he did, how hopeless it was. The Navy had been run like this for hundreds of years, and it wasn't going to change now just because a handful of men were tired and wanted to eat.

His shoulders dropped their aggressive hunch and his fists unclenched. "All right, lads," he said. "Let's get on with it. Come on, then, don't look so miserable—you won't be in the bloody Navy for the rest of your days."

Lithgow looked at him warningly, but the revolutionary feeling of the hands had fizzled out.

Dejectedly they turned to again, mumbling among themselves. Mulholland picked up his rag and the tin of shale oil and began wiping the deck again. Others began restacking stores and putting tools away. The fore-ends seemed to be in a greater shambles than ever, now that the last of the spirit had gone out of the men. A bag of flour had burst open, spilling its powdery contents. Oil and water slopped about. Boxes piled up kept falling over, and tins clattered noisily, racing about the deck like clockwork toys. The men's movements were listless. They no longer seemed to care what happened.

A half hour passed. Rice, just off watch, appeared in the doorway. The coxswain had told him to tell Titt that the rum was up. In his thin, quavering, southern counties voice he called out: "Up spirits!" Stanley gave the traditional answer.

"Stand fast the Holy Ghost," he yelled at the top of his voice.

Immediately everyone downed tools.

Titt knew better than to crack the whip. "Up spirits" was a near-sacred call. He prodded Stanley. "Well, what are you waiting for? Seeing you're so eager, go and get it—and chop-chop, we could all do with our tots."

Stanley grinned impishly. "Yes, chief. Three bags full, chief." He was off out of the mess like a shot.

Not long after he had gone, Dinsdale and the chief E.R.A. left, leaving only the two stokers working on the planes. The intricate machinery had been stripped down and lay around the fore-ends in bits and pieces.

Stanley was back again in a few minutes. His face was split in a broad smile from ear to ear. He ran his tongue around his lips as he held up the metal container with the mess's rum issue safely inside. Cups and mugs had been laid out on a couple of upturned tea chests. Titt took charge of the operation, balancing himself against the roll of the boat as he shared out the rum. The men seized the mugs gratefully. The rum cheered and warmed bodies that had run low on physical and mental reserves. Heaving and hauling for hours in the pitching compartment and constantly exposed to the dangers of a torpedo breaking loose, they were like soldiers returned from the front line. But it was only a temporary relief. Some of them would be going on watch soon. For the next two hours they would be up on the ice-cold bridge with the wind and water chilling them to the bone, or gazing heavy-eyed at the reeling compass strip as they struggled to keep the submarine on course. Those going on watch would be lucky if they got a hot meal, and for all they knew there would be no place to sleep when they came back off again. It might be hours yet before they could sling their hammocks. Longingly they looked at the stiff, wet, canvas sacks.

Squatting down, they sipped their rum. They were fairly quiet, and when they spoke at all it was in low monotones. Only the irrepressible Stanley showed signs of life. Hoisting his mug he began to sing: "If your drip tin's running over borrow mine. . . ."

A few of the men grinned weakly, but no one joined Stanley in the sailor's traditional song of protest.

Titt was the first to get to his feet. He put his empty mug down and scratched his chest. From the direction of the galley came the strong smell of cooking. They were all ravenous, having had nothing all day but lukewarm tea and damp sandwiches. Titt decided to go and see how long the meal would be. Outside the P.O.'s' mess he bumped into the coxswain.

"How's it going up forward?" Blow asked immediately.

"Well, that's what I came to see you about. It looks as if the engineers will be hours yet. I was thinking we might as well have the grub when it's ready. It'll be long enough before we get cleared up."

Blow rubbed his chin. "Hmmm. It's up to you, Tom, but it'll be a bit of a circus if they're still working there, won't it?"

Titt shrugged. "I know, but we're all starving. I think we should have it when it's ready."

"Okay, Tom. Let's go and see how Steve's getting on."

The two men walked aft toward the galley. The smell of the food nearly drove Titt crazy. Donahue, red-faced, his shirt clinging to his back with sweat, turned at their approach. A pile of empty tins spilled over the gash buckets in the galley.

"How long, Steve?" asked the coxswain.

Donahue mopped the sweat from his streaming face. "Ten minutes, 'swain. Yeah, about ten minutes. It'd been ready sooner but half the galley's out of action—those bastards knocked it for six." He spoke as if the Germans had broken the rules of war by damaging his equipment.

Titt grinned. Donahue caught the look, and his expression became almost that of a child resenting some adult outrage. "Well—" he protested. But Blow patted him on the back.

"Good, Steve. We'll say ten—no, fifteen—minutes, then. Okay?"

Donahue, not looking at Titt, still had the same look of indignation on his face. "I said ten minutes, 'swain. It'll be ready in ten minutes," he mumbled in a piqued voice.

Blow and Titt exchanged looks. They both grinned behind the chef's back, enjoying for a moment the relief of humor.

A chorus of welcome shouts greeted Titt when he reentered the fore-ends.

"What's on the menu, Torn?"

"How long's it gonna be?"

"What's the bastard serving up this time?"

Titt waved his hands. "All right, all right. One at a time. . . ." He waited till the noise had died down.

"Okay, then, if you want to know, it's steak and kidney pud and—"

"What's for afters?" somebody interjected eagerly.

"Hold on, I was just coming to that—there's steamed rice and raisins to follow."

Stanley gave a whoop and slapped his thigh. "Old cardboard and cat's meat and Chinese wedding cake. Goodo." He cut a couple of steps and began to sing again. Titt waited ten minutes and sent Moore and Renwick to get the food. Soon they reappeared with the steaming trays. The rest of the hands had done their best to clear out a space at the rear of the compartment. Plates and cutlery were produced. Titt, assisted by Big Jock Corr, ladled out the food, and the plates were passed round. A few of the lucky ones were able to get some place to sit but most of them had to stand.

Titt found himself jammed in against the bulkhead door next to Moore.

He scooped the food into his mouth with a spoon and wondered what it must have been like for his old man back in the last war. As a boy he'd seen pictures of the battlefields. He remembered the cheering Tommies giving the thumbs-up sign and waving their caps. He'd gobbled up the stories of the glory and heroism, stories enlarged upon by adult relatives who'd never been at the front or who had forgotten what it was really like and could only recall the comradeship. But his own father had seldom spoken about it. When he did, it was slowly and haltingly and with the breath going in and out of his ruined lungs like the sound of a punctured bellows. The prematurely old man would search for the words, but he never got very far; the strain on his respiratory system was too great. A simple everyday thing like speech was something that he'd left behind him on the battlefields of France.

Young Titt at that time saw only the excitement and the glamour. With a heartfelt, youthful devotion, he had sworn to himself that when he grew up and it came his turn he would fight for King and country like one of the ancient knights of the round table. But not in the Army. He was going to be a fighter pilot.

When he did grow up he joined the Navy—but it was to fight for a living. Economics, not heroics, determined his actions. There was no work to be had, and his father's small pension was barely capable of supporting two aging people, let alone a lusty young man. Titt, on a visit to Bristol to look for a job, saw the poster in the window of the naval recruiting office and was immediately attracted. The bronzed healthy sailor, looking as smart as paint against the background of the fleet at anchorage in some foreign port, appealed directly to him. It looked a clean, healthy and adventurous life. He'd stared at the poster for a long time before going inside to see the Sergeant of Marines. The sergeant assured him it was a clean, healthy and adventurous life. Just the thing for a young man.

His mother had protested weakly when he told her he'd joined up, but his father had said nothing, just looked at him with a kind of sadness, his unnaturally big eyes seeming even bigger.

Titt grinned bitterly to himself.

A clean, healthy, exciting life. That's what the sergeant had said. It was like some kind of evil joke when you thought about it. A sort of white-slave traffic encouraged and endorsed by state and church. Perhaps it was different for the lads who had joined up for the war. Maybe it had some meaning for them, some purpose. But the peacetime sailor had been press-ganged every bit as much as his forebears had been in the time of Nelson. Only the methods were different. Unemployment had been the cudgel, and glossy propaganda was used to soften the blow.

A clean, healthy, exciting life? He wondered where that Sergeant of Marines was now. Probably propping up some barracks and still writing out chits to send others into the fray. Still there was one thing about being in submarines. They mightn't be clean and healthy, but nobody could say they hadn't their moments of excitement. And when it came to it you weren't likely to get your leg or your arm shot off and you weren't going to get your lungs full of mustard gas. The submarine service didn't, like the other services, produce its quota of cripples and half men to be sent back into civvy street to rot away someplace out of sight. It was an all-or-nothing-at-all kind of arrangement.

You either got out in one piece or you didn't.

He turned to face Moore. The dark-faced seaman had his feet spread wide apart to balance himself against the heaving deck. His plate was held close to his mouth as if he was scared of losing any of the hot food.

Titt eyed the gypsylike face carefully. "How's the back?" he asked.

Moore gulped down another spoonful of food. He wiped his mouth with the sleeve of his greasy overalls. " 'S'okay," he muttered, his heavy jaws still working.

Titt cleaned his own plate with a piece of bread. "That was a pretty close call you had back there."

Moore grunted, still eating.

"If that rope end had caught you on the head it would have taken your eyes out."

Moore put his plate down, dropping it in a bucket of greasy tepid water. He straightened up. "Bloody mad set of bastards. Couldn't wait till we were dived. Oh, no. We had to have a kipper up the spout in case the skipper might miss the chance of another Jerry." His dark features twisted. "What's the matter with the bastard? He'll get his D.S.O. for sinking the U-boat. What more does he want—a pile of the bloody things?"

Stanley was within earshot. He sauntered over, attracted by Moore's sounding off.

"What's that you said about medals, Pony? Ah, you don't want to say that about medals. Medals are the thing these days."

Moore grimaced sourly. He was in no mood for Stanley's humor. "Piss off," he said bluntly.

Unperturbed, the bantam seaman went on. "Talking about medals, did you hear that one about the R.A.F. geezer that goes up to the Palace?"

Moore glared at him hostilely, but Titt chipped in. "Okay," he said, "let's have it, but it'd better be good. I'm not in the mood for bursting my sides, either."

Stanley's eyes rounded. "Oh, it's not funny, or anything like that. It's a true story—"

"Get on with it, you little bastard," warned Titt.

Stanley drew in his breath. "Well, you see, it's like this. This Raf type goes up to the Palace for a gong. He's standing there all attention like and the King comes up to him and says: 'Congratulations, f-f-flying officer. I hear you shot down a F-f-focke-Wulf?' The bloke answers straightaway: 'It was actually two Focke-Wulfs, Your Majesty.' And the King says: 'N-n-never mind that, you only get one f-f-fucken m-m-medal just the same.' "

Titt threw back his head and roared. Where did the comical little bastard get them?

Moore glowered. There were times when Stanley got on his nerves, and this was one of the times. You'd think the whole thing was nothing but a great big joke. "Why don't you get lost, Stanley?" he said. "Somebody should put a stop to your tot. That might cut your cackle."

Stanley drained his face of expression. He came to a position of attention and, putting his head to the side, flicked his hand in a salute. "Yes, chief. Three bags full, chief. Getting lost, chief." He made a smart about-turn and stumbled over the outstretched legs of Renwick, who was sitting down on one of the hammocks. The others pushed at him as they indulged in a bit of horseplay. Reeling about, Stanley spun forward to land on his back at the far end of the compartment. He got up still grinning.

Moore shook his head grimly. "*I* don't know," he said. "That's another one that should be locked up. Him and Cadbury'd make a right pair. They want to stick them together in one of those two-man submarines. They could spend their whole time laughing at one another telling jokes."

"Oh, come off it, Pony," Titt remonstrated. "What's up with

you? The little bugger's only having a bit of a skylark. Christ, we could do with more like him."

Moore made an unintelligible sound expressing his disgust. Someone handed him a plate of rice, but he refused it, saying that he was going aft to get a smoke and away from the madhouse.

Big Jock Corr, who was dishing out the rice, asked Titt: "What's up with him, then? Has he gone off his food?"

"Oh, let him be. He's chokker, that's all." Titt took the plate of rice that Corr offered.

Corr leaned up against the bulkhead. "Chokker, is he? Who's no'," he said. "We're all bloody chokker o' this outfit." The two men began eating their rice. Spooning the thick, gluey substance from his plate, Corr happened to drop some on the deck. The big seaman looked down at his feet. The rice, floating about in a pool of water, began to break up into separate grains, staining the dirty water a grayish white. Corr waved his spoon about. "It's a right old bluddy mess, i'n't it, Tom?" His spoon pointed in the direction of the foreplanes machinery that was strewn around. "Are they lot going to be working here for the rest of the patrol, that's what Ah'm asking. If so, somebody better let on, 'cause Ah'm no' staying if they are. It's beginning to gi'e me the boke."

Titt glanced at the pockmarked face amusedly. He finished off his rice. "Where were you thinking of going, Jock? Fancy a run ashore in Norway? It's a long swim if you do."

"Norway, Sweden, Russia, if it comes to it. Anyplace to get out of this lot. It gives me the shits," Corr said, licking his plate.

A voice suddenly piped up from behind: "What gives you the shits, Jock—Norway?" Stanley had come back.

Corr turned round, eyeing Stanley narrowly above the rim of his plate. "You give me the shits, for a start," he said.

"I know a bloke that was in Norway once, said it was a great place. No boozers, but loads of crumpet all flinging themselves about. I think I'll go there myself one of these days," Stanley went on as if Jock hadn't spoken.

"You, you bastard," Corr choked. "They wouldn't let you near the place."

"Yes, they would," Stanley replied confidently. "Anyway, it's a bloody sight better place than Haggisland, so what are *you* on about?" Stanley knew how Big Jock felt about his homeland and never lost the chance to rib him about it. Corr rose to the bait.

"Hey, watch it, mate. There's nothing a matter wi' Scotland. I don't see you staying aboard when we're in Dunoon."

"Dunoon?" Stanley howled. "I tell you there's only one place worse than Dunoon."

"Where?" Corr asked suspiciously.

"Oldham!" exclaimed Stanley triumphantly.

"Where? What was that?" Corr looked baffled. "Ah thought you said you came from Oldham."

"So I do," Stanley said firmly. From the corner of his eye he saw Moore coming back through the bulkhead door. "I'm telling you next to Bolton, Oldham's the worst place on God's earth, and that's a fact. If you don't believe me ask Pony, he'll tell you. Bloody awful place that Bolton, all factories and crawling with Yanks an' all."

Moore shoved his way past Corr and found a corner to sit down in. Why the hell couldn't they just leave him alone? Always babbling on about something or other. Corr was getting nearly as bad as Stanley. What the hell did he care for Bolton or any other place? He just happened to be born there, and if he never saw the place again he wouldn't worry. Bolton was just another big ugly city. England was full of them. Big ugly cities and all crawling with Yanks. They were right though, he thought. The U.K. was beginning to look like one big service camp for G.I. Joe. Well, let them have the bloody place. He'd nothing against the Americans—except that their pockets were stuffed with dollars, or whatever it was they used for money. Yeah, stuffed with money and their tunics bulging with rations . . . or silk stockings . . . or soap . . . or lipstick . . . or any other bloody thing that would get the women flocking around them. Not that *they* needed much encouragement from what he'd seen, flinging themselves at the G.I.'s in an ecstasy of whoredom.

Christ! The thought suddenly struck him—Alice.

What a fool he'd been. So that's what she'd been up to. And all the time he'd kidded himself she was the one who was different from the others. No wonder she said she was too tired to write these days. The Yanks would see to that. Long hours in the factory? That was a good one. Long hours of whooping it up in the camps more like. Christ, what a bloody fool. He'd thought there was something strange about her last letter. Something had been missing somewhere. So that's what it was. Here he was knocking his bloody pan in, and she was whoring it up back home. Christ, just wait till he got his hands on her, the bitch. He'd make Alice Bingham regret the day she'd ever been born.

Moore's face had gradually become more contorted as the wild thoughts ran through his head. He stared about him without seeing. His fists were clenched tightly, and his shoulders rose and fell as his anger placed more demands for oxygen on his lungs.

Titt, watching him out of the corner of his eye, frowned. It was clear that something was bothering Moore. His behavior had become odd recently. Little things, but all added up they amounted to something. It wasn't just the bad temper. They all suffered from that at times. There were moments at sea when it was quite possible to hate your best friends. You learned to live with it. He'd have to keep a close watch on Moore. A man with something deep troubling him inside could be a source of danger. So many things could go wrong on a submarine. Carelessness was something you had to guard against. One single foolish act and they could all be in it. Every submariner knew this. It had been drilled into him constantly, this need for vigilance.

"Do you not think so, Tom?" the voice rose and fell in the unmistakable singsong accents of Big Corr.

"Eh?" Titt's stream of thought died away as the voice caught his attention. "Eh? What was that you said, Jock?"

"Ah was saying about Poney, do you no' think he's acting kinda funny these days?" Corr repeated.

"Oh, Pony? Well—I don't know—he's okay, I suppose. Just a bit cheesed, that's all," he answered glibly. So Corr had noticed it too. He wondered if any of the others had.

"Mebbe Cadbury bent his ear when he went along to the control room for a smoke. That's enough to send anyone off. Yon bloody steward gives me the creeps. Somebody wants to ditch him overboard wi' the gash one of these nights. You know what he was trying to tell me the other—"

"Hold it," Titt butted in. "Gash? What am I thinking about? I knew there was something I had to ask the 'swain. That's it—the gash. Good. Thanks for reminding me, Jock. You can start collecting the buckets when I'm away. We'll ditch it all tonight."

"Oh, no!" Corr groaned and hit himself on the forehead with the heel of his palm. "Why didn't I keep mah big mouth shut? uuugh!"

"Come on now, Jock. Just look at those buckets. Here," he addressed the crew generally, "rise and shine, you lot. Get all the buckets together, will you? We're going to ditch the gash. I'll go and see the 'swain and see if we can get permission. And stop moaning. If we don't get rid of it now we'll soon be sleeping on the bloody stuff, so let's be having you."

Protestingly the men got to their feet. Nobody wanted to ditch gash. They were all dirty and unwashed, but somehow the thought of the gash reminded them of how filthy they were. The buckets, which they all looked at now, were brimming over with all sorts of refuse—a putrefying mass which gave off a strong, unpleasant odor.

"Why the hell can't we put the stuff in the tubes and blow it overboard?" asked someone half seriously.

Corr looked at the man disdainfully. "You've been seeing too many pictures about submarines, you have. And another thing, even if we could, what would we do with the kippers we've just spent the whole bastarding day loading into the tubes, you boneheaded goon."

"I was only—" the young seaman began to protest.

"Ah, shurrup," said Corr. "Let's get on wi' it, eh?"

They crowded around and began dragging the buckets out and forming them into some sort of order.

"What do you bet the skipper doesn't give his permission to ditch it?" Renwick ventured hopefully.

A look of infinite disgust came to Corr's features. "An' how no'?" he asked. "What's he gonna have against it?"

"Well," said Renwick, "he won't want all that muck floating about the hoggin to tell the Jerries where we are, will he?"

Corr looked at him pityingly. "You know, son, you're a real genius, you are. What do you think those destroyers are looking for—Moby bloody Dick? You're a right thickheaded lot, aren't you, firing gash out o' torpedo tubes—trying to kid on that the Jerries don't know we're here. You blokes want to see a 'trick-cyclist' when we get back." He bent down, grabbing the handles of one of the buckets. "Come on, let's get the bloody thing done."

Titt returned in a few minutes. "Okay, lads," he said. "Get all the buckets along in the control room. You, Raggy—and Jock—stack them up at the foot of the conning tower. Let's get weaving."

When the last bucket had been passed up the tower Titt detailed off a couple of the hands to go forward and make tea. The large metal container was sending up sweet-smelling clouds of steam when the gash party returned to the fore-ends. Eagerly they crowded in, fondling the heavy mugs in their bloodless hands. The engineers had reassembled the foreplanes and were running the motor through tests. Mulholland and those not on the gash-ditching squad had dragged the messtable out and rigged it up in the center of the compartment. It had the effect of restoring an air of homeliness to the fore-ends. The compartment was no longer just a seagoing workshop. The crew pulled up the locker benches and gathered around the table like a swarm of bees.

Titt had just managed to sit down and was sipping his tea

slowly when Monkhouse, the P.O.'s' messman, poked his head into the compartment. "Coxswain wants to see you, Tom," he sang out.

Titt put down his mug with an expression of disgust. "What does he want now?"

Monkhouse shrugged his shoulders. "Search me, Tom. He just said he wanted to see you, that's all."

Titt got up from the table, pushing his way through the mass of bodies.

Blow was waiting for him.

"Come in, Tom," he said as Titt appeared. "What I wanted to see you about was Mitchell."

"Oh?" Titt glanced up in the direction of the bunk where Mitchell lay. He'd forgotten all about the sick seaman.

"Yes," Blow went on. "I was thinking we might keep him in here for a few days. See how he gets on. . . ."

"Well—it's up to you, 'swain. He'd be a lot better off in here, there's no doubt about that. The lads try to keep an eye on him, but you know what it's like up forward," Titt said in a mollified tone.

"Of course, Tom. I know what you mean. Right, we'll do that, then. We'll hang onto him for a bit and see how he gets on. It'll make a bit more room for your blokes."

Titt glanced at the bunk again. "How's he doing, anyway? What's up with him?"

Blow stroked his smooth chin. "Mmmmm. Well, I'm not all that sure, to tell you the truth. He's still feeling sick and he's got a pain in his gut. We'll just have to wait and see."

He got to his feet. "How's Rice, by the way? You've had no more trouble, have you?"

"Trouble?" Titt gave a wry laugh. "No, we haven't had any more trouble. Not what you mean anyway."

"Send him along, will you, Tom? I want to have another look at him." He averted his gaze as he spoke.

Titt nodded dully. "Okay, 'swain. He's probably having a cup of char at the minute, but I'll send him along when he's done. Shouldn't be long." He pushed back the curtain and stepped out of the mess, leaving Blow gazing thoughtfully at the bulkhead.

Just about this time Cheney had asked the first lieutenant along to his cabin. Cadbury, going into the wardroom to collect the coffee cups, saw that only Robinson was there. He appeared to be dozing at the table. Cadbury scratched his head. Joyner had the watch, and there was no one in the officers' heads. That meant only one thing: the first lieutenant had to be with the captain. Cadbury dumped the cups in the pantry and skipped along the passageway. Sure enough, from behind the door of the captain's cabin came the muffled sound of voices. Before he had time to bend down and get his ear to the paneling the door was flung open and Brangwyn came bowling out, his face flushed. He looked upset and brushed past the steward apparently without seeing him. Cadbury waited a minute and bolted back to the pantry. When Bain came off watch a few minutes later, he caught sight of the steward doing what seemed to be a little jig as he dried the cups.

Bain was still shaking his head amusedly as he entered his own mess.

Blow, who was seated at the table, said nothing but looked up questioningly.

Bain gave a short laugh. "You'll never believe it, but I've just seen that bugger Cadbury doing an eightsome reel all on his own in the pantry—he must be right off his nut."

"Oh, *him*," Blow growled.

About to hang up his duffel coat, Bain spotted the recumbent figure of Mitchell in his bunk.

Blow intercepted the glance. "I meant to tell you, Jock. I want to keep him in here for a few days and see how he gets on. You don't mind, do you? I've seen some of the others—you can share bunks about."

"No, that's all right. I don't mind. It won't be the first time I've had to use a hot bunk, you know."

Both men turned at the sound of the curtain runners sliding over the brass rail. Bissel came in. His long, lean face was drawn, and there were heavy blue shadows under his eyes. He flung his cap into the far corner of the mess and leaned forward on the table, breathing heavily. "I'm just about shagged out, I am," he said finally, sinking down onto the bench locker.

"I'll get Monkhouse to make a pot of char," Blow offered.

"Tea? You old sod. It's the bottle you should be getting out. God, what I wouldn't give for a pint of mild and bitter." Bissel rubbed his tired eyes. "That was a bloody good job the Jerries done on us. They've just about smashed everything up that was worth smashing. You know something?" He raised his hand to his forehead, kneading the loose skin. "I'm beginning to take a real dislike to those squarehead bastards."

"How's the gyro, Perce? You got that working, I hope?" asked Bain.

Bissel shot him a look of suffering. "Don't talk to me about that bleeding thing. I had to strip it all the way down and then put it all back up again. That's you lot to blame. Call yourself sailors. Why can't you steer the ship by ordinary compass—or have you forgotten how? Sailors?" he snorted, his big arms flapping about loosely.

"Keep it down, Perce," warned the coxswain, jerking his thumb in the direction of Mitchell. "You'll wake him up."

Bissel twisted around. "Wake who up?"

"I told you before. I'm keeping Mitchell in here under observation for a few days."

"Oh, Gawd," Bissel groaned, "the poor bastard will never get better if he's got to stay in here with you lot. If I still had a hammock I'd move into his place in the fore-ends."

"Like hell, you would," said Bain scathingly. "One day out there in the bearpit and you'd be back here screaming for help."

Bissel gave an anguished moan. "How the hell did I ever get in submarines anyway? It must have been the Missus that put me up to it for the extra dough—either that or she's trying to drive me off my chump." He got up from the table. "Oh, bollocks. I'm turning in before we run out of bunks. Give me a shout when the boat's on fire, will you?" He lurched across the mess toward his bunk. In a few minutes he was stretched out, fast asleep.

Chapter Twelve

Lieutenant Brangwyn, who had the watch on deck, was in an unusual state of agitation. Raising his voice above the wind, he kept snapping at the lookouts and yelling down the voice pipe at the helmsman, warning him to watch his ship's head.

Brangwyn was still rankling from the tongue-lashing Cheney had given him about the mess in the control room. Cheney had stormed and raged, thumping his palm with clenched fist as he returned to his favorite subject: the morale and discipline of the ship's company.

Elbows hooked over the bridge capping, legs spread apart to maintain his balance, Brangwyn scanned the dull press of the surrounding blackness. The night seemed to reflect his mood as the wind stormed and howled about his head.

Despite his service-bred sense of loyalty toward his commanding officer, he found it hard to understand Cheney's attitude. The first lieutenant prided himself on being a reasonable man. He tried to look at things fairly and logically. How would he have reacted had he been in Cheney's position? It was a question difficult to answer. To Cheney the service was his whole life, and he'd been cheated of the promotion that even his fellow officers agreed he deserved. Marriage and bringing up a family could be a consolation to a man thwarted in his life's ambition, but Cheney had no children, and his marriage appeared to be one of convenience. There was always the challenge of civvy street, Brangwyn mused. He was looking forward to it himself, but then he had the family business he could get his teeth into. The Navy wasn't his life as it was Cheney's. Anyway it was impossible to imagine Cheney as a civilian. The man was a born sailor. He would be lost if he were ever to leave the sea. Yes, he supposed it was possible to see the reasons behind the bitterness and the acrimony. To fail to get a new command at this critical stage of the war could have disastrous effects on Cheney's future career. Going to the shore base at Fort Blockhouse was not going to help him at all. Still, sinking the U-boat would automatically bring an award of a D.S.O. It might just weigh the scales again in his favor. Surely he must realize that. Why then was he so unapproachable? Brangwyn had arrived back at his starting point and would have gone through the whole treadmill of his reasoning again had he not become aware of a subtle change in the night.

He lowered his glasses. Shielding his face against the wind with a mittened hand, he glanced up at the sky. The wind had torn gaps in the cloud. A dull silvery haze from the hidden moon spilled out, and a tiny needlepoint of light flickered as a lone star was revealed.

Brangwyn watched the broken scurry of the overhanging cloud anxiously. Hanging onto the bridge structure with one hand, he peered overboard. The light from the moon had become stronger. The sea, driven by the wind, was rising. He could see the white glint of the curling and breaking waves. They had been lucky. In conditions as they were now it would have been impossible to load the spare torpedoes.

At a steady six knots the submarine zigzagged her way north. Running on one engine, the battery not fully charged, she pushed her way stubbornly into the wind. Down below the crew dozed uneasily as the mass of hammocks began to sway with increasing violence. Occasionally a mess utensil would break free and clatter about the fore-ends noisily before catching up against some obstruction; then the noise would die as suddenly as it had started. The seas breaking over the casing were no more than a dull boom, like that of a distant drum. Though the wind screeched and howled, the inch-thick steel hull cut off the sound of its angry cries from the sleeping hands.

A shout, short-lived in the wind, brought Brangwyn whirling around. The starboard lookout had no need to point—the burst of light on the horizon was clearly visible. It was followed within seconds by a fresh glow. Again the light seemed to soar upward.

Brangwyn ran forward and seized the voice pipe and yelled for the captain on the bridge. Cheney arrived, breathing heavily as he fumbled with the buttons of his bridge coat.

"Looks like star shells, sir," shouted Brangwyn, pointing toward the horizon where he'd seen the glow of yellow light.

Cheney steadied himself against the periscope standards and raised his binoculars. Though he remained on the bridge a full half hour, no further lights were seen. With a curt word to Brangwyn to keep a good look out, he went down below.

Minutes after he'd gone Brangwyn glanced up at the sky again. More cloud had been ripped away by the fierce wind. He bit his lips nervously. If the sky continued to clear there would be no need for the German antisubmarine forces to use star shells to find them. Feeling ill at ease, Brangwyn wondered how many destroyers had joined in the hunt.

He jumped as a buzzing sound came from the voice pipe.

A little ashamed of his nervousness, he bent down and held his ear to the trumpet-shaped tube. Lieutenant Robinson, in the control room, requested permission to come on the bridge. The helmsman's voice sounded tinny and detached. Wearily Brangwyn gave his permission. Now that his watch had nearly ended he felt very tired. The submarine dipped her bows deeply into the mass of churning water, rolling as she broke free. Brangwyn swayed and clutched at the bridge capping. Regaining his balance he raised his night glasses to search the horizon once more. His arms felt like lead. A few seconds later he felt a tap on his shoulder. Robinson had arrived.

Brangwyn turned over the watch, warning his relief about the suspected proximity of a search force. He waited a few minutes until Robinson had settled in, then with heavy steps he made his way across to the upper hatch.

By the time he'd reached the wardroom he was absolutely exhausted. Stripping off his bridge suit and sea boots was an effort. He yawned heavily and crawled into his bunk, praying he would be able to get some sleep before the Germans showed up.

He had a strong feeling they would. It was only a question of time.

Half an hour after he'd retired, the rest of the watch changed over. Titt relieved Bain as petty officer of the watch. Renwick took over the helm. Rubbing the sleep from their eyes, both men settled down resignedly to face the long and miserable two-hour stretch in front of them. It was bitterly cold in the drafty control room. Titt was muffled up to the neck. He wore a heavy scarf and had fastened the top button of his duffel coat. Like most of the others, to help keep himself warm he wore a layer of jerseys. The top one was an emerald-green cable stitch his wife had knitted him. Wearing it comforted him and gave him a sense of security. It also helped him to remember that there was another world outside the stark brutalizing ugliness of his present one. Titt had no names for this other world, but it was a real and worthwhile thing to him. It was this conception that enabled him to keep going when he was sickened by the horror and carnage they helped to create. Deep down and hidden like the roots of a tree was his belief that the savagery and cruelty that was part of his daily life had to be suffered if the future were to have any meaning for any of them. Some day it would be all over, and he would go back to Ruth and the kids. The love and warmth she created from the depth of her serenity and wisdom would help to heal the scars and wounds. Titt thought himself lucky. Without Ruth he might have just been another beer-swilling, brothel-creeping, time-wasting service-man, his life dwindling away in a series of booze-ups in a thousand ports and pubs. A Jack-me-hearty with nothing to look forward to but a measly pension and a few stories to tell in the local. After a while the stories would become boring to the listeners and there would be nothing left but the beer. At forty-five he'd have a gut and the beginnings of an alcoholic flush on his face. He'd be living alone in a couple of rooms with only a ditty box full of fading photographs to remind him of the past glories of his youth. At least he'd been saved that. The only fear that troubled him was that something might happen to Ruth and the kids. He thanked God they were away from the bombing.

Unconsciously he slipped his hand inside his duffel coat. Underneath he could feel the jersey that was his link with home. The soft wool was warm and pliant to the touch. He wondered how many countless strands had gone into its makeup. Taken separately, one of them couldn't have held a fly captive, but cunningly woven together the soft threads had an amazingly defiant strength. There was a lesson here somewhere. It was a kind of biblical thing he was reminded of. Something about the ancient tribes bound together in a pattern that defied plague, famine and even war. It was the kind of thing he had with Ruth.

Angrily he broke off his thoughts. He jerked his hand free and thrust it into his pocket. Feelings of frustration and near despair bubbled in his mind. It wasn't good to think of Ruth when he was at sea. He'd told himself that a hundred times before. It only left him with a dull aching sensation in his chest that nothing would ease. Clenching his fists tightly, he tried hard to shut her from his mind.

The deck plunged and screwed wildly. Unprepared, he was thrown off balance and flung heavily against the for'ard periscope. It brought him back to the grim reality of his surroundings.

"Watch your ship's head," he yelled angrily at the helmsman. "Watch what you're bloody well doing, will you!"

The compass strip spun in a blur. Renwick was using full helm to correct the sudden swing away of the bows. He wandered off a full ten degrees before he was able to get back on his course.

"For Christ's sake," Titt bawled, "watch her, will you?"

Renwick mumbled protestingly as the wheel spun in his hands. The voice pipe buzzed angrily. A few feet away Titt could hear strident tones as the O.O.W. handed out a bollocking to the helmsman.

"Aye, aye, sir," replied Renwick automatically when Robinson had finished. He made a face at the voice pipe. *Aye, aye, sir. Three bags full, sir. You can go and get stuffed, sir,* he thought to himself, crouching over the wheel and grasping the spokes tightly.

Titt watched for a minute or two. Renwick was being extra careful. Titt fell into a mood of brooding silence. His head began to ache. Removing his balaclava, he ran his fingers through his stiff, sand-colored hair, massaging the scalp. It was all he needed now—a headache. With exasperation he moved over toward the foot of the conning tower. The rush of air, funneling down the narrow tower, flattened the skin against his cheekbones. He lifted his head to take deep breaths. He stood at the foot of the tower for perhaps half a minute before the violence of the draft and the bitter cold drove him away. His headache had eased a little by the time he took up his stance behind the helmsman again. He felt annoyed with himself for tearing Renwick off a strip. It was no easy task to keep a small submarine on her proper course in a heavy seaway.

After an hour at the helm you felt your eyes popping, and your arms ached. The constant effort to correct the ship's head as she yawed unexpectedly was enough to drive you near crazy. But that was submarines all over. There were a thousand things that could drive you out of your mind. You couldn't sleep, eat, sit down, stand up or walk about without effort or discomfort. Even to go to the heads was something you weighed up beforehand, and half the time you kept putting it off until you were really desperate. Going to the heads could even be dangerous. Look at that poor little bugger Kennedy. At the thought of the dead seaman and the unforgettable horror of the scene in the motor room, his mind shied away. But he couldn't help thinking of the youngster's widowed mother. What would they tell her? That her son had died gallantly in the course of duty? A teen-age hero with a bit in the local paper to mark his death. Maybe even a picture and something about his school and why he'd decided to join the Navy. The final act of hypocrisy would come later when his name would be carved in a piece of stone along with a couple of dozen others. Just one more dead hero and not even a medal from the King to thank him kindly for sacrificing his life so unselfishly. Medals? That was a laugh. Half of them would finish up in the pawnshops if they weren't made of tin. A whole chestful of them would be a fat lot of good when the brass bands stopped playing and all the heroes were back in civvies. There'd be a mad scramble for jobs. The same old lot would be fighting tooth and nail for power and privilege. Fear and envy would soon make everyone forget what the war had been about.

There would be the annual farce, of course, just to make it look as though some people did care. The old veterans from the First World War would be trotted out from soldiers' homes and there'd be kids with big bunches of flowers—but no daddies—and everyone would be dressed up in uniform or Sunday best, parading around in honor of the dead. Lords and ladies, civic officials and honorary colonels, would turn out to fill up the ranks—in front of course—some of the widows would shed a few tears and Brigadier Big-Wig would lay a wreath. After that they could all go home feeling much better for having paid tribute to "our gallant lads." If the "gallant lads" were alive and happened to be sick or couldn't get a job, well, that was their own lookout. If they wanted their share in the fun they should have got themselves killed. What did they think all the public expenditure of time and money was for—the living?

Titt produced an old pipe from his duffel coat and began sucking on it. He no longer smoked. When things got him down he gripped the stem between his teeth and chewed on it like a dog with a bone. The pipe jumping up and down in his mouth, he moved closer to Renwick, eyeing the compass strip.

Renwick sensed his nearness and without taking his eyes off the compass spoke over his shoulder. "Do's a favor, Tom. Take the wheel for a bit. I'm bursting for a slash."

Titt grunted. "You mean you want to skive off for five minutes—off you go then and don't be all night about it."

Renwick got up hurriedly from the stool and shot aft through the engine room door.

The wheel jerked in Titt's hands the moment he sat down. The strip of numerals tracked across the visor. He watched them closely, getting the feel of the helm.

015 . . . 014 . . . 013 . . . 012 . . . 011, the figures spun.

He felt the wheel kick back as he put the helm hard over. It went dead in his hands, and the markings on the strip began to reel off in the opposite direction. He swung the wheel until he could feel the rudder bite the water. The ship's head yawed over five degrees, steadied for a second and started to race back. Hampered by his heavy clothing, Titt wrestled with the wheel. He cursed softly to himself, thankful that Renwick wasn't there to witness his efforts. Any minute he expected Robinson to shout down from the bridge. But already he had began to sense the seemingly erratic behavior pattern behind the wild swinging of the bows. The next time the ship's head fell away he was ready for her and checked the movement. But he had to concentrate and work the wheel hard.

Renwick was back within five minutes and took over again.

He shot Titt a see-what-I-mean kind of look as he sat down. "She's a bugger, eh, Tom?" he remarked with a grin on his face.

Titt's lips curled. "Bugger be blowed. A half-blind, three-badge wren with rheumatics could steer this tub." He snorted contemptuously. "I don't know how you lot'd get on if you were ever caught in a real snorter."

Renwick started singing in a high-pitched nasal tone in imitation of a violin.

"Listen, mate, you're lucky you never had to steer an H-boat in the middle of the Bay in winter. Call yourself helmsman—I wouldn't put you in charge of a kid's pram," Titt said.

Renwick's smile widened as he settled himself into the chair.

Titt put his pipe back in his pocket and went over to have a look at the barometer. It was falling rapidly. They could be in for a blow. A real force-10 snorter.

"Watch her, Raggy," he said when he returned. "It looks like it's going to get worse."

Renwick nodded. "Don't worry, I'll watch the bastard. I've had enough of old shitface screaming down the voice pipe for one night."

Titt glanced up at the control room clock. "You've only another fifteen minutes to go and you can keep him company."

Renwick shivered. "It'll be bloody freezing up there tonight. I hope those fucking Jerries are not pissing about yet."

"Here, Tom," he added after a minute. "What's this buzz about the old man wanting to have a go at the boom up some bloody fiord? Have you heard?"

Titt grunted noncommittally.

"I don't know about you, but bugger that for a lark. He wants to stuff this Errol Flynn caper. The only boom I want to see is in the Holy Loch, and then it's me on that first liberty boat for Sandbank and into the nearest boozer."

"You must have spent too much time in the boozer, mate. When did you ever see a boom in the Holy Loch?"

"Well—you know what I mean. I don't care what boom it is as long as it's one of ours."

"Well, here's your big chance to get it off your chest," said Titt, glancing along the passageway. "Here's the old man coming."

Renwick sat up at the wheel.

A moment later Cheney swept into the control room. He shot Titt a glare, glanced momentarily at the helmsman and made straight for the barometer. He tapped it once or twice with his finger before crossing over to the chart table. A pool of light flooded the corner as he flipped the switch. For a long time he studied the chart. Titt watched, his curiosity aroused. The captain was busy with pencil and dividers.

Maybe the rumor that had been circulating the boat all day was right for once, thought Titt. There was a wildness about

Cheney's expression that he'd seen before. It invariably meant the captain was about to initiate some determined course of action.

Titt looked away quickly as Cheney straightened up from the table. He heard the light click out and, a second after, the sound of a foot scraping the rungs of the control room ladder.

Making sure that Renwick was on course, he nipped over to the chart table. Cheney, obligingly, hadn't replaced the canvas cover. Obviously he didn't intend to be long on the bridge. Titt switched the light on, blinking for a moment, his eyes unaccustomed to the brightness. He peered at the chart. From their last noted position a thin pencil line stabbed northward, passing the Kosters and crossing the 59th parallel to plunge toward a ring of islands. The line halted at the entrance to a channel separating the largest of the islands from its neighbors. Large sections of the area were marked with the familiar hatched lines that indicated the position of suspected minefields.

Titt put out the light. He was about to replace the cover when he remembered Cheney had left the canvas rolled back. With a quick glance to see that he had disturbed nothing he stepped away.

It looked as if the crew's latest buzz could well be right.

Cheney came back down from the bridge and walked straight to the chart table. Titt tapped Renwick on the shoulder, indicating it was time for him to get dressed. At that moment Cheney came over. Grabbing the voice pipe he hailed the bridge: "Steer 010, Robinson, no zigzag."

Both Renwick and Titt pricked up their ears as a muffled reply came from the O.O.W. Cheney swung the end of the voice pipe back toward the helmsman. "Call me in three quarters of an hour, Titt. And leave word with your relief that I want a word with the first lieutenant before he goes on watch, should I be in my cabin."

Renwick waited until he had gone, then excitedly he swung around to Titt. "Did you hear that, Tom? No bloody zigzag. What's the idea, does he want to give them a chance to get their own back or something?"

The same idea was passing through Titt's mind. Cutting out the zigzag meant they would be at the boom a lot earlier, but as Renwick suggested, they would be a sitting duck for anyone that spotted them. He gave no indication of his thoughts.

"No zigzag was the pipe, mate, and you're wandering all over the place. Here, give me the wheel. You'd better go and get dressed, anyway."

An hour later, the coxswain appeared to take over the watch from Titt.

"Anything happening, Tom?" He yawned as he rubbed the sleep out of his eyes. Some of the smoothness had gone out of his skin, and he looked a worried man.

Titt told him about the alteration of course and the cancellation of the zigzag before he passed on Cheney's message. Blow's eyebrows lifted slightly. "Hmmm. Must be in a bit of a hurry, eh? Anything else? Nothing been buggering about up top, has there?"

"Only Joyner, since he's taken over from Robinson," Titt remarked dryly.

Blow glanced at him disapprovingly. He was of the old school and always felt uncomfortable when he heard a rating criticizing an officer—even Joyner. Had it been anyone but Titt he would have admonished him on the spot. "Hmmm. I see. And there's nothing else?"

"Not a thing. Only that burst of star shells earlier, but you know about that. Mebbe they've called the hunt off and all gone back to their beds."

Blow was in no mood for humor. He turned to the two relief lookouts who were struggling into wet bridge suits. "Come on then, shake it up, the pair of you. Do you see what time it is?"

A high-pitched muffled cry came from the voice pipe. The helmsman spun around, calling over his shoulder: "Captain on the bridge!"

Titt beat the coxswain to the bulkhead doorway. Running along the passageway, he called out the message. He hadn't got more than a few yards when Cheney came tumbling out of his cabin. Titt flattened himself against the bulkhead to allow him free passage. A few seconds later, as Titt was returning to the control room, the night alarm sounded off.

The telegraphs clanged and the running charge on the battery was broken as the crew raced for their action stations. Titt felt the deck vibrate under his feet as the throttles of the diesels were opened wide. Heeling sharply, they came rapidly to port as they swung away on an opposite course.

In the fore-ends the heavy roll caused by the application of full helm dislodged the usual amount of crockery and spare gear. As Wells came hurtling through the doorway he half-tripped, half-fell over a bucket that blocked his path. Cursing savagely, he lashed out at it with his foot. It landed up against the table in the center of the fore-ends. He'd no sooner reached the tube space than the klaxon went.

At 30 feet Winch picked up an echo.

Cheney, standing by the afterperiscope, his hand gripping the hoist wire, was still breathing heavily from his mad dash up to the bridge. He arched his body in the direction of the asdic cabinet as if he were about to spring. "What does it sound like, Winch?" he snapped.

"Turbines, sir. Range closing. There's a few of them. Could be destroyers."

Cheney turned to look at the depth gauge. In accordance with standing orders on diving Brangwyn had gone to 80 feet.

"One hundred twenty feet, number one. Slow ahead both. Shut off for depth charging—they might have seen us."

Quickly the crew sprang to the heavy bulkhead doors, easing them quietly home and putting the clips on.

One hundred twenty feet.

From up top a sound was heard. Faint at first, it gradually increased in volume.

White-faced, the crew craned their heads upward as if they could see through the inch-thick steel plating. They listened.

"Range closing rapidly, sir," called Winch. "Bearing red 05."

No one needed to be told the ships were approaching. The

angry *swish, swish,* of the propellers was clearly audible now. Instinctively the crew began to crouch in anticipation of a depth charge attack.

The sound rose to a crescendo and began to fade. The men looked at each other, their tense expressions slackening to be replaced by humorless grins.

Cheney waited a full half hour after the ships had passed before surfacing. With the hunt moving to the south, it seemed his way was clear to the boom.

The crew fell out and made their way back for'ard. They surveyed the minor shambles in the fore-ends. What were a few broken cups? Wearily they climbed back into their hammocks.

Early morning found them close to the anchored boom vessel. There were no signs of activity, though occasionally a light was seen to flash high up on the rocky promontory of the island. A cold wind blew through the narrows, and the sea was stiff and choppy. No one was sorry when they dived just before dawn.

Breakfast that morning was greeted unenthusiastically. Many crew members were too tired to eat and left the meal half finished. The long night passage had produced a crop of alarms. Most of the time they had been closed up at diving stations.

"Well, if you're all done, let's get cleared up," Titt broke into the subdued conversation. "The quicker we get our heads down the better. We could be in for a busy day of it now that we're here."

There was a murmur of groans and protests. Nobody wanted to move.

"Come on," Titt chivvied them. "Finger-dinger. Let's get on with it." He stretched himself and got to his feet. Something brushed against his leg. He looked down and saw the bucket Wells had kicked forward in his mad rush. He picked it up. "What the hell's this doing here?" he said as he read the name on the side. "I thought I told—" He looked for Lacey, remembering as he did so that he'd only meant to tell him to get his gear out of the mess but somehow had never got around to it.

"Guns has relieved me for breakfast, if that's who you're looking for," Corr volunteered. "Ah'll tell him you want to see him when I get back."

"See him. I'll do the bugger, leaving his gear lying around. There's enough old garbage in here as it is," Titt said angrily, picking the bucket up and heaving it in the corner by the copper. It landed with a clang. Monkhouse, who had just stepped through the bulkhead, jumped back.

"What do you want?" Titt said as he caught sight of him. "Whatever it is, we don't have any."

Monkhouse peered around the doorway. "The 'swain would like to see you, Tom, when you have a minute."

"Would he? Well, he'll just have to wait. I'm not finished my breakfast yet." Titt sat down at the table and poured himself another cup of tea.

The hands began to clear the table. Titt waited a few minutes. Emptying his almost full cup in the slop kettle, he went off to see the coxswain.

Lacey arrived in the mess.

Renwick collared him. "Here, Guns, if I was you I'd get my gear out of here smartish like. Tom's got a real widgy on."

Lacey shook him off with a scowl. "What are you talking about? What gear?"

Renwick pointed to the corner. "That's yours, isn't it? It's got your name all over it if it isn't."

Frowning, Lacey walked over to where Renwick had pointed. An awful thought struck him as he bent down to pick up the bucket. He stole a quick glance behind him. Renwick's back was turned. His heart began to trip like a hammer as he slipped his hand inside the bucket. He felt the small piece of metal covered in grease. He had no need to look. He knew what it was. Feeling slightly sick, he slipped out of the mess and made his way toward the control room. In his haste he nearly ran into Robinson, who had just stepped out of the wardroom. Robinson glared at him but apparently didn't notice the bucket. It was just as well—he might have started asking awkward questions.

He stopped as he neared the control room, trying to decide what he was going to do. The first thing was to remove the bit of metal and hide it. Cheney would flay him alive if he ever found out. As he stood hesitating, not knowing what to do, Cadbury came out from the wardroom, carrying a tray of dishes.

"Wotcher, Guns," the steward sang out gaily.

Lacey shot around in alarm, nearly knocking the tray out of Cadbury's hands.

Cadbury's suspicions were immediately aroused as he stepped back neatly. He glanced down at the bucket, his little beady eyes twinkling. He noted the guilty expression on Lacey's face. "A-ha! What you got there, Trapper? Going to do your dobeying, eh?"

"Shut up," whispered Lacey fiercely.

Cadbury's eyes danced. "O-ho, o-ho. That's no way to speak to an old shipmate, is it? What are you hiding then? Stashing away your tot, are you?"

Lacey felt the sweat come out on his forehead. His mind raced. If he didn't do something to put the steward off the scent, and quick, the bastard would be yapping all over the boat that he'd caught the gunlayer hiding something. He thought quickly. It came to him what to do. He'd tell the truth—half of it.

"Jesus, mate, you gave me a right shock," he said with a relieved grin. "For a moment I thought you were Robinson."

"Oh," said Cadbury. "You're keeping out of his way, are you?"

Lacey shook his head frankly. "Well, you might say that in a way. You see he's got me stone cold if he finds out. . . ."

Cadbury drew closer. "Finds what out?"

Guns held up a finger and looked up and down the passage. "Don't tell anyone, but I forgot to put the locking pins in the Browning gun stanchions. It's nothing—I could fit them in a couple of seconds and anyway we seldom ever use the bloody things, but you know what he's like. He wouldn't half go on if he found out. . . ." Lacey took a breath. It was a calculated risk he was taking. The steward would tell everyone, of course, but as there were no such things as locking pins for Browning

stanchions they would just think he was raving again and ignore him. There was a chance that the steward also knew this,
but looking at the fatuous face bobbing about excitedly in front
of him, Lacey reckoned he was safe enough. Pleased with his own
cunning, he relaxed a little. "So that's the story, mate. I just
wouldn't like to get in Robinson's bad books, that's all."

Cadbury nodded with conviction. "You're right there, Guns.
He's a nasty bastard and all. Anyway, don't you worry," he
added with a conspiratorial wink, "your old mate's not going
to tell on you. Anyway, it's nothing, is it, just—what was it
you said again? Never mind, Cadbury's not the sort of bloke to
let an old shipmate down, whatever it was."

"You're all right, mate, for my money. I've always said that."
Lacey laid it on, stepping aside to let Cadbury into the pantry.

But the steward made no effort to move. Lacey began to feel
uncomfortable. He couldn't stand all day talking to the daft
bastard. Why didn't he go?

Cadbury put his head to one side and grinned suddenly.
"What was that you said again, Guns? It was something off the
Brownings, not the gun?"

Lacey shot him a startled glance as a warning bell rang in his
head. But the steward's smiling face wore a bland and innocent
expression. "It's all right, Trapper. I remember now. It was
the Brownings." With a kind of half laugh, as if amused at his
own folly, Cadbury eased past the gunlayer and marched into
the pantry.

Lacey gazed hatefully at the retreating figure. Bloody oaf, he
thought. Still, he hadn't time to worry about the steward. He
had something to do and in a hurry. A quick glance to see that
there was no one about, and he plunged his hand into the
bucket.

Wiping the grease from his fingers on his overalls, he stuck
the firing pin of the three-inch gun in his pocket.

What to do with the bucket now? Easy. Just put it in the
control room where it was normally kept. If anyone said anything, well, Titt had told him to get it out of the fore-ends.
With an air of nonchalance he began to stroll aft.

Cadbury's head appeared out of the pantry. "Pssst. Hey, Guns?"

Lacey could have killed him. "What is it?" he hissed angrily.

"Your overalls—they're covered in grease." Cadbury thrust a rag toward him.

Lacey shot him a venomous glance, but he took the rag. The white, thick, nonfloating grease seemed to be all over his suit. Cursing, he wiped it off as best as he could. He handed it back to the steward without a word of thanks when he'd finished.

Cadbury watched him as Lacey continued on his way to the control room. He gave a little chuckle to himself. What did the gunlayer take him for with all that flannel about stanchions and pins and not to breathe a word? So you thought you could take the mickey out of old Cadbury, he said to himself. Well, we'll just wait and see, Mister Lacey. You didn't get all that grease over you unless you were searching for something you'd left in the bucket. And a pound to a pinch of shit it was something to do with the gun.

The boom vessel lay at anchor less than a mile away. Cheney was watching her through the periscope. He'd been in the control room since first light. As yet there had been no signs of activity.

The water, racing through the narrows and driven by the wind, sent up flying showers of spray, forcing Cheney to raise the periscope high to see above the mist of spume. It was a calculated risk he was taking. Even in the turbulence four feet of periscope sticking out of the water could be spotted by a keen observer on the heights of the shore. The low gray cloud provided ideal cover for approaching aircraft. Occasionally he would train the lens upward to search overhead.

He swung around again to the boom ship. It seemed to jump across the intervening space at him as he switched into high power.

He saw the first signs of life on board the ship. A curl of smoke came from a point aft of her wheelhouse to be swept away in a long dirty streamer. A seaman came up on deck, made his way to the fo'c'sle and emptied a bucket overboard.

It all looked peaceful enough, but Cheney knew just how dangerous an illusion this was.

Beyond the boom defense on the eastern shore of the island, a group of houses seemed to cling like limpets to the barren rock, their whitewashed walls the color of putty in the light. Dull smudges of red and yellow paint had been added to window sashes and doors in an attempt to relieve the effect of bleak monotony. Half of it hidden by the rocky promontory, the tiny village appeared deserted but for the pennants of smoke that curled away from chimneys. On the foreshore a wooden jetty ran a short distance out to sea. A handful of fishing boats were moored on its lee side.

Cheney carefully searched the opposing cliffs for signs of gun emplacements, but if there were any they were so well concealed they escaped detection. He put the periscope down and left to grab a hurried breakfast. Alone in his cabin he bolted the food down mechanically and sent for Brangwyn.

In a few brief sentences he outlined his plan to the first lieutenant. They would beat up and down outside the nets without getting too close to the boom vessel. There would be no attempt to breach the boom that day, but a careful plot of all shipping going through the narrows would be made in an effort to determine the course of the swept channel. Use of the periscopes was to be kept to an absolute minimum and the big one only when necessary. All observations would have to be made quickly and accurately in consequence. By the following day they should have gained sufficient knowledge of the area to be able to make their attempt.

When he'd finished briefing Brangwyn, Cheney brought up the subject of Mitchell again.

The first lieutenant's anxious frown deepened. "He appears to be very ill, sir," he answered worriedly.

"You've seen him this morning?"

"Just after breakfast, sir. Blow—"

"Do you think his condition is worsening?"

Brangwyn paused before answering. "I should think it is, sir."

"What's his temperature now?"

"Well, sir, chief petty officer Blow tells me the last time he took it it was 103."

Cheney's fingers drummed the table. "103, eh? That's fairly high. Looks like the fever's reached a crisis. We'll just have to keep a close watch on him. Have another look at him in an hour or so, Brangwyn."

"Very well, sir," the first lieutenant replied, perturbed by the captain's apparent unwillingness to concede that Mitchell was suffering from anything but an infectious fever. He made to go.

"And, Brangwyn?"

He turned. "Yes, sir?"

"Let me know when you intend to visit him. I'll go along with you."

Back in the wardroom, Brangywn rang the bell for the steward. "Tell the coxswain I'd like to see him when he has a minute," he told Cadbury as the steward's head appeared through the curtain.

Cadbury shot off, his mind already beginning to seethe with speculation. In the passageway he bumped into Monkhouse.

"Hello there, Monkeyhouse," he giggled. "I was just on my way to look for you."

"Watch it, mate. Just watch it," warned the P.O.'s' messman, eyeing the steward threateningly.

Cadbury bared his yellow teeth in a grin. "Well, it's actually the 'swain I wanted. You can save me a journey if you're going back. Jimmy wants to see him in the wardroom."

Monkhouse growled. "What's the matter with you, then? Broken your leg? All right, piss off back to your piggery—I'll tell him."

He caught the coxswain just as he was about to turn in. Muttering under his breath about never getting any peace, Blow slipped his shoes on again.

Monkhouse stood around.

"Well, what's up with you, then? Haven't you anything better to do? I'll soon find you something if you haven't," Blow said testily.

The messman made no effort to move. He sniffed the air, his nose wrinkling. "Can you smell anything, 'swain? There's an odd smell about." His head pivoted slowly as he tried to locate the source of the smell.

Blow was halfway into his jacket. He stopped to sniff, compelled by the messman's example. "I don't smell anything," he growled, slipping into his jacket. "You must be imagining things."

Monkhouse gave a definite shake of his head in denial. "No, there's a strange smell somewhere, 'swain." He sniffed again. "It seems to be coming from here all right."

Blow had a quick glance at himself in the mirror. A thought struck him. "It's not like a smell of burning, is it?" he asked, swinging around quickly. Fire in a submerged submarine was a serious threat.

"No, no, it's nothing like that. It's—well, it's weird-like. I don't know how to describe it."

Blow squeezed around the table. Monkhouse stepped aside to let him pass.

"I'll be with the first lieutenant if anyone wants me, and after that they'll just have to wait because I'm going to get some sleep. And listen, you want to watch it, lad. You'll be seeing things next if you're not careful."

The curtain of the wardroom was drawn. Blow knocked on the paneling. Brangwyn's voice answered. Blow squared himself up and stepped inside. The first thing he noticed was that the first lieutenant had neither combed his hair nor washed. He wondered about it. Invariably Brangwyn would give himself a little spruce-up before breakfast. He couldn't help noticing, either, the heavy shadows under Brangwyn's eyes and the lines beginning to set in his face. After nearly three weeks at sea everyone began to look a bit haggard, but he'd never seen the first lieutenant look quite so beat before. If he hadn't known better he would have said Brangwyn was suffering from a hangover.

"You wanted to see me, sir?"

"Oh, yes, coxswain." Brangwyn's face wrinkled as if trying to clear his thoughts. He rubbed his forehead. "It's about Mitchell."

"Mitchell, sir?" Blow repeated in surprise.

"I know, I've just seen him, but . . . well, quite honestly, coxswain, I'm not happy about this whole business at all. Now are you quite sure—" His hand waved to dismiss Blow's protestations. "It's not that I'm doubting your judgment, coxswain. Please understand that. All I'm asking is . . . well, has anything happened at all that seems to confirm your opinion or vice versa? Anything at all?" Brangwyn's question sounded almost like a plea.

Blow set his lips in a straight line. "I've told you what I think, sir. I could be wrong, but I still think he's suffering from appendicitis. How bad it is I don't know, but from what I've read about it in the manual, it's always a dangerous condition."

Brangwyn appeared to think for a minute. "All right, coxswain. I just wanted to make absolutely sure. By the way," he said, bringing the meeting to a close, "the captain will be along later this morning to have a look at Mitchell himself. I'll let you know when. He's having a rest just now."

Cheney was lying on his bunk. His eyes ached, and an iron band of pain bit into his head like an applied tourniquet. He knew his slowly mounting nervous tension would only find release in action. The feeling wasn't helped by the knowledge that he could expect his recall any day now. Even with emergency rations there wasn't much food left, and they still had the long trip back to the Clyde. Four weeks was the maximum they could hope to spend at sea.

Restlessly he tossed about, unable to decide whether to make an attempt at breaching the boom that day. Since morning he'd been arguing the question with himself. Time was running out; another day could make all the difference. Ill-temperedly he looked at his watch. The hours were slipping by. It would soon be noon and half the day gone. The hour reminded him that he hadn't seen Mitchell yet. Another damned worry. Why in God's name had the man had to fall sick at this critical time? He cursed himself for not having gotten rid of him before. He'd known Mitchell was a weak link even before he'd examined his medical record. It was obvious the man was a weak type. Why the damned medical people hadn't spotted this and weeded him out he would never understand. It was all that damned psychological nonsense they seemed obsessed with. Common sense was all that was required to know whether a man had a backbone or not. Weed out the weak and the malcontents. And not only from the Navy. It was a thing that would have to be done on a national scale if they were all to survive. Germany, for all her faults, had recognized this, and she had become strong and powerful in a decade.

They had risen from the depths of defeat and crushed the Red menace which sought to destroy them from within, and all within a few years had created a state of such vigor that it had lifted the dull masses out of their apathy. They might be enemies—at the moment—but they were skillful and courageous enemies. One could admire such adversaries. War had created them, and war would destroy them, perhaps, but history would remember them as soldiers. Let the pacifists go on about war and all its horrors, but if you looked at the matter in a broader light it was easy to see that the wars that mankind had fought from time immemorial were nothing more than nature's way of ridding itself of the weak. If you had the courage to face it, then it was no more than a little bloodletting in the cause of evolution.

Cheney broke off his thinking and sat upright, his nostrils quivering like an animal's.

He was out of his bunk and along the passageway even as the O.O.W. called out for the captain in the control room.

Robinson stood by the column of the descending periscope.

"H.E., sir," he said quickly as Cheney came bounding in. "Red 175, sir. Can't see anything on the bearing."

Cheney bent down and grabbed the handles of the periscope as they neared the rim of the well. He snuggled close to the eyepiece as the periscope began to rise again. "Who's on the asdic set?" he asked Robinson over his shoulder.

"Rice, sir. He's—"

"Get Winch right away," snapped Cheney.

Seconds later, the senior asdic rating arrived, puffing and blowing as he forced his huge bulk into a trot.

With a few hurriedly whispered words Rice vacated the stool to allow Winch to take over.

Time seemed to stretch out unendingly as Winch fiddled with the controls.

Impatiently Cheney bit into his knuckle. He could contain himself no longer. "Well, Winch, what is it?" he barked. "Have you got an echo?"

Winch held up his hand for quiet as he bent forward listening.

Cheney glowered at him, but he knew how valuable the asdic rating was. He held silent, but his clenched fists showed white at the knuckles.

At last Winch confirmed the echo. "It's a diesel, sir, all right . . . red 173 now . . . sounds like an M.F.V."

Cheney signaled the big periscope up again. "Are you sure, Winch? It couldn't be a small U-boat?"

Holding the earphones to his head, Winch said, "Definitely not, sir. It's a fishing vessel, all right."

Cheney scowled in disappointment as he screwed his eye up to the lens. Breaking waves hindered his view, but toward the limit of his horizon he caught a sudden glimpse of a small box-like structure sticking up out of the water for a brief instant. A thin line, no more than a flickering image, danced about, and a moment later the wheelhouse of the fishing vessel heaved into sight. She appeared to be heading toward the narrows.

Angrily Cheney signaled the periscope down.

He changed his mind. "Up periscope," he barked, as inspiration hit him. There was no time to waste. He would follow her in through the boom.

"Robinson?"

The O.O.W. jerked. "Yes, sir?"

"Go to diving stations."

His hand trembling a little, Robinson unhooked the Tannoy.

"Damn it, she's turning away," Cheney cried in anger.

The speaker in his hand, Robinson paused uncertainly.

Cheney banged the handles of the periscope together, glowering at Robinson. He made a peremptory gesture with his hand. "All right, Robinson, you can—"

Winch picked up another echo.

Cheney dived for the periscope. He swung it on the reported bearing. *Clack, clack,* went the handles again. Cheney's eyes seemed to glow from within, as the periscope slid away silently.

"Diving station, Robinson." His voice vibrated excitedly. "Hurry, man, hurry!"

Within minutes of Winch's report the attack team had closed up as the leading destroyer of the convoy hove into view. Overhead a pair of A/S aircraft circled slowly. Astern of the leading vessel another destroyer and a slower A/S trawler flanked a 1,000-ton U-boat.

Cheney was transformed as he worked the big periscope. Beads of sweat oozed from his forehead as he started the attack.

"Port fifteen, steer 320 . . . group up . . . half ahead both . . . sixty feet." He turned to Brangwyn. "I must be back up in three minutes."

The crew felt the familiar butterflies crawling about their stomachs as they crossed the path of the convoy to maneuver for an attacking position.

When Cheney came up again he was within 4,000 yards of the convoy on a converging course. He was using the periscope for no more than seconds at a time, gobbling up all the information he needed in brief snatches as the lens broke the surface. Robinson fed the data into the fruit machine.

Both destroyers came up on the port, leaving the trawler to starboard. The leading destroyer gave four long piercing blasts on her siren as she approached the boom vessel.

As the sounds echoed and reechoed from the surrounding high cliffs, a burst of steam erupted from the foredeck of the anchored ship and the heavy winch started up with a *clank, clank.*

The leading destroyer now went hard about to come down on the starboard side between the U-boat and the trawler. One of the heavily clad officers on the bridge of the destroyer picked up a megaphone as they came abeam. He shouted instructions across the narrow intervening space to the U-boat's captain.

None of the lookouts on the surface vessels saw the long metal tube with its eye of glass break the surface of the water a thousand yards away.

At the other end of the tube at the periscope lens Cheney crouched tensely. The sweat which had gathered on his brow now ran down his face in tiny rivulets as he waited for his target to center on the hair-thin graticule of his sights.

In the nightmare setting of the control room with its tortured loops of pipes and cabling and its hundreds of shining valves, the men sat quietly at their controls and instruments.

The silence had the brittleness of glass. Cheney's heavy breathing could be heard above the low urgent hum of the main motors as they approached the point where they would launch their torpedoes.

"Clamp me on my D.A.," said Cheney in a hoarse voice to Bissel.

The E.A. leaned forward, his long arms stretching out. His hands overlapped Cheney's on the periscope handles, and he set his feet wide apart as he locked him on the director angle.

Ignoring the approaching destroyer, Cheney watched the thin pencil bows of the U-boat creep into the periphery of the lens.

Like a film running in slow motion, the U-boat's gun mounting appeared next, and then the forepart of her conning tower. Cheney glimpsed the large numerals painted on her side.

"Fire one," he snapped in a crisp voice.

A muffled thud from for'ard, and the submarine recoiled as the torpedo burst from the tube, propellers snarling as they bit the water.

"Fire two."

At ten-second intervals he fired two further torpedoes. Winch reported all of them running.

There was no time to wait and see the results. The second destroyer was approaching fast.

"A hundred feet . . . shut off for depth charging . . . silent routine," Cheney cried.

Everyone stilled as the destroyer scraped overhead. Hearts thumping, they awaited the retribution that was to come.

In a squirming dive Cheney headed for the safety of deeper waters.

Up top four torpedoes, strung out like miniature speedboats, tore toward the unsuspecting U-boat, but the leading destroyer, having turned, was coming up fast to port.

At twenty-five knots she caught the torpedoes intended for the U-boat. Two hit her in the forepeak and one amidships, engulfing her in a sheet of flame as her ammunition went up.

The fourth torpedo slipped astern of the U-boat and hit the trawler just under her hawse pipe, instantly lifting the bows in a jagged twisted mass of metal and killing all the hands in the fo'c'sle. Within seconds the stricken destroyer settled down in the water, her back broken and her two halves beginning to jackknife. Her crew, leaping into the sea to escape the holocaust on board, were caught in the concussive explosion of their own depth charges going off and were smashed to pulp.

The remaining destroyer, seeing that the trawler was still afloat, raced to help her companion. She arrived too late to be of any assistance. As the U-boat slipped through the boom she turned to begin a vengeful search for their attacker.

Ten miles farther up the fiord, two Emden-class destroyers slipped their moorings and headed south at full speed to join in the hunt.

All afternoon the three destroyers pressed the submarine relentlessly. In the village the windows of the houses shook to the thunder of continuous explosions. When the destroyers left eventually, the surface of the water was covered with dead fish. The air grew thick with gulls as they swarmed from all around to join in the unexpected feast.

Their hungry cries continued till late into the evening.

Chapter Thirteen

It was nine o'clock in the evening. Low gray clouds sagged heavily. The light had the faded quality of old tapestry. The sea was desolate and empty now, the destroyer having gone back up the fiord.

Some ten miles to the south of the boom the submarine that had been so mercilessly hunted limped along on one motor. Severely damaged by the continuous and heavy depth charging, she was making water aft. The pumps, running all the time, were fighting a losing battle as water continued to seep through the damaged stern gland.

Both depth gauges had ceased to function, and the depth had to be calculated from a small sea-pressure gauge in the engine room. One pattern of depth charges had been so close that all the fuses were blown off the board. A small electrical fire had started in the motor room. It had been brought under control but not before it had damaged a number of wiring circuits. The enormously concussive effect of the depth charging had burst open glands and joints on both the telemotor and high-pressure air lines. The foreplanes had been damaged and were again in manual control.

One particularly frightening incident had occurred when the master Sperry gyrocompass had leaped from its mountings and scythed through the control room like an angry cannonball. With an anguished screech it had plowed into the exchange, leaving shards of metal and a confetti of wiring in its wake. By some miracle no one had been hurt.

Oil and water dripped everywhere, gathering in pools on the deck.

Cheney straightened up from where he stood clutching the hoist wire of the for'ard periscope. His feet crunched on broken glass as he walked over to consult the barometer. The pressure on the gauge registered 22.6 pounds, almost 8 pounds above normal atmospheric pressure. He returned to stand in the midst of the wreckage which, a few hours before, had been the control room.

"Should be getting a little darker now, number one. We'll give it another half an hour and go up and have a look," he said, his voice breaking the silence.

Brangwyn's eyes were ringed with fatigue. "She's getting terribly heavy aft, sir. The pumps are not coping."

Cheney stroked his chin. "What's the depth now?"

A voice sang out from the engine room: "One hundred twenty-eight feet."

"Hmmm. Any H.E., Winch?"

Asdics reported all clear.

Cheney stared for a moment at the pool of oil and water at his feet. "All right, number one. We'll go up and have a look now."

Brangwyn bit his lip. They were slowly sinking deeper all the time. He was going to have a job on his hands to get her up to periscope depth without blowing main ballast. And if he blew the tanks and there was a destroyer up top lying waiting with her engines stopped. . . . He dreaded to think about it.

He took a deep breath. "Group up . . . half ahead port . . . thirty feet."

A protesting whine came from aft as the port motor was shunted into series and the revs increased. The ballast pumps shook noisily on their mountings as they raced.

"One hundred thirty-five feet," reported the engine room.

The men in the control room exchanged glances. They weren't going to make it without blowing main ballast. God help them if there was a destroyer up top.

Brangwyn shot Cheney a helpless glance.

Cheney never took his eye from the inclinometer. "How much have we left in the battery?"

"It was very low the last reading, sir. Shall I—"

"No, no. Try full ahead on the port motor."

Brangwyn passed on the order quietly. They all waited apprehensively as a tremor ran through the deck. The motor was at full speed now.

Cheney continued to watch the bubble.

"One hundred thirty feet." They were gaining.

Straining like a wounded sea creature, the submarine began to ascend.

"All right, Brangwyn," Cheney said when they had reached 80 feet. "I think you can group down now, but watch her."

A few minutes later they were at periscope depth and still nothing to report from asdics.

Cheney stretched out his full length on the wet deck as he ordered the afterperiscope up. Grabbing the handles as they cleared the well, he twisted on his side, scrambling to his knees as the lens inched upward. Bits of glass and metal clung to his oil-soaked clothes. "Keep her up, Brangwyn," he warned.

Brangwyn felt a pool of warm sweat collect in the small of his back. Whatever happened he mustn't break surface.

Cheney grunted heavily as he put his weight on the periscope. It was stiff and difficult to turn. He snatched his eye away from the lens. "Bissel," he called.

Two long strides and the E.A. was across the control room. He leaned his weight as Cheney tugged at the handles.

"Easy now," breathed Cheney between clenched teeth, "not too much."

The two men strained at the periscope. It eased free. Bissel was caught unprepared. His long legs tangled up as he lost his balance. Flinging out his arms he made a wild grab at the chief stoker. Beale caught him but in doing so accidentally dropped his wheel spanner. The heavy metal tool clanged noisily as it landed in the bilges behind the blowing panel.

Heads jerked around instinctively, and all eyes stared upward at the deckhead. No one breathed.

Cheney snapped the periscope handles together. "Sixty feet," he called to Brangwyn. "There's nothing about up top. Fall out diving stations. Get all hands off watch to start clearing up. We'll surface in half an hour."

It was midnight before the hands were able to stop for a break. The galley had been put out of action. Corned beef and pickles were served for dinner. It was like a refrigerator in the fore-ends. Because they were working hard, no one had seemed to notice the cold, but now it seeped into the very marrow of their bones.

Titt glanced at his watch. Almost time to turn to again.

"What time is it now?" asked Corr.

"Near the half hour."

Corr groaned as if in pain. "Christ, we've still got this lot to clear up yet and I'm on watch at two." He turned to Hollingsworth, the telegraphist. "Here," he said accusingly, "have you not got that bloody recall signal yet?"

Hollingsworth shook his head. "Nothing yet. It might be days yet for all you know."

"Days? What do you mean, days, you Jonas bastard? Just listen to him, will you? What's the matter with you? Don't you want to get back to Dunoon or something?"

The telegraphist smiled bleakly. "Get back? I wish we'd never left."

"Well, then, what are you on about? You'd think you were all for it the way you go on."

"All for it?" Hollingsworth laughed bitterly. "Look, mate, you're not the only one that wants to get back—but me, I'm not counting any chickens, that's all."

Corr made a sound of disgust. "Don't give us your ab-dabs. I'll bet you wouldn't mind getting a medal out of this lot. You bloody sparkies are all the same. Anyway," he went on, reaching for the teapot, "if we manage to get rid of those two fish we've left, they can stuff their recall. All we want now is a big fat ten-thousand-tonner with no escorts and *bang, bang,* and we've no torpedoes left and we're on our way home." He tilted the teapot over his cup. A thin dark trickle of liquid and leaves ran out of the spout. "Just look at that. No bloody tea now."

"You've had it, mate," said Renwick. "Unless you want to make some more," he added hopefully.

Corr banged the pot down. "Aw, shite! What's the time, Tom?"

Titt got to his feet wearily. "That's it, lads. Time to get cracking again."

There was a general moan of dismay.

"Come on. Let's be having you," Titt prodded, putting his hand on Corr's shoulder.

Corr shook it off angrily. "Christ, you never let up, do you?"

Titt felt his own temper flash for a second, but he let it go. He knew how Corr and the others felt. To live in the shambles of the fore-ends would try the patience of a saint. He looked around him in disgust. For nearly three weeks they had been at sea. The weather had been continuously bad, and everything was wet to the touch. In the permanently damp atmosphere clothes mildewed and metal tarnished. What happened to the crew was a damned sight worse. Sleep was the only anodyne they had recourse to, but even then it was more of a drugging of the senses than anything else. "That's right, Jock. And mebbe it's just as well." But there was sympathy and understanding in his voice.

"This bloody lot gives me the screamers," Corr protested, but he got to his feet.

"You should have thought about it before you joined," Renwick chipped in.

Corr turned on him. "You just watch it, mate, or—"

Titt motioned to Renwick. "Get the water, Raggy. Off you go. Chop-chop."

"He wants to watch it," Corr growled threateningly. "He's getting a bit too stroppy these days."

Nearly an hour later they had swept up the remainder of the debris caused by the depth charging. They mopped up the deck as best they could and repacked the stores and crates that had broken loose. Even with all their hard work they had only managed to introduce a small element of order into the chaos. No sooner had they finished than the engineers arrived to attend to the damaged foreplanes.

Titt called a halt and went to see the coxswain.

"All right, lads," he said when he got back, "that's it for now. Pack it up."

Nearly dropping with fatigue but unable to sling their hammocks because of McLintock and his crew working on the foreplanes, the men lay down where they could. Closing their eyes, they tried to blank off the heavy banging and hammering sounds that assailed their ears. It was like trying to sleep in a workshop. Groaning, they covered up their heads, but it was a restless night they spent.

0400 hours. The start of the morning watch and A.B. Moore had just taken over the wheel. He had an hour to do before taking over lookout.

Bain was petty officer of the watch. Both men were too tired to exchange conversation, and anyway, Moore, since his run in with the captain had retired into sullen resentment.

Moodily he kept his eye on the dimly reflected compass card as the submarine beat steadily to the south on one engine. Toward the end of his spell on the wheel he spoke to Bain for the first time since he'd come on watch.

"Mind if I nip for'ard? I'd like a cup of kye before going up top," he said.

Bain glanced at the clock. "Sure, off you go. Better hurry it up, though—you've only a few minutes."

Moore slipped out of the helmsman's seat and Bain took over the wheel. Hurrying forward, Moore helped himself to a cup of cocoa from the jug on the galley hot plate. He was back in a minute.

"You'd better see if there's a dry suit hanging up in the engine room," Bain advised. "It'll be cold and wet up top."

Moore shook his head.

"On you go," Bain insisted. "You might as well have a look —you've a minute yet. But shake it up—the old man's about and I don't want to get a blast for the watch relieving late."

Moore shrugged. More to humor Bain than in the belief that he'd find a dry suit he walked aft. Absently he put his cup down on the edge of the chart table as he poked his head into the engine room. Ford, one of the stokers on watch, saw him. He cupped his hands to his mouth to yell above the din of the hammering diesels. Moore couldn't make out the words, but there was no mistaking the stoker's meaning. Just as he thought— there were no dry suits in the engine room.

Moore turned and reached for his cup at the same instant Cheney came in the control room.

Cheney's face went white with rage. "Moore," he roared, his mouth working convulsively. "What did I tell you before?"

Moore stared uncomprehendingly up at the captain. His mouth fell open.

Cheney thumped his palm with his closed fist. "I told you to keep away from there, didn't I? What the devil do you mean by it, eh?"

Moore looked at the chart table and then up at the captain again. He waved his cup in front of him, his mouth opening and closing as he tried to explain.

"Answer me, man! Answer me," Cheney trumpeted. He strode over to where Bain sat on the wheel. He flung his arm out to point accusingly at Moore, who was standing with a stupefied expression on his face. "What is this man doing in the control room?"

Bain could only half turn as he tried to keep an eye on the compass. "Moore, sir?"

"Yes, petty officer—Moore."

Bain blinked, unable to understand what was going on. "He's on watch, sir," he said, jerking his head back again to watch his ship's head.

"Then what in heaven's name is he doing over at the chart table?" Cheney barked.

Bain twisted in his chair until he could see Moore. He motioned him with a jerk of his head. "Here, grab this," he said in a low voice as Moore stepped forward. He got up as Moore reached over and took the wheel.

"What's going on, Bain? You say this man is on watch and yet I find him over at the chart table. What is the meaning of it?"

"I'm sorry, sir," Bain answered. "I took over the helm from able seaman Moore so he could get dressed before going up on lookout."

Cheney thrust his face forward, the great beak nose stabbing the air aggressively. "Then what was he doing at the chart table? My implicit instructions were that no one, excepting the officers, were to be allowed near the charts. And yet the moment my back is turned I find him there. You're in charge of the watch, Bain. I expect you to see that my orders are obeyed."

Bain's face began to redden. He felt helpless in the face of Cheney's intransigence. "I'm sorry, sir—" he began, but Cheney cut him off with a switch of questions.

"What time is this man supposed to relieve?"

Bain stole a backward glance at the clock and groaned inwardly. It was already seven minutes past the hour. He bit his lip. He knew what was coming next. "0500, sir," he answered.

Cheney glared. "He's already seven minutes late, then. And it appears he's not even dressed yet."

Bain opened his mouth to protest, but Cheney cut him off again. "Put him in the first lieutenant's report," he said, glancing at his watch. "It is now eight minutes past—I will expect this man to have relieved the lookout in one minute from now." Cheney wheeled about and made for the conning tower ladder.

Bain, still dumbfounded by the injustice of the captain's behavior, turned on Moore angrily. "What the fuck were you buggering about over there for? You know bloody well what the old man's like about the charts."

Moore began to protest. "Save it till later," said Bain,

reaching over and grabbing the wheel. "You'd better get a bender on and get up on that bridge or you'll be ever deeper in it."

Moore got up. "I wasn't looking at the charts, Jock. Honest—"

"Never mind that now—get a move on."

Moore gave up. Fastening up the top of his overall suit, he made for the tower.

"Hey!" yelled Bain. "What do you think you're up to now? Get your bloody suit on."

Moore, one foot on the ladder, stopped. He gave a bitter laugh. "That's what he wants me to do so he can put me in the rattle again for being late. . . ."

Bain twisted around angrily. "Pony—" but he was too late. Moore was already up the tower.

You stupid bastard, thought Bain. *You'll get frozen to death.* He shuddered as he imagined what it was going to be like for Moore in the next hour. Of all the crazy bastards. Swinging the voice pipe around he informed the officer of the watch that the starboard lookout was on his way up. Joyner spluttered indignantly, wanting to know what was the meaning of sending the lookout up on the bridge without his permission.

"Ask the captain. It's his orders," Bain replied acidly and swung the voice pipe back.

Moore had been forty minutes on the bridge. A thin drizzle blew down from the fiords, chilled to near-freezing point by the icy wind. Moore's face and hands were blue. His teeth chattered in his head and he shook all over. On the exposed rear part of the bridge he took the full force of the north wind as they headed south for Bohus Bay.

For half an hour he'd been holding something back, his anger and misery masking his needs. Now he couldn't wait any longer. He spoke to Joyner: "Permission to use the pig's ear, sir," he asked in desperation, pointing to the urinal bowl on the side of the bridge structure.

Joyner hesitated. It was possible he would have given permission, but Cheney's keen ears had picked up the request. He snapped over his shoulder: "Tell him to wait till he gets down below."

It was enough for Joyner. "Certainly not," he said indignantly. "You'll just have to wait till you get down below."

Moore jerked back as if he'd been struck. "You bastards," he muttered under his breath as Joyner walked away. Uncaring, he stepped over to the pig's ear. His cold hands fumbling with the layers of clothing, he unbuttoned his flies.

Joyner happened to turn around again. In his astonishment he nearly dropped his night glasses. "Moore!" he squeaked in rage. "What the devil do you think you're doing?"

The incident might have resulted in little more than the able seaman's getting a severe ticking off had Joyner not made the mistake of seizing him by the shoulder.

It was the spark that set Moore off. His already overstrained nervous system exploded violently. He lashed out at Joyner, his fist catching the sub-lieutenant high up on the bridge of the nose. Joyner staggered backward and sat down on the deck.

Cheney whipped around in a flash at the noise. In a glance he took in what had happened as Joyner struggled to get to his feet. He shot Moore a glance of pure malevolence.

"You—Moore. Get down below at once," he hissed savagely.

Joyner was on his feet, his eyes watering with pain and humiliation. "Joyner," Cheney barked, "take over the starboard lookout." Dismissing Joyner contemptuously—an officer's being struck by one of the men showed he lacked power of command—he strode over to the voice pipe.

"Petty officer of the watch," he called down to the control room.

Bain came on the other end of the voice pipe.

"Petty officer Bain," said Cheney in a stern voice, "you will place able seaman Moore under arrest when he arrives in the control room. Have one of the hands coming on watch relieve early. And, Bain, send for the coxswain. I want to see him in the control room in five minutes."

Bain staggered back from the voice pipe unbelievingly. Had

the captain gone off his head? Moore? Under arrest? In Christ's name, what was happening?

Taking the wheel from Crabbe, he sent him forward to rouse the coxswain and tell Titt that a relief for one of the lookouts was required immediately.

He heard muffled sounds and the scrape of a foot on the ladder as a body squeezed through the lower hatch. An incongruous thought struck him: He'd have to arrest Moore while sitting down and with his back to him, unless he ordered him to take the wheel and reverse the positions. Either way the whole thing seemed crazy.

Chapter Fourteen

By the following afternoon they had reached Bohus Bay. The sea had calmed and visibility was good. All day the crew had been working hard to repair the damage they had sustained from the depth charging. They continued to steer by magnetic compass. Bissel had the Sperry gyro stripped down, but it seemed a hopeless task to get it to work again. But the leaks from the air and telemotor lines had been stopped, and the foreplanes were in operation again. The leak in the stern gland had also been checked and the pumps were now able to deal with the flow.

Cheney was prepared to take the offensive once more.

During the morning and the early part of the afternoon, accompanied by the engineer officer, he had visited each compartment to inspect progress. Only when he had satisfied himself that all repairs were well in hand did he retire to his cabin. He had been without sleep for the best part of twenty-four hours.

As the submarine slid through the water at a limping two and a half knots, her crew, weary to the bone, had fallen into a soporific sleep. A breathy murmuring sound, rising from the mass of hammocks, echoed around the contours of the deckhead and fell away in silence to be repeated in a regular kind of rhythm as they snored.

Two hammocks were absent from the crowded fore-ends. Mitchell was still in the P.O.'s' mess, and Moore, after being placed under close arrest for striking the O.O.W., had been moved right forward into the tube space, under surveillance of the duty watchkeeper.

Strict instructions had been issued that, except to use the heads, he wasn't to be allowed out from the tube space. His rum had been stopped and he was forbidden the use of tobacco. The coxswain had also warned Titt that there was to be no communication with Moore. He was a prisoner and as such was denied all privileges. Blow had also gone out of his way to caution Titt that the officers would be making regular visits to ensure that the orders were being carried out.

Immediately after his interview with the coxswain, Titt had warned all hands in the fore-ends that the wardroom was on the warpath and that they would have to be careful. Immediately after that he'd gone in to have a word with Moore. But the seaman, lying in his hammock, had been surly and uncommunicative, answering Titt's questions in clipped monosyllables.

During tea that afternoon the fore-ends buzzed with conversation as everyone discussed the incident on the bridge and Moore's subsequent arrest. Old stories were dug up and trotted out, but no one could remember a similar case. A yarn that most of them had heard at one time or other made its reappearance as the gossip grew. It was an old yarn and concerned one of the early P-boats. Apparently, and much to the resentment of her crew, on the completion of her running-up trials she had been sent straight out to the Mediterranean without leave being granted. On the eve of her departure, or so it was alleged, the men had mutinied and had to be forced on board at gunpoint. To add to her troubles, her number one was a real cat-o'-nine-tails character. On her way out to the Mediterranean, as she made passage through the Bay of Biscay, the two lookouts had grabbed hold of him and, in heavy seas, tossed him overboard.

Some of the hands discounted the story, but its truth was willingly accepted by the majority, who believed it for the illusion it gave them of the ultimate power of the lower deck. It was a fairy tale belief wherein they substituted Mr. Christian for St. George and the notorious Captain Bligh for the dragon.

When this subject, which always caused much argument, was exhausted, speculation turned next to what Moore was likely to get by way of punishment. No one doubted for one moment that he was headed right for the glasshouse. But for how long? Estimates varied from three months to two years. Only Stanley dissented on the question of imprisonment. He claimed he'd overheard the officers planning to have Moore hung from the yardarm of the *Victory* as a warning to all men who fancied having a go at snotty-faced subbies.

The usual ribaldry greeted his remarks, but it wasn't long before the crew became serious again as someone brought up Mitchell's name. By this time everyone realized he was very ill, though by some miracle they hadn't got hold of the story that he might be suffering from appendicitis. Blow had kept his suspicions well hidden, revealing them only to the captain and the first lieutenant.

Gravely they speculated on the cause of his illness. But it appeared nothing was sacred to the paperweight Stanley. With a perfectly straight face he implied that Mitchell could be suffering from leprosy. The bizarre statement would have sounded like sacrilege coming from anyone else. Only Stanley could possibly get away with such a thing.

Big Corr, who was sitting next to him, made a face of disgust. "Leprosy?" he said. "Who the hell ever heard o' anybody with leprosy in this country? You're off your flippin' rocker, mate."

Stanley perked up like a cock sparrow at the challenge. "All right, Jock, all right, but I'll tell you something if you want to know. . . ."

Corr squinted at him sideways, screwing up his big pock-marked face. "Tell me something? You couldna tell me your own name if somebody hadn't written it in your paybook for you."

Stanley held up a finger. "You didn't know that the submarine base at Malta was an old leper colony, did you?"

Corr laughed sarcastically. "When was that, Stan? Nineteen oatcake?"

"You can laugh, but I'll tell you one thing—they never wiped it out. Quite a few of the blokes went sick with it when I was out there. It gets in through the feet. That's where it gets in—through the feet."

Corr shook his head pathetically. "It's chinky toe-rot you're thinking of, that's what it is."

Rice frowned distastefully. He didn't like the seeming lack of concern shown by Stanley toward Mitchell. Corr, too—he was almost as bad for encouraging him. They should both know better than to make a joke out of a man's sickness. He coughed. "You shouldn't be talking like that," he said as Stanley turned around. "It's a serious matter. He's very ill."

Stanley looked at him innocent-eyed.

"And another thing," Rice went on, unable to resist the temptation of the born pedant, "you're talking a lot of nonsense, Stanley. Leprosy as a disease is practically wiped out. I don't suppose there are more than twenty cases in the whole of England."

Corr let out a great roar at this. "Ha! Ha! Ha! You're bloody right there, Ricey," he guffawed. "If there's any lepers back home it's a safe bet the bastards are all in England."

Stanley was watching Rice, his eyes twinkling. "Twenty, eh?" he said, "in the whole of England? Let me tell you something, my good chap, there's a hundred and fifty in Dunoon alone."

"You're a lying havering bastard," Corr roared.

Stanley held up an admonishing hand. "Just a minute, Jock. I didn't say they was haggis-wafflers. All I said was there's a hundred and fifty in Dunoon. And I'll tell you where they are—you know that big hotel up on top of the hill? You know the one, right at the back, with all those trees and things round it?" No such hotel existed, but Stanley made it sound convincing enough for half the crew at the table to be able to believe in it.

"What bloody hotel?" Corr said. "You're imagining things."

Stanley ignored his barracker as he turned to the others. "That hotel is full of lepers—and that's only one. There's hundreds like it all over the country, but the government's trying to keep it a secret so's we won't all get in a panic."

Rice looked away disgustedly. "You're talking absolute non-sense, Stanley."

Corr shook his head as he grinned. "He's off his nut. Clean round the bend. Stark, staring bonkers, aren't you, Stan? Here," he said, "how's it you know all about it if the government's trying to keep it a secret, then?"

Stanley stared at the table, silent for a minute.

"A-ha," cried Corr. "That's got you. Go on then, tell us how you know."

Stanley brought his head up, a look of proud defiance on his face. "All right. I'll admit it. I was one of them myself. That's why I—"

The rest of his words were lost as Corr let out a roar and dived on him, wrestling him to the deck. "You little bastard," he said as the hands exploded in laughter. "I'll do you this time—"

Titt, in spite of himself, couldn't help smiling. Like Rice, he didn't like the idea of Mitchell's illness being treated as a joke. But what could you do with Stanley? The little bastard would laugh at a funeral, even his own if he could. But it had gone far enough.

"Steady up there," he cried above the din. "You'll have the 'swain in here in a minute wondering what the hell's going on. Reaching over, he grabbed Corr by the arm and yanked him off Stanley. "Come on then, Jock. That's enough."

Corr got to his feet to allow Stanley to get up. Everyone seemed to be laughing and shouting and indulging in horseplay when Monkhouse stuck his head around the doorway.

Titt's face straightened guiltily.

"Coxswain says to tell you, Tom, that Robinson'll be along in a few minutes to see the prisoner."

The laughter died suddenly.

"Stuff my aunt's canary," said Stanley, able to get to his feet at last and breathing heavily. "What's he gonna do—flog him?"

Titt cut short the ripple of laughter. "That's enough. Let's get the table cleared before he gets here. Come on, chop-chop, the lot of you." Titt was very sensitive about officers visiting the fore-ends. It was a question of pride, not awe. They might live like pigs in the fore-ends, but he wasn't going to advertise the fact by allowing dirty dishes and mess gear to lie around for Robinson to see. He went forward to warn Mulholland, who was on watch in the tube space.

The lanky fore-endsman was sitting on the rear platform, arms clasped around his legs, his chin resting on his knees. He looked half asleep as usual. He heard Titt come in. Without moving he said: "What the hell's going on in there? Sounds like a sod's opera or something. Whose birthday is it?"

Titt ignored the question as he told him that Robinson was expected to visit the prisoner soon.

"Hmmmph. That poncy bastard. What does he want?" Mulholland grunted.

Titt kept his voice down as he glanced up at Moore's hammock. "Just watch it, Scouse. You know what he's like."

"He can get stuffed," Mulholland commented dryly.

"Well, watch it, anyway," Titt warned again and went back to the mess.

A few minutes later, by the time the sub-lieutenant arrived, the table was cleared and the hands had turned in. Robinson looked around the fore-ends, his aquiline nose wrinkling in disgust. He picked his way forward through the cramped compartment, feeling a certain loss of dignity as he had to clamber over the tables and the lockers. He reached the tube space and stuck his head through the bulkhead doorway.

Mulholland hadn't bothered to move from his sitting position.

Robinson saw the sprawling lanky torpedoman. His mouth thinned angrily. "Mulholland," he barked, "what do you mean by being asleep on watch?"

Mulholland inclined his head lazily. "I'm not asleep, sir," he answered in a level voice.

Robinson glared at him and turned his attention to the prisoner. Stretching on tiptoe, he peered inside Moore's hammock. Moore turned over. Robinson was sure he was awake. For some reason the idea that he was shamming sleep annoyed him even further.

"Have you any report to make about the prisoner?" he said, speaking sharply to Mulholland.

He got a negative shake of the head in answer.

His temper fraying, he raised his voice: "Don't you know that you should get to your feet when an officer addresses you?"

Mulholland uncoiled his long legs and stood up, a long-suffering look on his face.

Robinson was livid with rage. "I'm going to have to report this to the first lieutenant," he threatened.

The seaman raised a questioning eyebrow as he flicked a strand of hair back. What was the wet bastard on about now? The bugger should never have left barracks if he wanted to play at officers.

"You're not going to try and deny it, Mulholland. You were asleep, weren't you?"

"I wasn't asleep, sir," he replied in quiet denial. *You think you scare me, you pansy-faced git. A bit of gold braid and a lah-di-dah accent and you're all set to ladle out the Dartmouth stormtrooper stuff. Get stuffed, cobber.*

"You can tell that to the first lieutenant. I'm putting you in his report," snapped Robinson.

Mulholland's eyes flickered for an instant though they never left Robinson's face. He thought of Moore, lying just above, going back to do a spell of chokey. It was almost worth it. He'd like to hang one that long jutting chin of Robinson's, just to even up the odds a bit. Keeping a grip on himself, he held his tongue and continued to stare steadily at Robinson. Dumb insolence they called it, he thought, as he saw two tiny pinpoints of color mount the sub-lieutenant's cheeks.

"You'd better be careful in the future, Mulholland. I don't like your manner at all," Robinson warned as he turned on his heel and ducked through the narrow bulkhead doorway.

Mulholland heard him clambering his way back over the lockers and table. The bastard had been serious about putting him in the rattle. He was probably haring along the passage to get hold of Jimmy right this minute. It was no joke. To be charged with being asleep on watch was a serious matter. If Jimmy thought there was anything in it and put him in the captain's report. . . . He dreaded to think what might happen with Cheney in the mood he was in.

Mulholland sat down again and leaned back, but he'd been shaken by Robinson's threat.

The way the watches worked out it was nearly four hours before Robinson was able to get hold of the first lieutenant in the ward room. Brangwyn listened to him in worried silence. He had never known a patrol which had produced so many defaulters and so many serious charges.

"You're quite sure he was asleep, Robinson?" he asked again.

"Certain, sir. He was lying down on the platform with his eyes closed."

"He was actually lying down?" Brangwyn asked, glancing up from where he sat at the table.

Robinson hedged. "Well, perhaps not actually lying down, sir. He was sort of sprawling, if you know what I mean."

Brangwyn looked up again sharply. "I don't know what you mean. Was he or was he not lying down?"

"Well, sort of sitting down if you could call it that."

The first lieutenant made an explosive sound with his lips. "Good God, Robinson, this is a serious charge. You realize I have no option but to put Mulholland in the captain's report. Now once again—let's get this right. You say he was sitting down on the platform—"

"He was sort of sprawling—"

"But he wasn't actually lying down—yes?"

Robinson had to reluctantly agree.

"What makes you so sure he was asleep, then?"

"Well, it was his general appearance, sir."

"His eyes were closed?" Brangwyn probed.

"Yes, sir. That is, as far as I could see."

"As far as you could see? But if he was sitting down on the

platform as you say and slumped forward, how could you see if his eyes were closed or not?"

"It—it was the general impression I had, sir."

Brangwyn got to his feet slowly. He ran his fingers through his hair. "I'm not happy about this at all, Robinson. If Mulholland was asleep on watch, then he should be punished and severely, and I'll see to it that he is—but if there's any doubt in the matter. . . ." He sucked his lip thoughtfully. "Very well, Robinson. I want you to write me out a report on this. I want an accurate account of all the facts. I'll give the matter further consideration from there. One other thing," he added as Robinson made to go, "you did tell Mulholland that you were putting him in my report, did you?"

"Of course, sir," answered Robinson a trifle haughtily.

Brangwyn frowned. "Very well. You'll let me have that report then."

He sat down again when the sub-lieutenant had gone. He wasn't happy about the thing at all. Robinson's story didn't seem to ring true. But there seemed no way out of it now, since the leading seaman had been warned he was being put on report. It would look bad for discipline if he were to drop the whole thing as he felt like doing. He would have to go into it carefully when he'd read the report. If there was the slightest doubt in his mind then—well, the charge book had more than enough entries in it for one patrol.

When they surfaced that night the sky was clear of cloud, and miraculously the wind had dropped to a gentle breeze. Along with the drop in wind had come a rise in temperature, and for the first time in weeks the crew didn't feel as if they were living inside a refrigerator. Though they welcomed the change in the weather they also felt vulnerable and exposed as they slid through the glassy moonlit water, leaving a phosphorescent wake behind them like a paper-chase trail.

But stronger than their anxieties, a new feeling took hold of the crew as they sat down to dinner that night. They were in the grip of a fever. Since surfacing, rumors about their recall signal had swept through the boat like wildfire. Troubles were put aside and temporarily forgotten as the thought of returning home burst upon them like a glow of spring warmth after a long and hard winter.

Titt got up from the table as the sweet course of custard and stewed prunes was being ladled out. He couldn't stand the viscid yellow substance and the wrinkled aged appearance of the fruit. It made him odd man out in the mess, but that was the least of his worries. Picking his way across the cluttered, soaking deck he headed for the P.O.'s' mess to see how Mitchell was.

The petty officers were just finishing dinner. Titt poked his head in the doorway. Blow invited him to come in.

"It's all right, 'swain. I'll come back later when you've finished," he said, his face taking on an odd expression as he spoke. His nose wrinkled.

Blow pushed his sweet away. "Don't tell me we've got someone else who imagines he can smell something?"

Titt shook his head. "I thought I did smell something queer for a minute." He sniffed again.

The rest of the P.O.'s looked at him in annoyance.

"Whatever it is, you've brought it in with you from the bearpit," remarked Beale caustically.

"Look," Blow said, beginning to get irritated, "if you can't—" He broke off suddenly, following Titt's gaze.

Titt, a sickly expression on his face, was looking up in the direction of the bunk where Mitchell was lying.

Everyone stopped eating and looked round. As if released by Titt's action, the sweet, cloying, unwholesome smell hit them.

"Uuugh!" Preece was the first to get up from the table, his face paling. "I'm getting out of here," he said. One by one the others rose and followed him. In a few minutes the mess had emptied.

When everyone else had gone, Blow turned to Titt angrily as if in some way he was responsible for the smell.

Titt shrugged and spread his hands in apology. "Sorry, 'swain. I didn't mean—"

Blow cut him off with an impatient wave. He fumbled in his pocket and fished out some keys. "Here," he said, "Jock's on watch. Go down to the store, will you, and get a can of disinfectant—better make it two. And give Monkhouse a shout when you go out. Tell him I want to see him, at the double."

Feeling a bit nauseated, Titt took the keys and made for the second coxswain's store. One can or two cans, half a dozen cans, what did it matter? They might kill the smell, but they weren't going to help Mitchell.

Within minutes the awful smell seemed to permeate the length and breadth of the boat. Even Cadbury, who judging by the state of his pantry was impervious to smells, was affected by it.

As the hours passed, despite the liberal sprinkling of the P.O.'s' mess with disinfectant, the smell grew in strength. The men on watch complained, and those off watch stirred fretfully in their hammocks. Some of the petty officers took to sleeping at their duty stations. The remainder who couldn't get their heads down elsewhere clutched handkerchiefs sprinkled with disinfectant to their noses as they lay down. In reality the smell wasn't that bad. It was its source that lent it peculiarly offensive properties and led the crew to believe it was much worse than it actually was.

With the passing of the hours, Mitchell's condition gradually worsened. His temperature began to climb inexorably, and his pulse fluttered unevenly. His face had a drained appearance. His skin was yellow and waxlike. Blow, alarmed by the dramatic changes, went along to see the first lieutenant to be excused watchkeeping duties so that he could remain with Mitchell throughout the night. Brangwyn readily agreed after a short visit to the P.O.'s' mess to see Mitchell. Titt and Bain would have to share the watches in the control room between them.

Immediately after visiting Mitchell, Brangwyn went to report to the captain. Cheney was on the bridge but he came down. Brangwyn followed him to his cabin.

Cheney smacked the desk angrily. "No, Brangwyn, no. And I don't want to hear it again. I've told you before of the importance of our mission. I would be neglecting my duty if I were to call it off on the basis of vague suspicions and unqualified opinions. Now let's have no more of this."

"But you've seen him yourself, sir. He's very ill—I would say seriously—"

"Seriously. You take a lot on yourself, Mr. Brangwyn."

"But," Brangwyn protested again, "his temperature—his pulse rate—"

"No more than a fever crisis," Cheney said. He added in a snarling tone, "As for his pulse rate, well, we've been into that before. We don't have to be surgeon commanders to know what tachycardia means."

As the heated argument went on in the captain's cabin, the wardroom steward was prowling about like a stray cat. A non-watchkeeper, he fortunately got normal spells of sleep. Despite this he never seemed to take advantage of it and was frequently up and prowling at the oddest hours. He was making himself a cup of cocoa in the pantry and had just brought the pan of tinned milk and water to the boil when he heard the sound of angry voices coming from the captain's cabin.

Removing the pan from the hot plate, he wiped his greasy hands on his trousers. He was halfway along the passageway when the door opened to project a slab of light into the dimly lit tunnel. Quick as a flash he turned and raced back. In the sanctuary of his pantry he poked his head around the corner. Brangwyn was striding down the passage, his face white and his fists clenched.

Cadbury rubbed his hands together and replaced the pan on the hot plate. *O-ho,* he chuckled to himself, *somebody's just had a bollocking.* When the liquid in the pan came to the boil, he ground down a thick slab of drinking chocolate with an unclean knife and sprinkled the dark-brown shavings into the pan. After stirring the mixture for a few seconds with the knife, he poured himself a cup. Sipping at the hot sweet liquid, he wondered who was in the control room. He took another sip and decided to go along and see.

Bain had the watch.

Cadbury poked his head around the doorway and grinned fatuously. "Hi, Jock," he said in a sort of stage whisper.

Bain looked at the grinning face. It was a gray smudge of tone in the red light, and it was split like an old tennis ball. Bain was much too upset about Mitchell to want to talk to anyone, in particular the steward.

"Bugger off," he said to the round face.

Cadbury's head withdrew like a puppet jerked on a string. He went back to drink his cocoa. *So they're all getting a bit nasty,* he said to himself. *Well, you're not the only one who can get nasty, Mister Petty Officer Jock Bain. So can old Cadbury, just you wait and see, and you've had the cup of cocoa I was going to lash you up to.*

Finishing his cup, he pulled out a little folding stool, propping it up in the corner of the pantry. He sat down and folded his arms as he prepared to take a little catnap. Yes, just you wait and see. Old Cadbury can get nasty too when he wants. He grinned at the thought of the bombshell he was going to drop. Still grinning, he closed his eyes and dozed off.

Titt relieved Bain for the first half of the morning watch. As usual he wore his duffel coat, but with the rise in temperature he discarded his jerseys with the exception of his emerald-green one.

He stepped over the coaming, rubbing the sleep out of his eyes.

"Okay, Tom?" Bain greeted out of force of habit.

"Yeh, I suppose so. Bloody tired though. Where's the old man?"

Bain jerked his head. "Up top. He's been at the chart table for the last ten minutes, but he's away back up again."

"Hmmm. I wonder what that's all about? Anything happening?"

Bain shook his head. "No. Seems pretty quiet up top. Anyway, I'll be off and get my head down. This watch and watch business takes it out of you. See you in a couple of hours, then."

Titt yawned and rubbed his eyes. "Okay, Jock. We should be diving about then. I'll give you a shout."

Bain trudged off, leaving Titt alone in the control room with the helmsman. Titt made his way over to the for'ard periscope, leaning against the thick column. He stared at the helmsman's back for a second as he tried to figure what watch was on.

"Hey, Purgavie," he called, "who's up top on lookout?"

The helmsman twisted in his seat. "Crabbe and Lacey. I'm relieving Crabbe—I mean Lacey."

"You sound as bad as me, mate."

"I know, the watches are all to cock. Half the time I can't remember what watch I'm supposed to be in."

Titt grunted in answer and fell silent. Kennedy's, Mitchell's and now Moore's absence from the watch bill was making itself felt. As Purgavie said, everything was all to cock.

Cadbury stirred in his stool as he heard the muffled sound of voices from the control room. He shivered slightly and got to his feet, rubbing his shoulders. Blinking owlishly, he went to see if Bain had gone. He caught a glimpse of the duffel-coated figure by the periscope. So Titt had taken over. He went back to the pantry to put on the cocoa again. A few minutes later, as wreaths of steam curled up from the cups he carried, he stepped into the control room. He gestured to Titt.

Reluctantly Titt took his hand out of his pocket as he reached forward to grab a cup. It was something he was never very happy about. He imagined all sorts of things went into the steward's cocoa. But he accepted it. Anything to relieve the dull monotony of watchkeeping.

Cadbury handed the other cup to Purgavie.

Titt sipped at his cocoa, screwing up his face as a waft of hot oily air floated in from the engine room.

Cadbury looked at him anxiously. "Not sweet enough, Tom. Hang on, I'll—"

Titt cut him off. "No, no. It's okay. It's fine." It certainly tasted all right, whatever was in it.

Cadbury grinned and rubbed his hands together. "Cold, isn't it, Tom?"

Titt thought it was a lot warmer, but he nodded in silent agreement. Anything to keep the steward quiet.

Cadbury sidled up closer. He kept glancing down at a spot just beyond the helmsman's chair. "Some patrol, eh, Tom?" he said, his head weaving about as if looking for something.

Titt nodded, wondering what the hell was going on in the steward's weird mind as he noticed him glancing about. "Yeh, some patrol."

Cadbury rubbed his hands. "Still, we'll soon be on our way home. I'll be glad, won't you?" He looked up into Titt's face, adding significantly, "Just as well, eh? You never know what can happen at the last minute."

"Yeh, you're right there," Titt answered automatically.

"Yes, it's just as well. It would be awful if we were to drop a clanger now, wouldn't it?" Cadbury said slyly.

Titt looked at the steward. The bugger was up to something with his sly hints. Titt rolled his tongue in his cheek. "It would, but we're not likely to, are we?"

The smile left Cadbury's face. He made a ducking motion with his head. "I don't suppose so. But you never can tell. Lots of things can go wrong if people don't see to them properly."

"Like what?" Titt asked quietly.

Cadbury shrugged. "Oh, you know. Lots of things."

Titt's eyes narrowed. He knew for certain now that the steward had something up his sleeve. "Like what?" he repeated, an aggressive note in his voice.

"Well, you never can tell—"

"All right, you've had your fun. Now stop buggering about and tell me what you know."

Cadbury put on a look of surprised innocence. "Oh, I never said I knew anything, Tom. All I said was—"

"Cadbury," Titt warned. He noticed the steward's deliberate glance over toward the wheel again. He pivoted slowly. All he could see was a bucket just for'ard of the helmsman's feet. He faced the steward again. "Right, get it."

Cadbury's eyes rounded. "I'm sorry, Tom. I don't know—"

Titt took a step forward. "Don't play around with me, mate. You've been looking at that bucket since you came in. Now get it. At the double."

Cadbury scurried forward. Asking Purgavie to move over, he fished out the bucket from under the wheel. He brought it back to Titt.

A suspicion was growing in Titt's mind. He took the bucket from the steward and looked inside. He could see nothing.

Cadbury stood back, saying nothing, but his eyes were bright.

With a quick step forward Titt thrust the bucket against his chest. Cadbury drew back in alarm. "Right, mate," said Titt, "spit it out." He forced Cadbury back against the bulkhead.

"Leave go," the steward squealed as he wriggled about to escape.

"I'll give you ten seconds. If you don't tell me by then, I'm going to stuff this nonfloating grease down your throat. Right, let's have it then."

The steward coughed and spluttered, but bit by bit Titt dragged the story out of him.

Titt wasn't sure what to think by the time he'd finished. "And you definitely saw Lacey put something in his pocket. You're sure of that?"

Cadbury nodded vigorously. "Straight up, Tom. He's hiding something. He tried to spin me a lot of old malarkey, but I saw him. I'm telling you the—"

Titt stopped him. "Okay, okay, that's enough. Blow now, will you?"

"You won't tell Guns I told you, will you, Tom? I wouldn't—"

"I said blow, Cadbury," Titt warned again.

With a nervous laugh the steward skipped off.

"What was all that about, then?" asked Purgavie as Titt put the gunlayer's bucket back under the wheel.

"Just you pay attention to your course," said Titt and returned to the center of the control room to lean against the periscope. He stared thoughtfully to his front. The trouble with Cadbury was that he was such a liar. You could never trust him. But a vague suspicion, triggered off by the steward's story, lurked at the back of his mind. He was fairly certain that Cadbury hadn't made the whole thing up. He'd seen something, whatever it was. There was only one thing to do—he'd have to have it out with Lacey when he came off the bridge.

The air had become increasingly busy within the last forty-eight hours. The telegraphists on duty were picking up a lot of stuff. Signals were always the subject of much curiosity and wild speculation. Each time one was received, a crop of rumors would spring up like tropical plants. Knowing that the recall signal could be expected any day, the crew pestered the life out of the duty telegraphists. Not that they were able to learn much, as all-important signals were sent in code and routed through the wardroom for breaking. They could only guess at the importance of the communication by its priority designation.

Hollingsworth, on duty in the wireless cabinet, had just received a signal classified "most urgent." Immediately he went to rouse Robinson, who was responsible for decoding.

To get to the wardroom he had to pass through the control room. Titt saw the piece of paper in his hand. He made no comment as the telegraphist sped by. He had suffered far too many disappointments in the past to start wondering whether it was the recall signal or not, but he couldn't prevent a little nervous tremor from running up and down his spine.

Hollingsworth was back in a few minutes. Titt gave him a questioning look.

The telegraphist made a wry face and shrugged. "I don't know, Tom. It might be, but somehow I don't think so. There's a lot of stuff flashing about just now. Something big's going on, but don't ask me. It could be anything. Anyway, we'll soon find out if it's our recall or not—Robinson got cracking on it right away."

Purgavie was squirming in his seat. He kept looking around.

Unable to bear the suspense any longer, he called out, "Is that it, then? Have we got our recall?"

Titt broke off his conversation with Hollingsworth. "You just watch your ship's head, mate. We're a long way from home yet. So don't go counting your chickens."

After Hollingsworth had left to go back to the W/T cabinet, Titt found himself making a tour of the control room. Inspecting the barometer, he glanced at the rev counter before moving over to the planes and checking the pressure on the telemotor lines.

A foot scraped on the coaming of the bulkhead doorway leading to the passageway. Robinson entered the control room. Titt felt himself tense. Robinson grabbed the voice pipe. Instinctively Titt moved closer, but Robinson merely hailed the bridge to inform the captain he had received a signal and had decoded it.

Cheney came down off the bridge. He was frowning deeply, and his mouth was a compressed line. Titt stepped back to allow him past as he made his way to the wardroom.

Feeling restless, Titt began to pace the control room again. He looked at the clock. It seemed Cheney had been away for hours. He forced himself to stop. Standing behind Purgavie, he thrust his hands deep into his duffel coat pockets. The sound of the clock magnified in his ears as it ticked away between the regular beats of the diesels.

Cheney was back in five minutes. Without pausing he made his way straight over to the chart table. Titt heard the click of the light switch. He sneaked a glance behind him. Cheney was bent over the chart in deep concentration, his fingers nervously twirling a pair of dividers.

Titt looked at the clock again. It was almost time for Purgavie to relieve the lookouts. He heard the light click and turned in time to see the captain's legs vanishing up the conning tower hatch.

Instinctively Titt looked at the compass bowl. He had a strong feeling they would be altering course soon.

The voice pipe buzzed. Purgavie bent over to answer it. Titt heard the muffled instructions and the helmsman's dutiful reply as he swung the wheel over: "Starboard fifteen . . . steer north by northeast."

Titt felt the deck tilt. The strength seemed to go out of his legs.

They were going back up the fiord!

He swallowed his bitter disappointment and waited for Purgavie to settle on his new course before he tapped him on the shoulder.

"All right, mate, I'll take over now. You'd better get up top." He took the wheel as Purgavie rose. Easing himself into the seat, he stared at the compass card bleakly. North by northeast. Back up the front line when everybody thought they were going home. He dragged his hand over his face, pulling at the skin as he breathed out heavily through his nostrils.

Purgavie said he was ready to relieve. He looked far from happy as he fumbled with the buttons of his bridge coat. He began to curse in a low monotone, struggling with clumsy fingers.

"Bugger this for a lark," he complained. "I thought that was the recall. Instead we're going—" He broke off disgustedly with an angry shake of his head as if he just couldn't believe it. He looked like a man who'd been told he'd only three months to live.

"Well, nobody's going to ask you to take a vote on it so you might as well get used to the idea," Titt remarked cynically. "You're ready then?"

Purgavie nodded glumly.

Titt sang out to the bridge. A moment later Purgavie was on his way.

It wasn't until Lacey had taken over the wheel that Titt, still feeling a sense of chagrin despite himself, remembered the steward and his wild story. He took a couple of paces forward so he could ask the gunlayer face to face. Standing by the for'-ard bulkhead door, he looked down at the seated figure. Lacey's eyes were crinkled with tired lines, and his face bore the same strained look as had Purgavie's. He too knew they were heading back north. Titt stood for a minute, debating with himself whether to have it out with him there and then or wait until they were both off watch. He decided the matter was too serious to be shelved.

Lacey looked up curiously.

"Guns," said Titt, nodding toward the gunlayer's feet, "what was in the bucket?"

Titt's question hit Lacey like a blow between the eyes. "Bucket?" he repeated, trying to cover up his confusion. "W-what do you mean, Tom?"

Titt's eyes searched his face. "I'm not going to fart about, Guns. I'm told that you were seen taking something out of the bucket. And the way I got the story was that you were hiding it."

Lacey made a great play of concentrating on his steering, but his heart was thumping madly. That bastarding steward. He must have been blabbing his big mouth off. And it wasn't just that old flannel about the Browning gun mountings. He must have said something else to make Titt suspicious. But what could it have been? His thoughts raced as he played for time. Titt was looking at him fixedly, waiting for an answer.

Lacey's nonchalant grin came out more like a snarl. He laughed dryly at the back of his throat. "I see that daft bastard Cadbury's been on to you," he said.

Titt saw no point in either confirming or denying the allegation. He ignored it. "I'm asking you a question, Guns. Just give me a straight uncomplicated answer."

Lacey shook his head despairingly. "You're not going to believe what that goon told you, are you? I was only pulling his pisser. I told him—"

"Yeh, I know, about the Brownings. But I'm not interested in what you told him and you still haven't answered my question," Titt pressed, sure now that the gunlayer was hiding something important. He recalled the day they had left the parent ship. Lacey had been drunk then, hadn't he, and had to be helped down below not long before they had gone to harbor stations. Some of the gun parts had been stripped down. It was Corr and Renwick who had reassembled them. It all clicked.

Titt drew a deep breath. "Look, Lacey—" he began, but he never finished the sentence. A wild cry came from the voice pipe. Lacey flung the wheel hard over as the night alarm went off.

It looked as if the gunlayer had been saved once again by the bell.

Feet pounded along the passageway, and the control room began to fill up as the crew ran to their stations. The deck vibrated with the surge of power from the diesels as the throttles were opened up. Orders were passed with quiet urgency, and the remaining part of the switchboard that was still in operation began to light up. Titt slipped in behind the wheel as Lacey mustered the gun's crew at the foot of the conning tower.

"Wheel amidships . . . steady as you go," came the disembodied voice of Cheney from the voice pipe. They had completed a full circle, and now, with the engines throttled down, they were cautiously approaching the object which had been sighted from the bridge.

Titt gripped the wheel tightly. He had a big problem. There was no time to weigh it all up carefully. Every second counted. Supposing they went to gun action and—he had to decide now, this very second.

He twisted in his seat, trying to catch Brangwyn's eye. But the first lieutenant was busy as he issued orders and ticked off reports of readiness. Titt felt the sweat coming to his brow. He tried to gesture to Bain, but the second coxswain, his arms folded, was staring fixedly to his front.

Titt swung around, ignoring the compass card. "First lieutenant, sir," he cried. Brangwyn didn't hear him. He called again, louder this time.

Brangwyn's head pivoted sharply at the intrusion. "What do you want, Titt?" he snapped. "It'll just have to wait."

Titt took a quick glance at the compass and called again. All heads turned this time.

"What in the devil's name do you want, man?" Brangwyn glared at Titt as though he'd gone mad.

"Can you come here a minute, sir? It's important."

Brangwyn took a quick glance around the control room to see that everything was in order before stepping quickly over to the wheel. His face was like thunder. "Look, Titt," he rasped, "this is no time—"

Titt interrupted him. As briefly as possible he told him what he suspected. Brangwyn stepped back, his face white. He whirled on Lacey, who was staring at the back of Titt's head with demoniac fury.

"Lacey," Brangwyn yelled, "is the gun in order?"

The gunlayer looked wildly about him, his thoughts a confused jumble as he tried to escape the dilemma he found himself in.

"Lacey?" Brangwyn's voice shot up.

"Well, sir . . . i-it's all right," Lacey stammered out. "It'll only take a second—"

Few of the crew had ever seen the first lieutenant in such a towering fury. "What's the matter with it?" His voice quivered with passion.

"It's nothing, sir . . . it's just—"

"God, man," screamed Brangwyn. "We're at night actions stations. Will the gun fire?"

Desperately, Lacey shook his head. "But it's—"

Brangwyn silenced him with a look and strode over to the voice pipe.

All eyes were on Lacey. Bewildered at first, the crew had sympathized with the gunlayer, as they would have with any man getting torn off a strip in front of everyone. When the import of the brief exchange dawned on them, their sympathies vanished.

A shout from the voice pipe had all heads turning again. Titt turned to Brangwyn, who was standing by the for'ard periscope breathing heavily. "Call off night attack stations, sir. Carry on patrol routine . . . and, sir," Titt added as Brangwyn picked up the Tannoy, "the captain says able seaman Lacey has to remain in the control room; he's on his way down."

There was still a crush of bodies piling through the bulkhead doorway as Cheney stepped down the last rung of the conning tower ladder. Instinctively Lacey had backed away and was standing at the far end of the control by the asdic cabinet.

Cheney blinked for a moment, his gaunt shoulders swinging around slowly. "Lacey," he called in a low terrible voice as he spotted the gunlayer.

The gunlayer stepped forward on wobbly legs.

"I'm told by the first lieutenant that the gun won't fire." Cheney spoke in a voice that was all the more frightening because of its very quietness. His eyes bored into the gunlayer. "Why, Lacey?"

The gunlayer swallowed hard and tried to clear his throat, but he found it difficult to speak. His mouth opened and closed.

Cheney bent forward, the great beak nose no more than a few inches away from Lacey's deathly white features. In a voice that could be heard almost as far for'ard as the tube space he shouted: "WHY, MAN?"

Almost inaudibly Lacey answered: "I didn't fit the firing pin, sir."

For a moment it looked as if Cheney was going to strike him. His whole body trembled with fury. He turned to Brangwyn. "Put this man in my report." He swung again to face Lacey. "Where is the firing pin?"

Lacey produced it from the pocket of his overall suit.

"Get up top and fit it right away."

Lacey almost ran for the ladder.

As Cheney followed the gunlayer up the ladder, Brangwyn crossed over to Titt.

"Why didn't you tell me about all this before, Titt?"

Titt looked up in surprise. "Before, sir? I only learned about it less than an hour ago. . . ."

"Well?"

Titt frowned. "Sir, I only heard it as a rumor. I had to see Lacey first to ask him about it."

"Did you ask him?"

Titt glanced at the lubber's point easing the wheel. "Yes, I asked him, sir."

"And what did he reply?"

"Nothing, sir. He didn't get the chance to. That was when the night alarm went off."

Brangwyn changed the position of his feet. He looked at Titt searchingly. "And when the steward informed you of his suspicions that was the first time you'd heard about it? I mean, you had no reason to suspect anything yourself before?"

Titt shook his head firmly. "Not a thing, sir."

Brangwyn paused in his questioning. He rubbed his chin. "Titt? The day we sailed you were working on the casing right up till the time harbor stations was piped. Everything was all right then. I mean, as far as you know, able seaman Lacey had checked his gun and everything appeared to be in order?"

Christ, thought Titt, *I wonder if he suspects Lacey had a skinful that day and had to be carried on board.* If it ever came out that the gunlayer had been drunk and unable to reassemble the stripped three-inch, Cheney would have him on a warrant charge without the slightest hesitation. The gunlayer would finish up in the glasshouse along with Moore. "That's correct, sir," he lied.

Brangwyn eyed him narrowly. "I see. Very well, Titt. You realize you'll have to give evidence when Lacey is brought before the captain."

The way Brangwyn said it, it sounded like a threat.

At breakfast that morning there was a mood of sullen tension around the table. When the crew learned they were heading back up the fiord, their feelings of apprehension, temporarily on ice at the prospect of their recall, reemerged. Quarrels broke out and old hatreds were revived in the volcanic atmosphere.

All during the meal Corr and Thornley had been needling each other. Little things, like ignoring a request to pass the bread or the butter or an odd, muttered word that dripped with poisonous malice.

Titt sat, as usual, at the end of the table. Like the others he felt on edge. The Thornley-Corr feud that threatened to erupt in violence any minute didn't help to improve his temper.

"Aw, can it, will you?" he snapped after one slow smoldering exchange between the two seamen had taken place.

Titt's remark had been intended for both men, but Thornley, sitting nearest him, evidently thought it was addressed to him alone.

"Why don't you tell *him* to shut up for a change?" he said, glaring at Corr.

"I'm telling both of you to can it. Now just pipe down, will you?" Titt warned.

Thornley sneered and muttered something under his breath.

Corr half rose to his feet, the big pockmarked face looking hard and dangerous. "What was that you said?"

Thornley drew his mouth down at the corners. "Get stuffed!"

Titt was reaching for the teapot when Corr made a dive for the blond seaman. The cups scattered in wild confusion. Titt flung himself forward to grab one of Corr's flailing arms, blocking him off as he tried to swing at Thornley. A couple of hands grabbed the big Scot from behind. Corr stopped struggling.

"All right, all right, let go, Tom," he said, breathing heavily. "Ah'm in no hurry—Ah'll get that bastard yet."

"You'll get no one," Titt shouted.

"Okay. Just let go of me, eh? Ah won't do anything—not just now."

"You're bloody well right and you won't—now just watch your step." Titt let go of his arm. Corr sat down, pulling at his collar.

Titt waited a few seconds. His finger stabbed at the packed bunch of men. "So help me," he breathed, "the next one out of line and he'll be up in front of the Bloke quicker than that. Now just get that into your thick heads, the lot of you." He made to

sit down again when Lacey made a half-heard sneering remark.

"What was that you said, Lacey?" Titt asked in a dangerously
quiet voice.

The gunlayer shrugged and gave a little corrosive smile.
"Oh, nothing. I just said some blokes were good at putting you
in the rattle . . . if the cap fits—"

Titt was on his feet in an instant. He shoved a couple of the
hands aside. Grabbing Lacey by the collar of his overalls he
yanked him to his feet. "Listen, you bastard," he whispered
fiercely, "you open your mouth for the rest of the patrol and I'll
make you wish you'd never been born."

Lacey struggled in the iron grip.

Titt shook him. "Now I'm going to tell you something,
Lacey, and I want the rest to listen. I don't mind a bloke getting
pissed, but when he gets pissed and can't do his job then he
should get all that's coming to him. You dropped a clanger,
Lacey, and didn't have the guts to own up to it, okay? But that
little clanger, mate, could have caused us all a heap of trouble.
We might have all been dead ducks by now if we'd gone into
gun action and couldn't get a round off. You never thought of
that, did you? No, all you thought of was your own bloody skin,
mate"—Titt flung Lacey back on the locker bench—"and
that's why I don't want to hear another single word from you,
Lacey, for the rest of this patrol."

Lacey glared at Titt with hatred, shifting his gaze to the
badge on Titt's arm.

Titt leaned forward. "I know what you're thinking, mate,"
he said, tapping his sleeve. "Take a good look at it. That hook
gives me a lot of weight. I'll tell you something else—it gives
me all the weight I need to push bastards like you around without getting my hands dirty."

Lacey's mouth worked.

"But don't let it worry you, Guns. I don't need it when I'm
ashore if that's what you're thinking, so if you ever fancy your
luck, don't hesitate—you speak up." Titt's eyes narrowed to
slits. "Meantime, on board, you shut up. Got that?"

Lacey shut up.

The fore-ends had only been turned in an hour when they were called out for diving stations.

Brangwyn, on watch at the periscope, had spotted a coil of smoke rising from the horizon. Shortly afterward the masthead of a vessel appeared. Immediately he sent for the captain. It turned out to be a coaster of less than a thousand tons. Cheney called off the attack. He was after much bigger game.

It was the only time that day that the crew were alerted.

The next time they were called to diving stations, it was to surface the boat. The night was clear again. A huge moon hanging over the water shone with a pale spectral light.

Cheney cursed inwardly as he watched the water drain from the casing. By the look of the sky there would be no underbelly of cloud to screen off the light and give them cover. But he was more determined than ever to head back up to the boom. The signal he had received the previous night was the added spur, as it had hinted at the possibility of Germany's collapse.

He paced the bridge restlessly. The long day's dive had taken a lot out of the battery. It would be hours before it was charged and he could use both engines for propulsion, and they still had a long way to travel.

Some of his restlessness seemed to be shared by the crew. Though they had at least an hour or more to wait before "up spirits" was piped, not many of them had turned in. A small group had started up a game of crib, but it soon died for lack of interest. Books were picked up and put down again, and the hands looked at each other, began to speak and stopped again. There seemed nothing to say. An uneasy silence hung over the fore-ends like a black cloud.

Titt was one of the few who had gone to his hammock. He lay back trying to read Tolstoy's *War and Peace*. He found it hard to concentrate, and the strange names with their patronymic doubles refused to line up with the characters in the book. Rice had loaned him the book, practically insisting that he read it. No doubt the bookish-minded asdic rating had thought his education was in a sad state of neglect. And he was right, in a way. Just a dumb sailor with enough reading and writing to get by, that's all he was. It wasn't going to be easy back in civvy street, he thought as he thumbed through the pages listlessly. And it wasn't going to be much help either if he read Tolstoy or Shakespeare or that other bloke—what was his name?—Joyce, till he was blue in the face. He'd get around to reading them when he had a job and was settled. He closed the thick volume carefully so as not to mark the pages and placed it under his pillow as he got up to go to the heads.

He came back five minutes later to find the scene in the fore-ends transformed. The compartment buzzed like a market-place.

Renwick grabbed him wildly as he came through the door-way. "Have you heard, Tom?" he asked, grinning wildly.

"Heard what?"

"The buzz." Renwick threw his arms about. "It's all over the boat. Didn't you hear?"

Everyone was trying to speak at the same time in a babble of excited noise.

"What buzz, mate? Spit it out."

"We just got a signal and—"

"And you think it's the recall?" said Titt, twisting free from Renwick's grasp and pushing him away.

"Hollingsworth thinks it is," Renwick said eagerly, rubbing his hands together. "How about that, eh?"

"Hmmmph. We'll see." Titt made for his hammock.

All eyes swiveled around as Monkhouse appeared in the doorway.

"Well?" It was a loud expectant chorus.

The P.O.'s' messman blinked uncomprehendingly before the penny dropped. "Oh," he said, "the signal. I don't know anything about that. I just came in to tell you—"

The rest of his sentence was drowned in a roar of catcalls. No one was interested in anything but the signal.

The small piece of paper lay on the wardroom table as Robinson, poring over the ciphers, decoded it. Brangwyn stood by, unable to hide his impatience.

At last Robinson finished. He rose up slowly like an automaton, holding onto the pink slip on which he'd written. What the devil was the man playing at, thought Brangwyn, snapping his fingers and reaching out with his hand.

Robinson passed the slip over without a word.

Brangwyn scanned it hurriedly. His mouth fell open. "Good God," he said. "Good God." Leaving Robinson still standing at the table with a bemused look on his face, he hurried into the control room.

Bain was on duty. He stepped aside smartly to allow the first lieutenant to get to the voice pipe. Joyner answered as Brangwyn hailed the bridge. Speaking in a clipped voice, Brangwyn told him he wanted to speak to the captain immediately. Cheney came on.

"I have a most urgent signal from Northways, sir. Will you come down?"

Bain and Corr, who was on the wheel, exchanged significant glances as Brangwyn moved over to the foot of the conning tower to await the captain's arrival. In a few moments Cheney's legs appeared through the lower hatchway as he clambered down the ladder. He reached the deck. Brangwyn handed him the signal.

Cheney shot him a querulous glance and began to read. His dark eyes flickered for an instant and the line of his mouth tightened. He gave no further signs of emotion as he folded the signal and put it in his pocket.

"I'm going back up on the bridge, number one," he said. "I will address the ship's company in five minutes' time."

Brangwyn took a half step forward and opened his mouth to speak.

Cheney gave him a cold discouraging look and mounted the ladder.

Corr turned to Bain when both officers had gone. His eyes were large with excitement. "Did you hear that, Jock? Address the ship's company—there must be something big happening."

Bain pulled nervously at his lower lip. Little flutters of apprehension were rippling in his stomach. Something big, all right, like a bloody great German cruiser with a thick ring of destroyers packed around it and the sky black with A/S planes. That was the way the big stuff traveled.

The sudden flurry of activity hadn't escaped the steward. He'd been listening in on the brief exchange between Brangwyn and the captain. He waited until the first lieutenant had gone back in the wardroom. Five minutes, the captain had said, and a couple had gone already. He didn't have much time. Grabbing a dishtowel, he nipped out of the pantry and sped along the passageway. He wasn't going to miss the opportunity of letting the crew know in advance that the captain intended to address them. Like a successful racing tipster, his stock would go up with this piece of information.

Bobbing and grinning all over his round face, he ducked through the bulkhead doorway of the fore-ends. It was seldom the steward was seen as far for'ard as the fore-ends. As soon as he was spotted he came under a heavy crossfire of barracking:

"Piss off!"

"Go and get knotted!"

"Get back to the piggery!"

Undismayed, he waited for the barrage of catcalls to die down. When it didn't he began to get a little worried. Time was passing. He had only minutes, perhaps only seconds. He held up both his hands, imploring silence. His plea had no effect on the crew, who were enjoying themselves. Dancing with rage in his frustration, he began shouting.

The Tannoy crackled warningly.

Instantly the fore-ends was silent as all eyes gazed up at the speaker in hushed expectancy. The crew half rose, ready to make a dive for the doorway.

Again the Tannoy speaker crackled, the noise pitching up into a plaintive whine.

Slowly the men sat down again as they recognized the voice that came over the speaker.

"Captain here. I have some very important news for all of you and I want you to listen very carefully to what I have to say. . . ." A pause followed. "I have just received a signal from

Rear Admiral (S). Germany has surrendered unconditionally. All German naval units have been informed by Admiral Doenitz that they are to cease hostilities." Another pause followed. Cheney's voice seemed to drop a tone. "We have also been recalled and are returning to base."

The men in the fore-ends looked at each other in dumbfounded silence. They shook their heads unbelievingly. Somebody jumped up on the table, and then the shocked silence erupted into a wild burst of cheering that was heard as far aft as the engine room.

Cheney, standing in the control room, Tannoy in his hand, frowned disapprovingly. He waited until the noise had died down.

"Attention, please. . . . I want you all to realize that we still await confirmation of Germany's surrender. Until such time as we receive it we must still consider ourselves as being in a state of hostilities. However, under the circumstances, we will no longer attack enemy shipping. We have no guarantee that they will do likewise. Remember we are still in the enemy's waters and we must not relax our vigilance for a single moment. . . . You will carry on as before. . . . That is all."

Another wild burst of cheering broke out in the fore-ends. Stanley grabbed hold of Oak and began to waltz him around in the few feet of clear space.

A high-pitched humming sound came from the speaker on the bulkhead.

"Shut up, you lot," yelled Titt. "Quiet, will you?"

"I would just want to add"—it was the first lieutenant speaking—"to what the captain had to say. Understandably you are all glad at the news you've just heard, but we are still a long way from Dunoon. We must not make the mistake of allowing ourselves to think it is all over. Even if the news is confirmed it is quite possible that some enemy units, and particularly the U-boats, will not adhere to the instructions of their High Command. In view of this it would be both criminal and dangerous to allow ourselves to relax. Any man who does not fully understand this and fails to act accordingly will be dealt with most stringently. . . . I have only one more thing to add. As from now we will be making passage back to H.M.S. *Forth*. Keep on your toes and remember there will be plenty of time and opportunity for celebration when we return to Dunoon."

As a wild hubbub of conversation sprang up around the table, Titt remembered something. He got up, and squeezing his way past the crowded table, he clambered forward into the tube space. Barbour was on watch, but he was standing in the bulkhead doorway, not wanting to miss the excitement. He stepped aside for Titt.

Moore lay in his hammock, his eyes open and staring at the deckhead. Titt shook the hammock nettles. Moore didn't move, but his eyes swiveled in his head.

"You heard then, Pony?" Titt remarked.

Moore only grunted in reply.

"Well, cheer up, mate. It looks as if it's all over. We're on our way home."

The prisoner gave a half-strangled bitter laugh. "All over? It's too late for it to be all over. It should have been over a long time ago," he muttered cryptically and turned his head away.

Titt shook the hammock nettles again. "Pony?" he called, but Moore had gone back into his strange withdrawn state and made no reply. With a sad shake of his head Titt gave up and returned to the fore-ends.

At a steady rate of knots the submarine, with the help of the ebbing tide, pushed her way south. By four in the morning the charge on the battery was broken. Running on both engines now, she forged stiffly ahead, parting the smooth waters like a plowshare as if eager to be home.

Toward the first light of dawn the port of Kristiansand lay abeam.

Ahead was the minefield. A grim reminder that the war hadn't finished yet.

They dived and went down to 120 feet. All bulkhead doors were shut. The crew remained at their diving stations, silent and subdued in the presence of the minefield. With red-rimmed eyes, for not many of them had slept the previous night, they stared at the inch-thick steel hull. It seemed to offer no more protection than a thin sheet of glass. Within half an hour of diving Winch picked up his first contact. The crew stiffened. Silently they prayed that nothing would happen to them now, each man offering up entreaties to his own particular god-image. All day long Winch continued to report the presence of mines in his heavy, flat-voweled Yorkshire accent. Cheney stood gripping the hoist wire of the for'ard periscope. Two deep lines scarred either side of the beak nose, and his face had a hollowed-out appearance. Hunch-shouldered and with a permanent scowl on his face, he spoke only to give occasional helm orders.

Toward evening the minefield began to thin out and there came a time when there were no more reports from the M.D.U. Shortly afterward, they went up to periscope depth. Cheney had a long careful search around. He put the periscope down and went over to the chart table. When he came back he spoke to Brangwyn.

"All right, number one. Go to sixty feet and fall out diving stations. We'll surface in an hour."

The men filed out of the control room. Cheney retired to his cabin to snatch some sleep. But within an hour Cadbury was knocking quietly at the door to tell him it was time to surface.

There was an air of expectancy in the control room as Cheney stepped over to the for'ard periscope. He motioned it up. A careful look and down again. He stepped back and turned to Brangwyn.

"All right, number one. Surface!"

They had cleared the last hurdle, and the gateway to the North Sea was open.

Chapter
Fifteen

It was an eager and animated crew that crowded the control room after surfacing. In boisterous mood they joked and chattered like a bunch of schoolboys going on holiday. They sucked in deep drafts of fresh air, stretching their arms and puffing their chests out.

Blow had to shout to make himself heard.

"Come on then, me lucky lads. You're not aboard the *Skylark*. You know the standing orders as well as I do." He spread his arms, shepherding them toward the passageway. "Come on then, don't clutter up the control room."

Titt was the last to leave. Making his way for'ard, he saw Bissel standing outside the P.O.'s' mess at the same time as the awful stench hit him. The disinfectant was fighting a losing battle. Titt screwed up his face as he approached the E.A.

Bissel was thumbing through an electrical manual. He looked up as he heard Titt's step. "God," he groaned, "if it isn't the fore-ends gauleiter himself."

Titt ignored the typical sally. He jerked his head in the direction of the mess. "How's Mitch, Lofty?"

The light vanished from the twinkling eyes. Bissel shook his head ponderously. "Pretty bad, mate. They're sending off a signal to have him picked up as soon as possible. With a bit of luck there might even be a corvette or a destroyer buggering about someplace near hand. But they'd better hurry up—that's all I can say."

Titt rubbed a weary hand over his face. "Well, I've got to get for'ard, Perce."

"Aye, I suppose so. You'll have to use the knout on them. It's the only thing they understand." Bissel was back to his old self.

Titt smiled weakly. "I'll do that, mate. I'll be back later to see how he is . . . if there was only something we could do." He shrugged his shoulders helplessly and stomped off.

It was after midnight before they received a reply to the signal requesting immediate medical aid for Mitchell. A Hunt-class destroyer was on its way from Dundee and would rendezvous with them the following afternoon.

Brangwyn took the signal to Cheney, who was in his cabin. Cheney read it and handed it back. Brangwyn waited for instructions, as Cheney stared at the deck, his lips pursed as if he were engaged in some internal debate. Finally he looked up. "We won't dive tomorrow morning. We'll proceed on the surface. It'll save a few hours. Have Robinson work out a course and tell him to let me know the new E.T.A. for the rendezvous. We'll send off another signal when he's worked it out. What is the condition of Mitchell now?"

"Not at all good, sir. He appears to be in a sort of coma. It—"

"Thank you, number one. Get Robinson cracking right away. I want to get that signal off as soon as possible."

Brangwyn swallowed hard and left. Reaching the wardroom, he sat down. Robinson was in his bunk and appeared to be asleep. He was about to shake him when he remembered something. He went into the drawer of his locker and extracted two sheets of foolscap. He studied them for a moment or two, gazing abstractedly at the sub-lieutenant's signature at the foot of the second page. He removed all doubt from his mind and with quick decisive movements ripped Robinson's written report into small pieces and deposited them in the wastebin. All things considered, it was best that the Mulholland incident be forgotten. He got up from the table and shook Robinson.

The sub-lieutenant left for the control room a few minutes later in a sleepy-eyed staggering gait. Brangwyn pressed the buzzer for the steward. When Cadbury arrived he sent him along to tell the coxswain he would like to see him. Nearly five minutes elapsed before the steward returned.

Brangwyn, on the point of asking what had kept him so long, paused as he noted Cadbury's expression. The fatuous smile was gone. He looked pale and shaken.

"What's the matter with you, steward?" he asked irritably. "Are you ill or something?"

"No, sir," Cadbury answered in a strained voice. "It's just that I went along to the P.O.'s' mess to give the coxswain your message like you said, sir, and. . . ."

"Go on."

"Well, it's Mitchell, sir—I think there's something the matter with him, sir."

Brangwyn's fingers drummed the table. "What do you mean, something the matter with Mitchell? Did you or did you not give the coxswain my message?"

Cadbury's eyes widened. "Oh, yes, sir," he said earnestly, "I gave him the message all right, but—"

There was a discreet cough from behind the steward, and the figure of chief petty officer Blow appeared in the doorway.

Brangwyn stood up, dismissing the steward with a wave of his hand. "Ah, there you are, coxswain. I sent for you to tell you that we received a reply to our signal. A destroyer is on the way. We should—" He broke off as he saw the expression on the coxswain's face. "Is there anything wrong, coxswain? What's—"

Blow's head came back a fraction. "I'm afraid it's too late, sir," he said.

"Too late?" echoed Brangwyn. "What do you mean it's too late?"

"Mitchell. He's dead, sir."

Brangwyn sat down. "Dead?" he gasped.

"Yes, sir. He died a few minutes ago."

"Oh, my God!" breathed Brangwyn.

The big signal lamp on the destroyer flashed a yellow light.

On the bridge of the submarine they could hear the *clack, clack,* of its shutters in the quiet of the afternoon air. Sailors lined the decks to gaze curiously across the intervening space that separated the two vessels. A whaler was lowered away from the destroyer.

Titt and Bain struggled with their heavy bundle. Half-dragging, half-carrying the canvas-wrapped body of Mitchell, they staggered along the casing. Just forward of the three-inch gun mounting they lowered the sack gently on the deck and leaped down onto the saddle tanks. In a moment their feet were awash as the long swell rippled and broke over the bulbous contours of the tanks. Titt grabbed the whaler's painter as she came alongside.

Unceremoniously the heavy sack was grabbed by the boat's crew. It draped inertly over the gun'ale, the canvas catching up somewhere. Bain heaved and the men in the whaler pulled. The sack broke free and landed with a dull thud in the stern sheets.

No one spoke. In a moment the whaler had pulled away.

Titt gazed after it, unmindful of the water that swirled to his knees. He felt a sense of deep loneliness. The dead always left an aura of finality behind them. Bain was already halfway toward the bridge. Titt jerked himself back to reality. He clambered onto the casing and hurried after the second coxswain, conscious of the noise as the loose plates rattled under his feet.

When the two men were back on the bridge, Cheney ordered everyone down below. He pressed the klaxon. Great gouts of water shot up from the tanks as the vents slammed open. The deck was awash when Cheney squirmed through the upper hatchway and pulled the lid shut after him. Levering the clips home, he climbed down the ladder. It wouldn't be wise to remain on the surface in the area. Officially the war was over, but it might not be for some fanatical U-boat commander intent on killing as many of the hated enemy as possible before they finally caught up with him.

Only the occasional chatter of the ballast pumps and the

steady hum of the electrical motors broke the quiet down below. The men went about their duties, speaking in hushed tones in an atmosphere that had become morguelike. Mitchell's death had shocked everyone. That he should die was bad enough, but to die on the very day that armistice had been declared and when they were returning home was a cruel, sickening twist of events.

Brangwyn was deeply affected by the death of the seaman. In an unguarded moment he tried to communicate some of his feelings to Cheney. Cheney had just looked at him with dark smoldering eyes and had made no comment.

It was almost as if he believed that Mitchell had been guilty of a gross act of cowardice, his dying the final act of a born malingerer who hadn't the guts to fight for his life when the crunch came.

Brangwyn had always respected and admired his commander. He still did, but for the first time he began to see him in another light. It was something he did not want to think about.

The following night they picked up their escort at the entrance to the Pentland Firth. With the steady improvement of the weather, the turbulent race of water in the Firth had become unusually calm, but a long swell rolled through the gap from the Atlantic. After the wild motion of the previous weeks, it was as if they found themselves borne along on a huge roller coaster. Unaccustomed to the long gliding movements and fatigued by the long spell at sea, the crew began to suffer from feelings of nausea. Some of them were seasick.

The state of the fore-ends didn't help. More than ever it resembled an old garbage dump. Sick and temporarily dispirited by Mitchell's death, the men did little to combat the daily accumulation of filth and debris.

Rice suffered badly. His skin had taken on a tinge of pale green, and he went about clutching first his head and then his stomach. He approached Titt in a state of misery to see if he could be allowed up to do a spell of lookout duty in the hope that the fresh air would help. Titt went to see the coxswain, who raised it with the first lieutenant. Permission was granted.

On his very first spell as lookout Rice was as sick as a dog as he climbed the conning tower ladder. Clinging to the metal rungs in agonized misery, he retched violently, no longer caring whether he lived or died. Both the ladder and the space around the lower hatch were covered with vomit.

It wasn't until the next man went up to relieve that the mess was discovered. There was a wild torrent of oaths. Had Rice owned up to it no doubt it would have been forgiven and forgotten soon enough. Ashamed of his action, he kept silent.

The incident became magnified out of all proportion. Corr, who had been one of the hands detailed to clear up the mess, swore he would find the bastard responsible. In the end it boiled down to three suspects: Crabbe, Renwick and Rice, who had all been watchkeeping at the time it was discovered. These three names cropped up again and again as the matter was heatedly argued in the fore-ends. It was Mulholland who pointed out that it could just as easily have been the officer of the watch. As this had been Joyner at the time, the idea found a certain amount of favor. But nevertheless the three seamen continued to be treated with hostility and suspicion.

Guiltily Rice took to spending long periods in his hammock. He seldom appeared at the table to eat.

Six days after receiving their recall signal they had cleared the Pentland Firth and stood into the Minches with the island of Lewis to starboard. It had just gone eight bells of the last dog. Cheney arrived on the bridge. The evening was mild, and he was clad only in his jacket. Grunting sourly to Robinson, who was O.O.W., he took his stance up in the forepart of the bridge.

A few cable lengths ahead, the corvette, looking plump and matronly, lifted and fell to the gentle swell. The islands fringing the rim of the Atlantic stood up in vivid coloring, a mass of ocher and russet tints. Overhead the sky was a flawless blue span, edging along the spectrum band as it met the ocean in a soft bright green.

Down below a flow of hot oily-smelling air from the engine

room hit Winch as he made his way to the asdic cabinet to do his spell. He grimaced and ran a plump white hand through his hair. Rice vacated the stool with a sigh of relief.

"Anything doing?" Winch's question was rhetorical.

Rice shook his head as Winch eased himself into the chair and adjusted the earphones over his head. With a bored air Winch settled himself down and began to carry out routine sweeps. For the first time since they'd received the recall he allowed himself to dwell on the prospect of going home. He smiled to himself as he created the scene in his mind, going over it stage by stage. First the liberty boat to Sandbank and then a bus to Dunoon. There it would be into the nearest bar for a drink with some of the lads. The first round would be on him. He felt a glow of pleasure at the thought of unbuttoning the moneybelt, fat with four weeks' pay, hauling out a note and slapping it down on the counter, the tight little group of his mates pressing around, laughing and shoving, eager to get at their beer, their faces bright and glowing and all their hardships, miseries and fears forgotten till the next time. Stanley would be there, convulsing them all with his fanciful stories, and Titt—or would he? That was the funny thing about Tom. He was one of the lads all right, and yet in another way he wasn't. It wasn't just because he was a killick or anything like that, it wouldn't have made any difference even if he'd been a P.O.—no, it was nothing like that. It was—well, even when he got drunk he seemed to be able to give the impression he was sort of two people, one of them whooping it up with the lads and the other one looking on, not critical or anything, but just watching as a man would watch a child at play. It gave him a certain dignity. That was the funny thing about Titt. He seemed no different from the rest of them, and yet without saying anything or doing anything he impressed. He had that kind of strength about him that everyone accepted without the need for demonstration. Still, Tom or no Tom, they would have. . . .

He stopped his train of thoughts, his body stiffening imperceptibly as he became alerted. What was that? An alien whisper of sound filtering in between the beat of the corvette's propellers? He listened again. Nothing there. He frowned and bit his lip. Was he getting a bit jumpy now that they were so near home?

In the fore-ends someone had brewed a pot of tea. Renwick had managed to scrounge some corned beef and a jar of pickles, though not many of the hands felt like eating. There was no bread left, and it didn't look as if Donahue intended to bake any more. The chef had just grinned good-humoredly when Stanley accused him of using glazier's putty instead of yeast to make his bread. But when Corr had suggested it was only fit to be stowed in the ammunitions locker the good-natured Donahue had lost his temper. He and Corr had nearly come to blows.

Corr was one of the hungry ones. Encouraged by the bantam seaman, who made hawking noises and flapped his arms like a bird, he helped himself to more corned beef and biscuits. Munching audibly, a vulgar nerve-grating sound in the sepulchral quiet, he asked someone to pass the butter. Thornley was nearest the dish. He deliberately ignored the request.

"What's the matter wi' you, then? Have you got cloth ears as well as a bone dome?" Corr said truculently, blowing crumbs from his mouth.

A growling sound came from Thornley's throat.

"Did you no' hear what I said, you ponce-faced cockney gett?" Corr half rose from the table.

Thornley also got up, his fists balling.

Corr was about to launch himself at the blond seaman when the boat heeled over sharply. The cups, suddenly animated, slid across the table as the alarm buzzer went off with a strident clamor of sound.

Since his first suspicions, a sense of doubt had remained in Winch's mind. It bothered him like a nagging tooth. He continued to carry out routine sweeps but, motivated by an inner compulsion, kept returning to search the bearing where he'd first thought he heard the sense-alerting near whisper.

In an instant, and in some unfathomable way, his doubts were resolved.

In a voice loud enough to carry above the roar of the diesels he sang out, "H.E. bearing green 030."

On the bridge Cheney didn't hesitate. He ordered the helm over and pressed the alarm tit. When Winch reported an echo, it meant that there was something there.

In a sea empty but for themselves and their escort, it could mean only one thing.

"Aircraft bearing green 085." Oak's shouted report momentarily drowned out the sound of Beer's clacking signal lamp.

Cheney watched the slow ponderous approach of the *Catalina*, one eye on the corvette as she began to come around in a boil and thresh of water. Coming out of the sun the *Catalina* glided in like a giant gull.

A huge column of water shot upward, and seconds later a thunderous explosion shattered the stillness of the evening.

The escort was racing madly toward the spot where the *Catalina* had dropped her depth bombs. As her stem cut through the greasy rope of smoke coiling from the aircraft's marker, there was a muffled sound as her depth charge throwers went off. Soaring into the clear air, the ugly black canisters seemed to hang in space before plunging down into the water.

A staggering series of eruptions followed, and great gouts of water reared up in thick columns before mushrooming and falling back in a shower of rain.

A patch of oil appeared on the surface, thick and evil-looking, like clotted blood. Seconds later the water swelled. A hemispheric bubble rose briefly upward to burst like a lanced abscess.

The corvette, with the *Catalina* in attendance overhead, circled the area. A cry came from the starboard lookout of the *Scorpion* as a black, water-glistening object lurched drunkenly to the surface.

Men began pouring from the conning tower of the surfaced U-boat to form a ragged line on her forecasing. Tiny toylike figures, they waved their arms and held shirts and other articles of clothing aloft in surrender.

It was the last action of war that the *Scorpion* was to witness.

Leaving her escort to deal with the U-boat, she continued south and an hour later, as it was still forbidden to make passage through the Minches at night, dropped anchor in a small bay on the island of Lewis.

After the evening meal a few of the hands gathered on the bridge. Stanley had the trot sentry duty. Dressed in overalls, his cap flat aback and the heavy service .45 tugging at the band of webbing around his waist, he looked like a caricature of the fighting services. Leaning on the capping by the forepart of the bridge, Titt sucked thoughtfully at an empty pipe. The sinking sun showed as a blood-red orange segment balanced on the edge of the Atlantic, its rays broken into bands of color by the prismatic atmosphere. To the east the sky had begun to darken. A faint tremor shook the deck as the port engine fired and burst into life. From the stern ugly blue puffs of smoke rose to contaminate the air.

The omnipotent calm of the island roused a deep response in Titt. The scene seemed to have an existence outside time. Something beyond the range of your own narrow individual experience, thought Titt, reflecting on life and what it meant. That was the really crazy thing. There was all this—the word sounded so soft—beauty, and he was seeing it only because he'd been caught up in a war. Did it mean anything other than something to look at? Was that its only reality, just a kind of picture postcard with nothing written on the back to convey regards or meaning? He sucked at his pipe, allowing his piled-up tensions to dissipate in the flow of his thoughts.

Well, whatever it was it made him feel good and maybe that was the answer—you just had to accept these things and not think about them. He smiled as an analogy sprang to his mind. The most beautiful girl he had ever met—he'd been in charge of a squad sent up from the base at Blockhouse in answer to a mayoral request for a naval turnout at the local War Weapons

Week—was at a dance in Wimborne. She had knocked all the blokes out. She claimed to have hailed from Bury St. Edmunds and had the language of a trawlerman and the manners of an aging whore—but she'd looked gorgeous.

People? You'd sit and drink with a bloke—one of your mates —and but for an accident of fate or history or whatever you wanted to call it, the same bloke would be wanting to cut your throat. It all depended on which direction somebody pointed him. A few days ago his own feelings had verged on the murderous, but at least it had been at a personal level. But you just upped that kind of feeling a bit and handed out uniforms and you made it possible for a man to kill someone he had no personal quarrel with and had never even seen in his life before. Once you had become involved in the killing you were never the same again. It changed your mind, twisted it so that you became a kind of mental hunchback, crippled so deeply inside that you were unable to prevent the generation coming up after you from making the same mistakes.

It was said this war was different. There would never be any more. Maybe so, but that's what they'd also told his old man. And they'd probably said it about every war in history. What was it they'd tell his own kids? Would young Brian ever find himself in the position of standing over another man, bayonet poised and ready to plunge, or. . . .

"What's up with you, then?" Bain's voice behind him cut off his thoughts. "The scenery too much for your miserable Sassenach soul?"

Titt turned to see the second coxswain beaming with a proprietary pride. He collected himself. "You built it all yourselves, did you?" he said with a good-humored smile.

"Every square foot of it, Clyde built. We got Para Handy to tow it up and dump it here so's you foreigners would never see it."

"Para who?"

"Forget it. I wouldn't expect an ignorant southerner to know such a great sailor man as Para Handy. Just you carry on and enjoy the scenery, mate. It won't be long now before you're back on the wrong side of the border."

Titt's pale blue eyes focused over Bain's shoulder. "Have you ever been up here before, Jock? I mean as a civvy, in peace-time."

Bain shook his head. "No, never. It was just a place on the map to me. All we did was to sing about it. You know—'Over the sea to Skye.'" He whistled the first few bars of the tune.

"All this on your doorstep and you don't even visit it. You don't deserve it, you lot."

"Listen, mate," said Bain, "before I joined the *Andrew* I was down the mines and had about as much chance of getting up here as I had of getting free beer from the mine owners."

Titt rested his chin on his folded arms. "You know, I'd like to bring the wife up here someday. She'd go a real bundle on this."

Bain looked at him. "You're getting a bit romantic in your old age, aren't you?"

"Well, you know what I mean, Jock. It's . . . well, it's so peaceful and quiet-like. . . ."

"Aye, there's nothing like the Highlands. But don't visit them when the gentry are after the deer. You might get a bullet up your bum for your trouble."

Harbor stations were piped at 0700 the following morning. By late afternoon they had rounded the Mull of Kintyre and pass-ing Southend entered the lower reaches of the Clyde. The weather was sunny and warm and already the lookouts on the bridge were beginning to lose their deathly pallor. As they passed Arran a light breeze came up, and by the time they had reached the Cumbraes they were rolling gently.

Up and past the two islands they passed within a few cables' length of the steamer on her last trip of the day from Rothesay to Wemyss Bay. Passengers crowded the rails to wave gaily to the tiny cigar-shaped vessel. They'd seen lots of submarines in the Clyde. Chipped paint, rust patches and a general bedraggled appearance told them this one was returning from the wars.

Half an hour later Cheney ordered the helm over. They swung to port and rounded into the Holy Loch. The freshening wind blew ripples over the deep blue water. Even from a distance the parent ship, a fat hen with her brood of chickens gathered around her, looked solid and secure.

Cheney sent signalman Beer down below. A few minutes later he had returned. Under his arm he carried a black roll of cloth. At a signal from Cheney he unrolled it and, bending it to the halyard, ran it up aloft. Picked up by the wind the flag broke free from its folds.

The *Scorpion* had hoisted her Jolly Roger to signify one more successful patrol.

On board the parent ship lower deck had been cleared. The whole of the ship's company had turned out to pay tribute to their brave little champion.

Coming in on the floodtide, Cheney circled the parent ship. Blue-clad figures packed the decks and hung over the rails. A great swell of spontaneous cheering echoed and reechoed from the surrounding hills of the loch.

Titt, standing in the cable well on the forepart of the casing, felt a tingle in his spine as the massed voices carried across the water in a great oratorio of sound. He knew it was an experience in his life that would never be repeated. In a paradoxical way it brought him a feeling of nostalgic sadness.

Maneuvering on main motors, Cheney came alongside the free berth to starboard. Chief petty officer Blow, some of the ruddy tinge gone from his cheeks, but looking smart and spruce, eased the wheel over. Titt glanced toward Bain, who was manning the capstan. There was a white flash of teeth, and Bain nodded his head as if to say: Make it a good one. Titt withdrew his right arm. The heaving line shot out and sped upward like an arrow to land on the towering fo'c'sle of the parent ship. He got a cheer all to himself.

Breasts and springs were passed and secured. The telegraphs

clanged in noisy relief as they rang their last order: Finished
with motors. Eagerly the two motormen wound down the field
regulators and broke the chopper switches. With the power shut
off, the two men turned to stare at each other in dazed disbelief.

Minutes later the hatches were flung open and a group of
filthy, unshaven men staggered out into the light. Blinking
and rubbing their eyes as they held onto each other, the crew
raised their heads to stare lovingly at the parent ship. The rising crescendo of cheers dinned their ears.

They were home at last.

It needed a few minutes to evening rounds. Much of the earlier
feverish excitement had gone, soaked up by the wearying tasks
of cleaning out the boat and transferring the mess gear inboard.
Titt had the duty watch. After supper, together with Renwick
and Corr, he went back aboard the submarine for a last minute
tidy-up before rounds.

The "ticket collector" was duty officer. Knowing just what
sort of an officious little bastard he was, Titt wanted to make
sure everything was in order. Joyner was the kind of officer
who felt he had failed in his duty if he couldn't spot some small
misdemeanor, no matter how trifling. But Titt knew how to deal
with him. Knowing how fussy he was, Titt would quite deliberately set up something for the "ticket collector" to pounce
upon. Joyner, of course, knew nothing of this. When he came
upon the offending article a triumphant look would come over
his dyspeptic features, and he would congratulate himself
on his eagle eye. After admonishing whoever was on duty,
his honor satisfied, he would race around the rest of the boat
with barely a pause.

On this occasion Titt had arranged for a bucket, half filled
with oily rags, to be left under the platform in the tube space.
As expected, the "ticket collector" began his rounds with
clinical thoroughness. He found the half-hidden bucket and
delivered a short lecture to Titt on the need for order and
cleanliness. While he was yapping away Renwick made faces

behind his back. It was all Titt could do to prevent himself from laughing.

The little farce over and Joyner having gone back inboard, Titt unlashed his hammock and laid it out on a locker bench in the P.O.'s' mess. The other members of the duty watch had slung their hammocks in the strangely empty fore-ends. Only one other person shared the P.O.'s' mess with Titt—Mc-Lintock, the duty E.R.A.—but he was busy in the engine room.

Titt sat down to compose a letter to his wife. He wanted to say so much to her, but he could never seem to find the right words. What he felt looked kind of soppy when he put it on paper. Sucking the end of his pen, he was struggling to get beyond *My dear Ruth* when a noise in the passageway warned him someone was coming. Renwick appeared, dressed up in the ridiculously long watch coat. The big Colt was strapped at his waist, and a whistle was secured to the lanyard slung around his neck. He had obviously made a fast descent from the casing. Leaning against the doorway, he struggled to get his breath back.

"Somebody coming down. I think it's the skipper, but there's another bloke too," he gasped out.

Titt jerked his thumb. "Okay, Raggy. You'd better get back up at the double to cut the old man off a slice of cake when he steps on board or he'll do you."

Renwick sped off again.

A few seconds later Titt looked up in time to see the tall figure of the captain go past, his body bent forward as he stooped to protect his head in the low passageway. He'd no sooner gone by than a second figure appeared. He stopped in the doorway.

"Looking for someone, mate?" Titt asked.

The sailor squinted at the piece of paper he held in his hand. "Leading Seaman Titt. I was told he was on board. Do you—"

"That's me." Titt held his hand out, his features going pale as he recognized the familiar buff-colored envelope. His fin-

gers trembled slightly as he ripped it open. The seaman waited
in silence.

Titt seemed to sway, and a pulse beat in his temples.

The messenger took a half step forward. "Is there anything
the matter, mate?"

Titt slowly shook his head. Like a man in a trance he walked
past the messenger and made his way aft toward the captain's
cabin.

Cheney handed the telegram back, a look of compassion
twisting his dark features. "I'm very sorry, Titt. I can't tell you
how sorry. . . . I'll see Captain (S) immediately. We'll try
and get you away tonight . . . If there's anything else I can do,
please let me know. . . ."

Cheney pulled all the stops out. In less than an hour Titt,
having packed a few things, reported to the master-at-arms'
office. His travel warrant and ration book were lying on the desk.
Brangwyn, looking immaculately clean and fresh, came down
from the wardroom to offer his sympathy. His breath smelled
slightly of gin and the odor of cigar smoke hung about his uniform. His eyes were big and liquid.

In the quiet of the passageway, outside the office, Titt felt
a warm breath of air from the ventilation trunking louvers play
soothingly on the back of his neck as he listened politely to the
first lieutenant's earnest words. A faint tremor ran under his
feet; the purr of the ship's auxiliary machinery had a comfort-
ing sound. Somehow they all went together. Brangwyn's voice,
the pleasant feeling of warmth and the steady living throb of
the machinery. They were real, part of his life. The other thing
was a crazy nightmare. He would wake up in a second to find it
was just an ugly lie.

Brangwyn was saying that the captain had also sent his sin-
cere condolences and that he'd made arrangements with Captain (S) for a special boat to take Titt across to Greenock where
he would catch a train for Glasgow and the south.

Titt mumbled a few words of thanks and checked he had his

travel warrant and paybook inside his tunic. He bent down to pick up his case.

The master-at-arms stepped from his office. "Better get going, lad. The boat's waiting for you up top." He placed his hand gently on the leading seaman's shoulder.

With a final pat of his tunic pocket Titt turned and walked across to the ladderway.

He never saw the first lieutenant or Cheney again.

Chapter
Sixteen

Waterloo Station was the usual seething mass of servicemen queueing up for warm tea and soggy buns, or wandering about in a semibemused state watched by the hard-eyed M.P.'s who strutted about like prison guards.

A large draft of navymen had arrived from Portsmouth. Red-faced petty officers shouting at them on all sides, they struggled to get themselves sorted out, as they formed a shapeless mass around the barrows piled high with hammocks and kit bags. Badgered by the P.O.'s, the new draft sweated freely in their ill-fitting, heavy, blue serge suits. It was unusually hot for the late autumn day. Robbed of their natural dignity by the comic-opera uniforms and bewildered by the strangeness of their new life, the men in the draft appeared witless and clumsy as they shuffled about in an amorphous mass.

Leading seaman Titt, D.S.M. and bar, who had traveled up in the same train as the draft, eyed them with pity and understanding. They were in for a hard time of it. An ordinary seaman in the Navy was the lowest of all living creatures, subject to whims and ill humors from all sides.

He skated his way around the outer edge of one group, who turned to gawk, their eyes lighting up in sour envy as they caught sight of the gold badges surmounted by an anchor, the glittering cap tally with its proud legend, H. M. Submarines, and the tiny colored pieces of medal ribbon.

Titt smiled to himself as he headed for the bar. Passing the R.T.O.'s office he became aware that he was being surveyed by a couple of white-belted and gaitered naval M.P.'s. He gave them a cold discouraging stare. He didn't want to be bothered with questions about travel warrants or identification. Heads set back on stiff shoulders, the two M.P.'s returned the stare, eyes slowly swiveling in their sockets as Titt walked past. Titt could see that the bigger of the pair was itching to have a go. He half hoped that he would. The glance shifted to the decorations on his tunic. *Yeh, have a good look at them, mate,* Titt muttered to himself. *They don't hand them out for hanging about railway stations trying to cop deserters.* The M.P. looked away, trying hard to appear unimpressed. He nudged his pal and the pair of them began to move off slowly and arrogantly.

Titt had only gone a few yards when he heard a shout. He spun around, ready to deal with the patrol. A stocky red-bearded figure was bargaining through the crowd.

"Tom, you old bastard." The ruddy face split in a grin showing bone-white teeth. "Well, are you not even going to say hello?" Bain gasped, planting two heavy suitcases down and grabbing Titt by the arm.

"Christ, Jock, I didn't recognize you for a minute with your beard. And a new uniform too—just look at all that gold. What made you do that, then?"

Bain laughed. "What, get a new uniform?"

"No, you clot. I mean—"

"I know what you mean." Bain's hand went up to his beard and stroked it proudly to a point. "It was the wife, mate. She said she couldn't stand the sight of my face any. . . ." His voice trailed away in embarrassment. "I'm sorry, Tom. I didn't mean. . . ." He stared uncomfortably at a space between his feet.

"Forget about it, Jock."

"Tom, I'm sorry. Most of us had gone by the time you got back and . . . well, I meant to write and—" He broke off to shrug helplessly.

Titt grabbed his arm and gave it a little shake to emphasize his words. "Jock, it's happened and there's nothing anyone can do about it. I was just one of the unlucky ones, that's all. Lots of blokes— Oh, come on—" he shadow-jabbed Bain in the ribs—"what are we hanging about here for? The bar's open."

Bain rubbed his mouth with the back of his hand. "Tom, I just wanted to say—Christ, it's good to see you, mate."

The station bar was crowded. As usual there was a shortage of glasses. Bain shouldered his way through to the counter. Shouting above the babble of noise, he called up two pints. There were no pint glasses. He got four half-pints. He handed two over to Titt, and they headed for a corner. They found a table. It was covered with beer slops and food debris. Bain made a grimace of disgust as he sat down. "It's near as bad as the fore-ends," he remarked.

The two men were silent for a moment as they sipped at the weak, watery beer. Bain wiped his mouth as he finished his first glass. He started on his second, eyeing Titt above the rim of the glass. Titt looked thinner, and the pale blue eyes had a washed-out appearance. There were slight hollows in his cheeks. *Poor bastard,* thought Bain. To lose his wife and both kinds when it was all over. He'd got the full story from Blow months after it had happened. A Flying Fortress on a routine flight from its base in Oxfordshire had got out of control near Shrewsbury. The pilot apparently had managed to steer it away from the thickly populated town. It had crashed on the outskirts near a handful of cottages. Titt's had been one of them. His wife and son had been killed instantly, but his little girl, three years old, had lingered for days. In the end she died from the massive burns she had sustained. What a terrible thing to have happened. Looking at Titt next to him, he wondered how he had managed to survive. What would he do now? Would he stay in the Navy or get out into civvy street as he'd always said he would?

Bain finished off his beer. "I'll get them," he offered as Titt made to rise.

Titt smiled wanly. "Are you loaded, then? Don't tell me you've become a black-market baron." But he got up anyway and in a few minutes had returned with another four half-pints.

"Where are you heading for, anyway?" he asked as he sat down.

"Me? I'm on my way to Blockhouse. I'm taking the coxswain's course. Somebody's got to supply the talent."

"You're staying on then?" asked Titt.

Bain shrugged. "Some of us have to stay on if we want to keep a Navy. I mean we're mebbe going to need it yet. Just look at the way the Russians are playing up. . . ."

Titt's finger traced a pattern on the beer-stained tabletop. It had started already. They had nearly finished the war to end all wars and here was Jock talking about the next one. He didn't communicate his thoughts to Bain. Instead he switched subjects. "Have you just come down from Dunoon, Jock?"

"Sort of. I've been up at Loch Goil for the last four months."

"Loch Goil? What were you doing up there?"

Bain's smile was almost apologetic. "I had a cushy number."

"Good for you."

"Yeh, I was P.O. in charge of a bunch of Jerries. They brought this cable layer back from Hamburg and stuck in Loch Goil. They needed a smart intelligent P.O." He spread his hands. "Anyway, they also needed someone who could speak the language to the Jerries."

Titt looked at Bain in surprise. "I never knew you spoke German."

"I was talking about English. Anyway, I was telling you about this cable layer. She wasn't a cable layer, in a way—she was a sort of asdic ship. She'd nip out off shore and dump this asdic gear, some kind of hydrophones, and run a cable back. Remember all those patrols off Bergen and Stavanger when Jerry would be out looking for us almost as soon as we arrived on the billet? Well, that was our friend. That was how they got the tipoff. They could hear us."

"And what were you supposed to be doing up Loch Goil?"

"Well, as I say, we brought this thing back to take apart and have a look at it."

"And all the Jerries were still aboard?"

"Yeh, the whole crew. They weren't a bad bunch of blokes except for the skipper and this scientist bloke in charge. They were a right pair of heel-clicking bastards, they were. Christ, they didn't half hate our guts. But the rest were all right."

"I suppose you were real matey-like?"

Bain laughed. "In a way. They were a poor bunch of bastards really. No money or fags or anything. I used to take a couple of them ashore now and again for a pint. It was a laugh. There we would be sitting at the bar of the hotel with all the locals —" He stopped as he became aware of Titt's disapproving silence. "Oh, just a minute, Tom. They were only civvies, and the poor bastards had bugger all—"

"I know. You said that already."

"Ach, Tom. They're not all bad, you know. This was just a bunch of blokes doing a job."

Titt sipped at his beer. "And it was a fucken good job they did too, wasn't it?"

Bain frowned and looked at the tabletop. "Well, you know—"

"Yeh, I know," Titt interruped. "They weren't all tarred with the same brush. It's funny, Jock, but everybody I know who's been over to Germany have all said the same thing and that was they never met one single Nazi. We must have killed the lot and left all the good ones because according to what they say there's no Nazis left in Germany."

Bain rubbed his jaw. "I don't know anything about that. All I'm saying is that this wasn't a bad bunch of blokes. I can tell you this—they did what they were told and worked hard."

"I can believe that all right, Jock," said Titt with a bitter laugh. "They did what they were told all right. And they must have worked hard to kill all those people in the concentration camps. I'll bet that brought them out in a sweat."

Bain felt uncomfortable. He didn't want to argue with Tom. Anyway, he hadn't been defending the Nazis. He decided to get off the subject. "Ach, well, let's forget about it, Tom. You haven't told me where you're heading for."

Titt stared for a moment. "Me? Oh, I'm just going up the line. Ruth's folks have asked me up for a long weekend. You know how it is." He grinned lopsidedly. "They're getting on a bit and feel a bit lonely at times, especially now that—"

"Sure, Tom, sure I know what you mean," Bain hurriedly sympathized. "You're down at Blockhouse, then?"

Titt sighed heavily. "Yeh, just waiting for demob. And I can tell you it's bloody grim, mate. It's not the old Blockhouse you and I used to know. It's all pusser now. No more sod's operas in the canteen and all that. You won't know it, Jock."

Bain smiled as he recalled the old days when they'd both been able seamen. "It used to be good. Remember that band they used to have? That cockney bloke that used to play the trumpet —Jimmy something or other. He was great."

"That's right. I remember that. And there was that young Scots bloke on the guitar that was always raving about Django somebody or other, some gypsy who'd lost a couple of fingers or something. What was his name again?"

"Who, the gypsy?"

"No." Titt shook his head. "I mean the Scots bloke—what did they call him again?"

"I can't remember, Tom. It's a long time ago." Bain began laughing. "Christ, remember Stanley? Were you in the canteen that night when he got a pint that was a bit off and he marched right back to the bar and when the barman wouldn't change it poured it all over his head? He was a hell of a bloke, Stanley was. What was that he always used to recite when he got the beer up? Remember he used to knock his pint off in one go and put the glass down, and then he'd turn around and recite this—what was it again?"

Titt scratched his chin. "Something about bad beer, wasn't it?"

"That's it," cried Bain. "I remember now—

> O Lord above, send down a dove
>   With wings as sharp as razors,
> To cut the throats of them there blokes
>   Wot sells bad beer to sailors."

They both laughed. Bain looked at his glass. It was empty again. There was an awful din going on all around. Bain had to raise his voice when he stood up. "Same again, Tom?"

"See if there's any stout, Jock, will you?"

Bain pushed his way to the bar. They'd no stout. Cradling the half-pint glasses in his arms, he headed back for the corner, nearly tripping over the outstretched feet of a drunk lolling at the next table. Careful not to spill any of the beer, Titt eased the glasses from the crook of Bain's arm.

"Drunken bastards," Bain muttered as he sat down. "They shouldn't drink if they can't hold it. And there's no bloody stout, Tom," he added as if it were the final indignity.

Titt raised his glass. "Never mind, Jock. Down the hatch, mate." The beer tasted thin and flat. He reckoned he'd need about fourteen pints of the stuff before he could get half a glow on. He took another gulp, remembering he'd meant to ask Jock about some of the others. He hadn't seen them when he'd come back after. . . . *Steady now, mate,* he said to himself. No good thinking about that again. It's done and nothing's ever going to alter it. Take a grip and don't start feeling sorry for yourself or you'll finish up crying in your beer, and once that starts that'll be the end of you, mate. You can still walk and breathe and there's a lot of years in front of you yet. So just keep putting one foot in front of the other and soldier on. If it had been you that had got it instead of Ruth, what do you think she would have done? Lain down? Not on your Nelly, mate. She would have kept going, and her sorrow would have been her own. She wouldn't drag it around like a ball and chain for everyone to see. Anyway, everybody gets hurt one way or another—some worse than others, that's all. It was just like fighting in the ring in a way. If the other bloke clobbered you hard you just had to grin because once he knew he'd hurt you he'd be in there piling it on and you might finish up with a real tanking. When you were hurt, you started punching—that was the rule. And never give up. If you were going to be licked, then you made sure it was by a better man and not yourself. And remember you still had a lot of friends at the ringside. If you threw the sponge in you wouldn't have any. . . .

He smiled at Bain. "Bloody awful beer, Jock, isn't it?"

Bain made a face. "There's only one place you can get good beer."

"Yeh, and we all know where that is, but before you get started tell me what happened to the others—Pony, Big Jock and Stanley and all that lot."

Bain twirled a finger in his ear as he raked his memory. "Well," he began slowly, "I don't know what happened to Stan, but Pony clewed up in some 'trick-cyclist' hospital or other. He went a bit around the twist, I think. And you know about Trapper? No? Well, he was lucky in a way. He lost his badges and got a packet of stoppage of leave and all that, but he didn't go to chokey. Thornley did though. I think he got fourteen days."

"And how about Corr and Renwick and that mad bastard Cadbury? What happened to him?"

"Cadbury? Him? I've no idea, but if ever a bloke should have been locked up it was that bugger—" He stopped speaking suddenly as a thought occurred to him. He shot a glance at Titt. "You haven't heard, then?"

"Heard? Heard about what?"

"You didn't know about old Bill?"

"Bill Blow? No. What happened?" Titt's brows furrowed.

Bain took a long pull at his beer. He licked the froth from his lips. "He was on the *Triumphant* out in the Far East. I didn't know about it till a couple of weeks back."

Titt's mouth dropped open. "Oh, no! I can't believe it," he said, shaking his head. "So old Bill bought it."

"And the old man?"

Titt looked up sharply. "The old man? You mean—"

"Yeh, Cheney. He was the skipper. He got his other half stripe, you know. It was their first patrol, too. Hit a mine they reckon, in the Malacca Straits.'

Titt was silent. The news of Blow's death had stunned him. He eventually spoke. "That's rough, Jock. I can't believe it. But how did he happen to get another boat? He'd done his whack, and anyway he was getting too old for it. You remember how he looked when we got back from that last patrol? He was absolutely sold, he was."

Bain agreed. "Aye, it was funny, that. He was all right till we got back and then he seemed to age overnight. I think that business of Mitchell shook him up more than he let on. He had a good idea that Mitch was in a bad way. Not that I blame the old man. You just can't turn back from patrol every time a bloke goes sick. I mean for all the old man knew Bill could have been all wrong. He'd have looked a right dummy if he'd gone all the way back to Dunoon to find there was nothing seriously wrong with the bloke."

"But there was, wasn't there?"

"Oh, there was, all right, but it's easy to be wise after, isn't it?"

"What was it, appendicitis?" Titt asked.

Bain raised an eyebrow. "That's what Bill thought it was. But how did you know? Anyway, it doesn't matter now and it wasn't appendicitis."

"What was it?"

"Mitchell had an ulcer, and it burst. He must have strained himself or something and it burst and he got peritonitis. They reckon he would have been all right if it hadn't burst, but there you are, that's the way it goes."

Titt tilted his glass back.

Outside on the platform, half hidden by dense clouds of steam, the P.O.'s were rounding up stragglers from the draft. They had to shout to make themselves heard above the noise of the escaping steam, the rattle of carriages and the heavy clank of the engines. The scene had an air of bedlam about it. But underneath the apparent chaos was a pattern that encompassed all of them. Even the prowling M.P.'s had a purpose.

Titt glanced at his watch. "I've just got time for another one before I get over to Paddington, Jock. Same again?"

Bain leaned back in his chair and patted his belly. "Fill them up, mate. I've got all the time in the world."

Titt picked up the empty tumblers. "I don't think any of us have got that, Jock." Elbowing his way through the crowded bar, he made his way to the counter.

OCLC (S)

MacHardy

Send down a dove.